Edexcel GCSE

Health and Social Care

Written by

Elizabeth Haworth
and Andy Ashton

edexcel
advancing learning, changing lives

Published by Pearson Education Limited, a company incorporated in England and Wales, having its registered office at Edinburgh Gate, Harlow, Essex, CM20 2JE. Registered company number: 872828

www.heinemann.co.uk

Edexcel is a registered trade mark of Edexcel Limited

Text © Elizabeth Haworth and Andy Ashton 2009

First published 2009

12 11 10 09
10 9 8 7 6 5 4 3 2 1

British Library Cataloguing in Publication Data
A catalogue record for this book is available from the British Library

ISBN 978 1 846903 47 2

Typeset by Saxon Graphics
Original illustrations © Pearson Education Ltd 2009
Illustrated by Sam Thompson CalowCraddock Ltd
Cover photo © Pearson Education Ltd/Chris Parker
Printed in Italy by Rotolito Lombarda

Acknowledgements

The author and publisher would like to thank the following individuals and organisations for permission to reproduce photographs:

Alamy Images/Bubbles Photolibrary/Angela Hampton – page 107
Alamy Images/David Hoffman Photo Library – page 94
Alamy Images/David Taylor – page 96
Alamy Image/Jeff Greenberg – page 167
Alamy Images/Nick Gregory – page 136
Alamy Images/Image Source Pink, page 11
Corbis/Jeff J Mitchell/Reuters – page 134
Corbis/JLP/Deimos – page 143
Getty Images/ColorBlind Images/Iconica – page 200
Getty Images/Reportage/Mischa Photo Ltd – page 220
Getty Images/Shaun Botterill/Allsport – page 165
Getty Images/Steve Finn – page 146
ImageSource – page 104
iStockPhoto/Aldo Murillo – page 33
iStockPhoto/Joshua Blake – pages 27, 37
PA Photos/Ian Nicholson/PA Archive – page 218
Pearson Education Ltd, pages 8, 12, 14, 24 (top), 26, 45, 64, 69, 70, 98, 206, 212
Pearson Education Ltd/Debbie Rowe – page 18
Pearson Education Ltd/Jules Selmes – page 148
Pearson Education Ltd/MindStudio – page 152
PhotoDisc/Jim Wehje – page 76
RCN Publishing Company – page 199
Rex Features – pages 22, 98
Rex Features/Alix/Phanie – pages 102, 156
Rex Features/Jonathan Hordle – page 100
Richard Smith – page 139

Robert Ford/Shutterstock – page 24 (bottom)
Topfoto/Ellen B. Senisi – page 82
Topfoto/Ellen Senisis/The Image Works – page 182

Crown Copyright material is reproduced by the permission of the Controller of HMSO

Every effort has been made to contact copyright holders of material reproduced in this book. Any omissions will be rectified in subsequent printings if notice is given to the publishers.

The websites used in this book were correct and up to date at the time of publication. It is essential for tutors to preview each website before using it in class so as to ensure that the URL is still accurate, relevant and appropriate. We suggest that tutors bookmark useful websites and consider enabling students to access them through the school/college intranet.

Disclaimer

This Edexcel publication offers high-quality support for the delivery of Edexcel qualifications.

Edexcel endorsement does not mean that this material is essential to achieve any Edexcel qualification, nor does it mean that this is the only suitable material available to support any Edexcel qualification. No endorsed material will be used verbatim in setting any Edexcel examination/assessment and any resource lists produced by Edexcel shall include this and other appropriate texts.

Copies of official specifications for all Edexcel qualifications may be found on the Edexcel website - www.edexcel.com

Contents

Introduction

This book has been written to help you pass either Single or Double Award GCSE in Health and Social Care for Edexcel. The qualification will give you the background knowledge and skills needed if you are considering working with people.

What will I learn, and how will I be assessed, during the course?

Double award

The double course is divided into 4 units:

Unit 1 aims to help you understand how people grow and develop from birth through to later adulthood. It also looks at the personal relationships people have during their lives and how growth and development affects them. This knowledge will not only help you understand others but maybe also yourself. At the end of the unit you will sit a 1 hour 15 minute written exam paper made up of multiple choice questions and a series of questions based on case studies and short scenarios.

Unit 2 will require you to carry out an investigation into the needs of one person and look at how health, social care and early years organisations meet these needs. You will select the person you base your research on yourself and use this research to write a report for your coursework.

Unit 3 looks at what it means to be healthy, the factors that affect health and well-being and how health is measured. For your coursework you will design a health plan for an individual based on details provided by the exam board.

Unit 4 combines everything you have studied in the first three units but looks at them very much from the point of view of a worker in a health, social care or early years service. This will help you develop a more in-depth understanding of the core principles needed to work with other **service providers** and **users**. At the end of this unit you will sit a 1 hour and 15 minute written exam paper made up of three compulsory questions based on case studies and short **scenarios**.

Single award

If you are taking the single award course you will study units 1 and 2 only. They are exactly the same as units 1 and 2 of the double award course.

Service provider – someone who works in a health, social care or early years organisation, so offering a service

Service user – someone who needs to use a health, social care or early years service

Scenario – an outline or description of a real life situation

What will I need to know before taking this course?

This will be a new course for all students so everyone will start from basics. However you will already have studied some relevant issues in subjects such as RS, Citizenship, Science and PE.

What kind of person should I be to take this qualification?

You should be interested in working with people, particularly in the areas of health, social care or early years. It will also help if your attendance and attitude at school are very good, as this will help you in several ways, such as completing the research and doing the coursework assignments in the time allocated for this in school. As part of your research you will also be speaking to people outside school, such as service providers, so good behaviour is also important.

What skills will I be using during the course?

You will be expected to plan and carry out tasks in which you will:

- analyse issues and problems
- identify, gather and record relevant information and evidence
- analyse and evaluate evidence
- make reasoned judgements and present conclusions.

You will also need to use and further develop your personal, learning and thinking skills, shown by being:

- an independent enquirer
- a creative thinker
- a reflective learner
- a team worker
- a self-manager
- an effective participant.

Other skills you will need are the functional skills of English, Information and Communication Technology (ICT) and Mathematics that will allow you to work confidently, effectively and independently in life.

How will this course help me once I have got the qualification?

This course allows progression onto an A Level course or a BTEC National qualification. You could also move on to working in an area of health, social care or early years, or to a training provider, to take NVQ/SVQ. All these can be taken in health and social care or other similar subject areas.

We hope you enjoy this course.

Liz Haworth and Andrew Ashton

Authors acknowledgements

Elizabeth Haworth would like to thank her husband and her children for their continued love and support throughout the writing process. She would also like to thank her parents and the rest of her family and friends for being there for her and providing the inspiration for many of the characters and case studies, as well as factual information.

She would especially like to thank Paul and his family, for sharing experiences of the disability and life changing events based on their suffering and courage after his brain injury.

Andy Ashton would like to thank all those who supported him during the writing period particularly Gary for his patience and encouragement. He would also like to thank his father Norman and mother Kathleen, who is never far from his thoughts. Without her support with learning reading in junior school this book may never have been written. A big thank you also goes to friends, such as Annie, for their advice and Steve for his technical wizardry.

How to use this book

This book has been written specially to support you in your study for the Edexcel GCSE in Health and Social Care. This will be the first time you have studied this subject, so we have included lots of features to make your learning experience interesting and worthwhile. Take a look below to find out more:

Independence days

Here you look at the key physical, intellectual, emotional and social changes that take place in early adulthood, from the ages of 19 to 45.

Early adulthood (19–45 years of age)

Do you look forward to the time when you are independent and can do what you want? Looking forward to having a job and earning your own money? Do you want to settle down with a partner and have your own home? Would you like to have children? These are all the sorts of things that may happen in early adulthood.

It is often seen as a time when people reach their physical peak and maturity. It is a time when you may feel completely 'grown up', yet in fact you are still growing and developing in important ways.

Physical development

During early adulthood, physical development continues, with most individuals reaching their physical peak – or reaching **physical maturity** – in their early twenties. People are at their strongest at this time and, in sporting terms, perform at their best – most athletic record holders are in early adulthood.

As individuals move towards the end of this life stage, their physical capabilities begin to decline. Fertility starts to drop for both men and women, and the signs of ageing begin to appear. Some women may start to go through the menopause, although this is more common in middle adulthood. As people's **metabolic rate** drops, they may begin to put on weight, hair may go grey, wrinkles may appear and eyesight may decline. However, many of the physical changes can be countered by exercise and diet control. If people in early adulthood look after themselves well, you may be surprised to discover their real age!

Intellectual development

Adults continue to develop their intellectual skills during early adulthood. For many, it can be a time of great progress. As people reach their productive peak at work, they often get promoted to jobs where they need specialist education and training. Many individuals follow further education courses to develop the skills they need for their chosen profession (for example, doctors, lawyers or architects).

Your world

Joy is an occupational therapist and Steven is a personal trainer. They have shared a house for over five years as friends. Draw a spider diagram of the possible benefits of having a long-term friendship.

Physical maturity – having reached the peak of physical capabilities

Metabolic rate – the rate at which the body burns up calories

Cohabit – live together

Other people return to education if they did not achieve their full potential at school and want to get further qualifications. 'Lifelong learning' is now recognised as being very valuable. One good thing about intellectual development is that we do not lose our intellectual capability as we age, and can continue to learn throughout our lives.

Emotional development

It is in early adulthood that many people develop close and intimate relationships with others. Sometimes this leads to people choosing to **cohabit**, marry or go through a civil ceremony. Most people choose to develop steady relationships, as this creates a feeling of security and allows them to give and receive love. Other people choose to live alone, or find themselves living alone as the result of relationship breakdown.

Early adulthood is also the time when many people choose to start a family, and begin to create emotional bonds with their children. The responsibilities of having children are great, but the emotional benefits for parents are, in most cases, very positive. Having children often gives people in early adulthood a sense of purpose and gives life added meaning. There are not many things that give adults more pleasure than hearing their children say their first words, watching them take their first steps or finding they can now cycle without stabilisers!

Social development

In adolescence, most people have few responsibilities and this may still be the case in the first part of early adulthood. Many people in their early twenties enjoy a life built round socialising, meeting new people and making new friends. Others may choose to follow a career, form a steady relationship and possibly start a family. Once these decisions are made, people begin to have responsibilities. A mortgage may need to be paid and the bills will have to be met. Financial responsibilities mean that, for many, work becomes more important. Balancing work, family life and a social life may become tricky. In most cases the social life of someone who is 20 is very different from that of a 40-year-old person.

Dear Lindy

My name is Jeff and I live with my girlfriend Becky and some other friends in a large flat.

I have been living with Becky for some time now, and we get on with our flatmates well. I would like to start a family in the future and get married. I want us to move out to our own flat and become more independent. Becky is concerned about the cost. She also wants us to stay with our flatmates as we have a good social life at the moment. Should I push Becky to take on more responsibility, or just carry on as we are? What do you think?

Just checking

1. Identify four physical changes that occur in early adulthood.
2. How might the social life of a person who is 40 be different from that of a person who is 20?
3. Why do many people in early adulthood choose to cohabit before they marry or go through a civil ceremony?

Your world – Activities and scenarios that get you thinking for yourself about certain aspects of your health and social care learning.

Key terms – Provide you with definitions of key terms and concepts, so you can be sure you understand exactly what is being covered in the topic you are learning about.

Dear Lindy – Read the problem page excerpts then help our agony aunt Lindy to give advice connected to the topic you are covering.

GCSE Health and Social Care for Edexcel

228

You've got the power!

This topic looks at how effective health promotion and support is built on through careful implementation of the care values.

Implementation of the care values

In Unit 2, you looked at the care values implemented by health and social care professionals. Here, you look at how these are implemented, through promoting choice, respecting identity and culture, and empowerment.

Promoting choice

When a service user, or the service user's family, is faced with a decision to make, they need to know what choice is available to them, so information has to be readily accessible to them. For example, if a person has dementia and it is not safe for him to live on his own anymore, his family will want to know what residential homes are available in the area and which will be best for him.

Your world

A life-changing experience

As Aaron has grown, it has become clear that he has special needs. He has struggled to communicate until recently, when his mother read a magazine about a new method being used in a nearby special school. He is now a pupil there and is making amazing progress. How will he have felt before and after the move to the new school?

Have you had an experience, no matter how small, that enabled you to move forward in your life? Have any of your group? Discuss this.

Activity

1. By talking to someone and finding out their preferences and dislikes, and giving them choices, a care assistant can start to help a person newly arrived at a residential care home to settle down and feel happy to be there. Think about someone who is of a different culture from most other people in the care home. What should a good care assistant do to help them settle in quickly? Explain your answer.
2. Answer the same question for someone who does not believe in taking medicinal drugs unless it is unavoidable. Explain your answer.

Think about it

This is fine if the person has a family who can read well and who have access to information sources such as the internet. What do you think happens if they have no family, or the family does not know where to look for information? What do you think the doctor will do as soon as he diagnoses dementia? Which services will he alert?

Respecting identity and culture

If a person's identity and culture are not acknowledged and taken into account in their care, it will affect how their needs are met, and affect their state of mind and willingness to use the service concerned. For example, a health promotion leaflet in a selection of languages will mean that someone from a particular culture will be a...

...information, encouragement and support to enable her to understand what is happening and to say what she wants and what is important to her, she is empowered, and is making progress towards being more independent and making a better recovery.

It may be that someone has been fighting a long battle against cancer and has now decided that he would rather spend what time he has left at home with his family, rather than suffering more treatment that makes him really s... just for the sake of a few more mo... and his wishes are respected, he w... control of what is left of his life. Th... help him through the rest of the ill...

Activity

Research cases of people with cancer, including children, who have decided not to have treatment to prolong their lives.

- Pick a case that touched you most. Why did the person decide to refuse the treatment?
- Do you think it was the right decision? Explain your answer.

Take it further

Look into alternative treatment options. For example, how can yoga or reflexology benefit a patient who has a life-threatening illness? How will a person providing a service such as yoga use the values of care that someone such as a nurse will use?

Just checking

1. Why is promoting choice important in the care of a service user?
2. How will a person's...

Callout descriptions:

Activity – A variety of fun tasks and activities that encourage you to apply the knowledge you've gained in the topic.

Think about it – Thought-provoking questions that give you the chance to reflect more deeply about something related to the topic you are covering.

Take it further – Give you plenty of opportunities to extend the knowledge and understanding you have gained of a topic or issue.

Case study – Scenarios with questions that link theory with practice to help contextualise your learning in the real world of health and social care.

GCSE Health and Social Care for Edexcel

86

What a team!

This topic looks at partnership... agency working, how the diffe... providers work together to meet client needs and how these services are integrated.

Working in partnership

As you will have realised, health, social care and early years professionals rarely work alone. They are more likely to work as part of a team.

Service providers from any of the sectors will meet at case conferences, usually with the client and their family, and work together to provide the right care. This **collaboration** of multi-agents leads to a **holistic** approach to care, so that the client's needs are more likely to be met.

Working collaboratively like this is a move away from the traditional structure of services based on professional discipline: for example, health care services working together and social care services working together, but each sector working separately from the other. The Childcare Act of 2006 is one example of how the Government reinforced what local authorities were already doing – working in partnership with the private and voluntary sectors.

Now you will learn about some good examples of working in partnership.

Sure Start Children's Centres

These are 'service hubs' – central points from which children under the age of five and their families can access integrated services and information. The idea is that this will help make sure that every child gets the best start in life. By 2010, every community (a settlement of 3,500 people) will have such a centre.

The services offered may vary between centres but could include early education and childcare with a qualified teacher, advice on...

think these agencies improve your life as part of a community of students?

Collaboration – working together
Holistic – looking at all the different needs of the client
Advocate – someone who speaks on someone else's behalf

Did you know?

By June 2008, almost 3,000 centres around the UK were offering services to over two million young children and their families.

Activity

Go on the Virtual Ward website. Go onto the Partnerships page and draw a mind map of the various partnerships shown.

87

Case study Edward

Edward is 45 years old and has lost his job as an accountant in a large company, due to cutbacks rather than any fault of his own. He is depressed: there are few jobs available at his level, and he will have to look after the children, because his wife has found a job to make ends meet. He starts to drink too much and becomes aggressive towards his wife and children, who are three, six and eight years old. He feels it is his role to support his family, and he now feels worthless.

1. What services can the family call on to help them through this situation?
2. How will these services work together to give the best possible support to the family?
3. How will Edward feel about calling on outside agencies to help him and his family?
4. How must the service providers approach the situation so as not to make Edward feel even worse about his situation?

health services can share good practice. Everyone can access information about positive and innovative practice, read supporting policy and to use examples of training underpinning those examples. There is an editorial board, where people share ideas, discuss innovations and review resources. The most useful resources are moved across into the Virtual Ward.

If you knew someone with mental health problems or were working in mental health, you could use this online resource to get help and advice.

Multi-agency disability team/key workers

A person who has a disability may be involved with a range of care providers, who will form a team to manage her care so that she can live as independently as possible.

- The local Primary Care Trust will look after her if she falls ill, and will see to routine needs such as sight tests or dental work, as well as helping if she needs more specialist help, such as speech therapy.
- Social services will be responsible for needs such as housing and financial entitlements.
- She will also have a key worker, who will act as an **advocate** to help her keep in touch with her family and with things such as...

The Virtual Ward homepage (www.virtualward.org.uk)

Just checking

1. Why do different services work together to provide care?
2. Why have Sure Start Children's Centres been set up across the country?
3. What is a key worker and what do they do?

Callout descriptions:

Did you know? – Interesting and useful facts that relate to the topic you are learning about.

Just checking – Summary questions at the end of each topic to check you've understood the most important aspects of what has been covered.

The Green

Many of the issues in this book affect people in their day-to-day lives. To see the impact of these issues on how people live, throughout the book you will meet the inhabitants of the Green, a multi-cultural town with a diverse population. By exploring the situations in their lives, you should be able to see how some of the theory you have learnt applies to 'real' world contexts.

Back row (left to right): Julia; Carol; David; Wendy; Felicity; Lewis; Emma; Joy; Steven; Mike; Colin; Nicola; Ben
Front row (left to right): Ahmed; Aaron; Sabah; Amina; Alina; Husna; Carmen; Saalm; Muhammed; Enrico; Barbara; Allegra; Francesca; Paul; Maud; George

The Green itself where the characters live!

Unit 1: Understanding Personal Development and Relationships

Your world

Working with a partner, decide how you might split the residents from The Green, shown on page x, into different groups. How many groups do you think there might be? What names could you give to these groups?

Learning objectives

- The stages and patterns of human growth and development
- The different factors that can affect human growth and development
- The development of self-concept and personal relationships
- Major life events and how people manage the effects of these
- The role of relationships in personal development

Introduction

Have you ever wondered what it is that makes people different? Why do we become close friends with some people and not others?

This unit will help you understand the factors that influence how people grow and develop throughout their lives.

The stages and patterns of human growth and development

During a person's **lifespan** they are said to go through six **life stages**. Whether a person goes through all six stages depends on how long they live. Some people can live to an age of 90 or 100 years, whereas some other people may only live till they are 20 or 30. George, who lives on The Green, is 90 years of age, so will have passed through all six life stages.

Factors affecting human growth and development

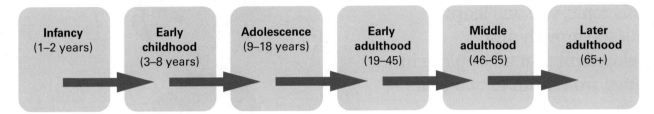

| Infancy (1–2 years) | Early childhood (3–8 years) | Adolescence (9–18 years) | Early adulthood (19–45) | Middle adulthood (46–65) | Later adulthood (65+) |

The six life stages

A number of different **factors** affect how people grow and develop. Some aspects of growth and development are determined by the genes that we inherit from our biological parents. We call these **nature** influences. How tall we grow and our body shape and weight are influenced by the genes from our parents.

The effects of the environment people live in also influence how people grow and develop. We call these influences **nurture** influences. A person's height and weight is also influenced by the diet they have and the exercise they take.

Effect of relationships

The different types of relationships people have in their lives also affect how they grow and develop. People are particularly influenced by family, friends, the people they work with and the close and intimate relationships they have with partners.

Effects of life events

As people pass through the different life stages, a whole range of events can affect how they grow and develop. Some events are expected, such as starting school; others are unexpected, such as accidents and serious illnesses.

> **Lifespan** – the period of time between birth and death
> **Life stage** – one of a number of distinct phases people pass through during their lives.
> **Factor** – something that has an influence on other things, or is a part or element of something larger
> **Nature** – the influence of our genes
> **Nurture** – the influence of our environment, our circumstances and the way we are brought up

How you will be assessed

You will be assessed by examination for this module of work. The examination paper will consist of:

- multiple-choice questions
- short, medium and longer questions based on case studies presented in the examination paper.

All the questions in the examination paper are compulsory, and will give you the opportunity to show examiners what you know.

4

Welcome to the world

In this topic, you will learn about the growth and development that takes place in infancy, from birth to two years of age.

Infancy (1–2 years of age)

From being born weighing just a few kilos, to reaching the age of two, an infant changes in many ways. How could so much change have taken place in such a short time?

During infancy, **growth** and **development** is at its most rapid, and is very noticeable to those closest to the infant.

To help to make it easier to understand just what happens, we can look at it under the four PIES headings: physical, intellectual, emotional and social.

Physical changes

These changes can be split into gross and fine motor skill development. Changes in gross motor skills mean that the infant can start to control the larger muscles in its body; fine motor skills mean that it can control the smaller muscles. By the age of two, an infant can usually do things such as walk, hold a spoon and point – changes that will progress further in childhood.

Intellectual changes

Intellectual development, sometimes called cognitive development, is about thinking and the way the mind works.

A newborn infant tends to respond to the world about them through their senses, in basic ways: for example, if it is hungry, it cries. By the time the infant is two, its ability to think has developed hugely: it will be using language and have the ability to grasp some basic concepts. For example, if a parent hides a toy from view, a six-

Your world

Ahmed and Sabah have two children. Aaron has just had his first birthday and is proving a handful for his mum, dad and sister, Alina. What sort of skills will Aaron have developed by this age? Think about PIES to help you structure your thinking.

Activity

With a partner, design a diagram to show:

- the sequence of the gross motor skill changes that happen in infancy
- the sequence of the fine motor skill changes that happen in infancy.

You might want to use a flow diagram, or a design of your own.

month-old infant will think it no longer exists and may cry, but a two-year-old will know that it still exists even though it cannot see it, and will seek it out – a concept known as object permanence.

Perhaps the most important part of intellectual development for infants is the development and use of language.

Emotional changes

Emotional development is concerned with understanding our own feelings and those of others. This begins and develops from birth.

During the first two years of life, an infant 'bonds' with those who care for it. An infant needs to form a strong attachment with its main carer, and to receive love and affection in a positive way. This bond helps create a sense of security, and influences the infant's development throughout future life stages. This process is part of what is sometimes called **attachment** theory.

Social changes

Social development is concerned with interaction with others and the relationships we form. The early relationships formed in infancy act as a model for future relationships.

By the age of two, an infant has learned a lot about how to interact with others. At first, the main relationships are with the primary carers, but this then extends to brothers and sisters, wider family members and other people the infant meets. A great deal of learning about relationships takes place through the process of play. In early infancy, the infant plays alone – solitary play – and is not able to think of others. By the age of two, the infant can play alongside others – parallel play – and the process of being able to share starts to develop.

Growth – the changes in size and mass of the infant
Development – the new skills and capabilities an infant acquires
Bond – grow closer and develop emotional ties
Attachment – the bonding process between an infant or child and its carer. Attachment is achieved through close contact over a period of time

---

Just checking

1. Explain the difference between fine and gross motor skills.
2. Explain the difference between growth and development.
3. Identify two ways in which a carer may promote 'bonding' with an infant.

Activity

Physical	Social	Emotional	Intellectual
Hold head up	Play alone	React to carer by smiling	Learn through senses such as taste
Hold a small toy	Learn to socialise with carer	Bond with brother/sister	Speak 100 words

1. Can you add two other changes to each area?
2. At what ages do you think the infant could have achieved each of these developments?

Stepping up

Here you will learn about the key physical, intellectual, emotional and social changes that take place in early childhood, from three to eight years of age.

Early childhood (3–8 years of age)

Early childhood continues to be a period of growth and development across all the PIES areas. It is a time when many of the skills we use in later life are developed. Children seem to be programmed to learn particular skills at particular ages, and love the process of learning them.

Physical development

The physical skills that children have develop greatly during childhood. At the age of two, an infant has limited skills that become much more developed as they pass through childhood. By the age of 5, most children can walk up stairs unaided, and can hold a crayon or pencil to draw and write. By the age of eight, children learn to catch and throw, develop a good sense of balance and can use a bat and ball effectively – many top-class athletes were already good at their sport by the end of this life stage.

By the end of early childhood, a child has established facial features that will be recognisable into adolescence and adulthood.

Intellectual development

By the end of childhood, a huge change will have taken place in intellectual ability. A child will no longer just experience the world through their senses, but will be able to begin to think about things, even if this is mainly only from their own viewpoint – which is called **egocentrism**.

Children's communication and language skills improve greatly in this stage. Children now use full sentences, can count and start to sequence and order events: for example, they will know which days of the week follow each other, and the order of the months of the year.

Children learn by asking questions and by watching the behaviour of others. It is important that adults show children how to behave in certain situations: for example, a parent might let their children watch how they behave at the dentist, so the child knows what to do when they go. This is known as **modelling**.

Your world

During childhood, boys and girls often play differently. Think back to when you were this age. Who did you play with and what sort of games did you play? In a small group, draw up a list of all the differences you can think of in how boys and girls play. Be prepared to feedback into a whole-class discussion.

Think about it

If you become a parent or carer in adulthood, what sort of values would you expect your child to have by the time they are eight?

- Draw up a list of the different things you expect them to know as being wrong by the age of eight.
- Discuss your views with others in the class in a whole-class discussion.

At this stage, children can also think about problems, learn about the difference between right and wrong, and begin to be able to work out solutions. During adolescence this process will become much more refined, but it is important that parents correct inappropriate behaviour in childhood and encourage acceptable behaviour.

Emotional development

Between the ages of three and eight, a child will experience a range of new feelings, and will have to learn how to handle them. Having bonded with their main carers, children now play and work with others. They have to learn how to share and cooperate – and this means that they experience emotions such at love, hate, fear and jealousy. As children are still very self-centred or egocentric, many may have **temper tantrums** and want their own way a lot of the time.

Social development

In early childhood, cooperative play begins to take place: children share, use their imagination and are often involved in role play. Children love to dress up and learn about the different jobs people have in the world. Children gradually learn how to handle relationships with others and how to behave as a friend. By the age of eight, a child will have a number of friends, and sometimes a person they call their 'best friend'.

In building relationships with other children and adults they learn how to behave appropriately in society.

Activity

In pairs, select three different sorts of games you played as a child or that children play together. For each game, explain how it would stimulate a child's development. Remember to use PIES to help you with this.

Egocentrism – seeing things from only your own viewpoint
Modelling – demonstrating behaviour for others to copy
Temper tantrums – poor behaviour by children such as screaming, throwing themselves to the ground, and getting really angry, designed to try to get their own way

Just checking

1. What sort of new skills and capabilities do children have by the age of eight?
2. Why do young children have temper tantrums?
3. Describe three new social skills that are developed in childhood.

Are teens so terrible?

This topic looks as the key physical, intellectual, emotional and social changes that take place during adolescence, from nine to eighteen years of age.

Adolescence (9–18 years of age)

Is your body changing shape? Do you worry about how you look and what other people think about you? It is common for people in adolescence to worry about how they look and what other people feel about them.

Some people see this life stage as a time of transition, as the child enters adolescence, goes through **puberty** and matures, becoming an adult. Different young people enter puberty at different times. The key point to remember is that your body programmes you to experience the changes in adolescence at exactly the right time for you.

Physical development

In adolescence, a rapid process of physical changes takes place in the body. These changes occur as a result of hormonal releases, which turn a child into a fully reproductive adult. The physical changes in girls are primarily shaped by the release of oestrogen; those in boys by the release of testosterone. This diagram shows the major changes that occur.

Dear Lindy

My name is Alina and I am 14 years old. I have just started going out with David who I have known since primary school. We both go to the same school and see each other twice during the week and at weekends. I fancy him like mad and he makes me feel good about myself. At the moment, he is getting a lot of spots and has become very moody. His spots don't really bother me, but he says he can't understand why I would want to go out with him anymore when he looks like this. He is talking about ending our relationship.

What can I do?

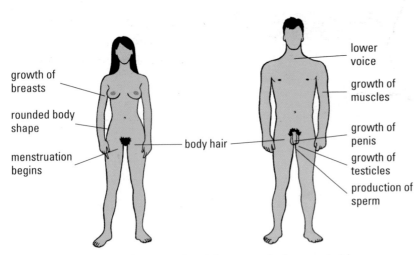

The physical changes that occur in adolescence, for boys and girls

growth of breasts

rounded body shape

menstruation begins

body hair

lower voice

growth of muscles

growth of penis

growth of testicles

production of sperm

Intellectual development

One of the biggest changes that happens intellectually in adolescence is the development of an ability to think about concepts and ideas rather than actual things – an ability known as **abstract thinking**. You can probably begin to see this in your own thought patterns already – you can imagine what it might be like to be a top-class football player or musician.

Adolescents can also think in a more logical way to solve problems, as well as being able to see things from other people's perspectives. Unlike children, they do not believe that the world is totally centred round them.

Intellectual development does not stop at the end of adolescence, but continues throughout adulthood life.

Emotional and social development

The large hormonal releases in the body that occur at this stage can make this a very difficult time for some teenagers. Many experience mood swings, frustrations, insecurities and confusions. There is also the added problem of feeling physical attraction to others – something that has not happened before. Adolescence is a time when sexuality is explored, with the opposite sex and sometimes the same sex. Close and intimate relationships are formed. The teenager has to work through this new range of feelings and handle rejection as they search for a unique and individual identity.

As well as forming close and intimate relationships, teenagers also begin to be more influenced more by what their friends do and think, rather than what their parents believe. This is called the influence of the **peer group**. Relationships also tend to be a lot closer in adolescence and may last throughout the whole of adult life.

Puberty – a period of physical change caused by hormonal changes in the body
Abstract thinking – the ability to think about something that might not be there or even exist
Peer group – the influence of people similar in many ways to the individual concerned: for example, of the same age, sex or class

Activity

In adolescence, many young people disagree with their parents/carers more than they used to.

- What do you think are the main issues young people disagree with parents/carers about?
- Why do you think conflicts happen more often at this time than during infancy or childhood?

Think about it

What can you do to be well prepared to produce the highest exam marks you can? Draw up a list of things you could do.

If you can do this, you are beginning to think abstractly. A six-year-old child would find this really hard to do.

Just checking

1. Identify two physical changes that happen to girls, two physical changes that happen to boys, and one physical change that happens to both girls and boys in adolescence.
2. In what ways is a teenager able to think differently from a child?
3. Describe three ways in which teenage behaviour may be influenced by peer-group pressure.

Independence days

Here you look at the key physical, intellectual, emotional and social changes that take place in early adulthood, from the ages of 19 to 45.

Early adulthood (19–45 years of age)

Do you look forward to the time when you are independent and can do what you want? Looking forward to having a job and earning your own money? Do you want to settle down with a partner and have your own home? Would you like to have children? These are all the sorts of things that may happen in early adulthood.

It is often seen as a time when people reach their physical peak and maturity. It is a time when you may feel completely 'grown up', yet in fact you are still growing and developing in important ways.

Your world

Joy is an occupational therapist and Steven is a personal trainer. They have shared a house for over five years as friends. Draw a spider diagram of the possible benefits of having a long-term friendship.

Physical development

During early adulthood, physical development continues, with most individuals reaching their physical peak – or reaching **physical maturity** – in their early twenties. People are at their strongest at this time and, in sporting terms, perform at their best – most athletic record holders are in early adulthood.

As individuals move towards the end of this life stage, their physical capabilities begin to decline. Fertility starts to drop for both men and women, and the signs of ageing begin to appear. Some women may start to go through the menopause, although this is more common in middle adulthood. As people's **metabolic rate** drops, they may begin to put on weight, hair may go grey, wrinkles may appear and eyesight may decline. However, many of the physical changes can be countered by exercise and diet control. If people in early adulthood look after themselves well, you may be surprised to discover their real age!

> **Physical maturity** – having reached the peak of physical capabilities
>
> **Metabolic rate** – the rate at which the body burns up calories
>
> **Cohabit** – live together

Intellectual development

Adults continue to develop their intellectual skills during early adulthood. For many, it can be a time of great progress. As people reach their productive peak at work, they often get promoted to jobs where they need specialist education and training. Many individuals follow further education courses to develop the skills they need for their chosen profession (for example, doctors, lawyers or architects).

Other people return to education if they did not achieve their full potential at school and want to get further qualifications. 'Lifelong learning' is now recognised as being very valuable. One good thing about intellectual development is that we do not lose our intellectual capability as we age, and can continue to learn throughout our lives.

Emotional development

It is in early adulthood that many people develop close and intimate relationships with others. Sometimes this leads to people choosing to **cohabit**, marry or go through a civil ceremony. Most people choose to develop steady relationships, as this creates a feeling of security and allows them to give and receive love. Other people choose to live alone, or find themselves living alone as the result of relationship breakdown.

Early adulthood is also the time when many people choose to start a family, and begin to create emotional bonds with their children. The responsibilities of having children are great, but the emotional benefits for parents are, in most cases, very positive. Having children often gives people in early adulthood a sense of purpose and gives life added meaning. There are not many things that give adults more pleasure than hearing their children say their first words, watching them take their first steps or finding they can now cycle without stabilisers!

Dear Lindy

My name is Jeff and I live with my girlfriend Becky and some other friends in a large flat.

I have been living with Becky for some time now, and we get on with our flatmates well. I would like to start a family in the future and get married. I want us to move out to our own flat and become more independent. Becky is concerned about the cost. She also wants us to stay with our flatmates as we have a good social life at the moment. Should I push Becky to take on more responsibility, or just carry on as we are? What do you think?

Social development

In adolescence, most people have few responsibilities and this may still be the case in the first part of early adulthood. Many people in their early twenties enjoy a life built round socialising, meeting new people and making new friends. Others may choose to follow a career, form a steady relationship and possibly start a family. Once these decisions are made, people begin to have responsibilities. A mortgage may need to be paid and the bills will have to be met. Financial responsibilities mean that, for many, work becomes more important. Balancing work, family life and a social life may become tricky. In most cases the social life of someone who is 20 is very different from that of a 40-year-old person.

Just checking

1. Identify four physical changes that occur in early adulthood.

2. How might the social life of a person who is 40 be different from that of a person who is 20?

3. Why do many people in early adulthood choose to cohabit before they marry or go through a civil ceremony?

Mid-life crisis?

This topic is about the key physical, intellectual, emotional and social changes that happen in middle adulthood, from 46 to 65 years of age.

Middle adulthood (46–65 years of age)

When people reach mid-life, it is often said that they have reached maturity. It is easy to think that, by reaching 45 years of age, most people should have worked out what life is all about and how it works. Just ask someone in this life stage if this is true. You might be surprised by the answer you get!

In some ways, the older you get, the wiser you get; but in other ways, the older you get, the less you know …

Physical development

In middle adulthood, the **ageing process** begins to take effect on the human body. The physical developments taking place in the body are often judged as being negative, but ageing is just a natural process. Physical capabilities begin to decline as the body does not function as effectively as it did in early adulthood. Skin loses its elasticity and wrinkles appear more obvious; muscle tone slackens; sight and hearing may not be as good.

At this stage, women produce less oestrogen and men less testosterone. These hormonal changes mean that women will go through the **menopause** and complete this process by the end of this life stage. In men, sperm production decreases.

Intellectual development

Intellectual development may continue throughout middle adulthood. Many people may return to education and choose to study more, perhaps wanting to move their life in a new direction and needing new qualifications to do so. Due to the ageing process, a person's memory may not be quite as quick as it used to be, but people in middle adulthood have the benefit of experience: hence the saying 'older but wiser'.

Emotional development

For many people, the physical changes of middle adulthood lead to confused emotions. Just as in adolescence, the body is in a period of hormonal change, and hormones can create a wide range of feelings and emotions.

Your world

In middle adulthood, people often begin to review their lives. They realise they are no longer young, but they do not yet feel old.

Draw up a table with two sections. In section one, list the positive points of being in middle adulthood; in the second section, list the negative points.

Ageing process – the biological change that takes place over time to the human body, affecting its structure and functioning

Menopause – the natural and permanent stopping of menstruation (periods), occurring usually between the ages of 45 and 55

Empty nest syndrome – the feeling of loss and sadness when one or more children leave the family home

Mid-life crisis – a dramatic period of self-doubt caused by the passing of youth and the move into later adulthood

Case study George

George is 90 years of age and lives on The Green. He attends the local community centre and often helps people deal with the problems they face in their lives. He often tells people that, when he was 25, he thought he knew most things and that he had life sorted. As he grew older, he realised that life can throw up unexpected events that make you feel a whole range of emotions, and question all aspects of your life and where you are going.

1. George has married twice, both times during his middle adulthood. How do you think the divorce from his first wife made him feel?
2. When George re-married he remained close with most of his children. However, one of his children found the re-marriage difficult. Why do you think this might have happened?
3. What steps do you think George could have made to re-build this relationship? What would you have done if you had found yourself in this position?

At this stage, people often no longer feel young. Their children may have grown up and be leaving home, creating the **empty nest syndrome**. Some people will become grandparents, with all the emotions and feelings that may bring. People may have been doing the same job for a number of years, and it might now have become routine. Some will have become bored with work and want a change; others might realise they have gone as far as they can go in their line of work, and be wondering what comes next.

Put together, these factors lead many people to review their lives at this time. Some may try to recapture their youth and go back to behaving as if they were in their twenties; others may wish to move on and try things they have never done before. This is why we talk about people having a **mid-life crisis**. It happens to many men and women and is quite normal. This process might last for a number of years until people settle into feeling happy with who they are again.

Social development

Being in middle adulthood offers many people the chance to extend their social development. If children have grown up and left home, the parents have less responsibility and more money to spend on themselves – so they can go out more to socialise with friends, try out new activities and travel.

However, this may not be the case for all middle-aged people. Many young people go into higher education, and their parents often have to support them financially well into their twenties. There is also a recent trend for children to stay in the family home for longer before they become independent. Also, the ageing process means that, as people move towards the end of this life stage, their energy levels may not be as great as before, so they may not want to socialise as much as they once did.

Activity

Ask people in your own family in middle adulthood about how their social life is different now from when they were in their twenties.

What are the main reasons for the differences in social activities in middle adulthood and those in early adulthood?

Just checking

1. Identify three physical features of the ageing process.
2. Describe two factors that might result in someone having a mid-life crisis.
3. Identify three physical features associated with the menopause.

14

Time on my hands

In this topic, you will learn about the key physical, intellectual, emotional and social developments that happen in later adulthood.

Later adulthood (65+)

Later adulthood is a period when people have more time on their hands than ever before. Many people who are over 65 years of age are very active – and wonder how they ever used to fit work into their lives!

Physical development

By the time people reach the age of 65, the ageing process is very clear. Their skin will be less elastic and thinner; their joints stiffer; their muscles weaker; their bones more brittle. As a result of these changes, many people in later adulthood start to stiffen up and begin to lose height. The changes to eyesight and hearing that started in middle adulthood continue.

People at this life stage need to avoid falling, as much more damage is likely to be done should they fall. Every year over 400,000 older people die in the UK as result of hip fracture. Falls can cost a lot to treat too: falls cost the NHS about £600 million per year, and social care around £400 million per year.

Although this may seem rather negative, there is a lot people can do to counter the effects of ageing and keep themselves fit. A regular exercise pattern and good diet can help people to improve their muscle tone, maintain joint flexibility and strengthen their bones.

Intellectual development

Although some people in later adulthood may not be as quick-thinking as they once were, intelligence is not something that deteriorates with age. The brain is just like a muscle – the more it is exercised, the better it works!

Many people at this stage in their lives are very active intellectually, enjoying activities such as reading, problem solving and keeping up with the news, as well as taking up new pursuits. While physical ability may be on the decline, people in later adulthood can still

Your world

Look carefully at the picture above of people in later adulthood exercising together. With a partner, list five reasons why these people might benefit from playing golf together regularly.

Activity

Look at a sudoku and a crossword puzzle in a newspaper.

With a partner, consider all the benefits that completing these tasks may have for person in later adulthood. Remember to use PIES to help you think of the possible benefits.

Case study George and Maud

On The Green, George has a very active social life, and Maud is involved with various groups connected to her church.

With members of your class, research the sorts of social activities available in your local area for people in later adulthood. Draw up a list and identify and explain how these activities are linked to development. Remember to use PIES to help shape your response.

apply the experience and knowledge they have gained over the years to great effect: indeed, the political leaders of many countries are in their sixties and seventies.

Some people may experience **dementia** in later adulthood. Dementia affects the functioning of the brain and particularly affects short-term memory, though long-term memory is also ultimately affected. For the members of the person's family, who have to live with a person experiencing dementia, this can be a very distressing time.

Emotional development

Later adulthood is often a rewarding period as, after retirement, people can spend more **quality time** with partners and family. Many people will enjoy spending time with grandchildren and other friends too. When people have finished full-time work, their stress levels may also be lower. These sorts of changes can lead to a happy and contented retirement.

However, later adulthood can be a challenging and upsetting time too. Partners and lifelong close friends will die, and some older people will feel isolated and alone. Having spent a lifetime with a partner and friends, losing the security and contentment of these relationships can be hard to cope with. The support of family and friends can be crucial in facing the challenges such changes bring.

Social development

With the extra time people have in retirement, it is possible for them to develop a very active social life. It is possible to split later adulthood up into two parts.

The first age section is 65 to 75, sometimes called 'early later adulthood'. During this time, many people may still be very active. They may meet their friends at the local swimming pool or possibly go on holiday together. This gives people the chance to become closer and support each other as the ageing process takes place.

As people age beyond 75, they do tend to slow down a little, but this doesn't mean that they have to socialise less. It just means that the pace may not be as quick. There is still the opportunity to spend time with others and enjoy the benefits of a good social life.

Dementia – various brain disorders that have in common a loss of brain function that is usually progressive and eventually severe

Quality time – time spent relating closely to and focusing on others, which may be more rewarding than a longer period of time spent being less engaged

Just checking

1. What sort of physical changes will people notice in their bodies after the age of 65?

2. Why might many people in later adulthood see this stage as the start of something new and exciting?

3. Explain two ways in which a family may support a person in later adulthood in dealing with the death of their life partner.

Born this way

Here you will learn how growth and development are influenced by nature, looking at hereditary characteristics.

The influence of nature

Genes, chromosomes and heredity

Every new baby that is born is a unique individual: no two people are exactly the same. But have you noticed that brothers and sisters from the same family often look alike and have similar features? Do you know any people who are identical twins? The physical similarities you've seen are linked to the natural influence of **heredity**: the **genes** we inherit from our parents, which strongly shape the way we develop and grow.

How heredity works

The human body is made up of cells. Each cell has two sets of 23 **chromosomes**: it is these chromosomes and the way they combine that influence the way we grow and develop. The chromosomes carry genetic information – a kind of code for the different features of a human being. At the point of conception, when the egg is fertilised by the sperm, nature combines two sets of genes: one from the father and one from the mother.

Your world

Look at the picture of Enrico and his family and identify the physical ways in which they look similar.

Which features do you think the daughter has inherited from Enrico and which from his wife?

Identify two ways in which we can change the way we look by the lifestyle choices we make.

Did you know?

Identical twins have exactly the same set of genetic information because they came from one egg, which only split after if was fertilised. With non-identical twins, the mother produces two eggs at the same time and they are fertilised by two different sperm – this is why these twins may not look that much alike.

The resulting child will inherit some characteristics from each parent – this is the process that makes us all so individual and interesting. If both parents have black hair and dark brown eyes, the child is likely to inherit these features. If parents are physically very different from each other – perhaps being of different sizes and with

Activity

Famous sisters Venus and Serena Williams are top-class tennis players, who have both won Wimbledon and other major tennis tournaments. They started playing tennis when they were four years old, and were leading players by the time they were 14.

Research these two sisters and identify which of the physical features determined by genes make them top-class players.

different hair and eye colours – the instructions from one set of genes may be **dominant** over the other: for example, dark eyes are usually dominant over blue eyes. If neither set of genes is dominant, then both sets of genetic instructions are followed.

Examples of physical features that are determined by genes

- Sex
- Height
- Body shape
- Skin colour
- Eye colour

What else is influenced by our genes?

Scientists have already discovered a great deal about how our genes affect us, and their research continues to find new links all the time.

We know that specific genes can be responsible for certain illnesses, such as **Huntington's disease**. We also know that the information in our genes can lead people to have a tendency to develop certain illnesses in later life – heart disease and certain types of cancer have been proved to be genetically linked. However, whether people go on to develop these diseases is also influenced by how they lead their lives.

If you were to look back at your parents' and grandparents' health, you might see a pattern emerging – for example, a tendency towards heart disease in the family. If this were so, you would be wise to eat healthily, have your cholesterol levels checked and exercise regularly. Decisions like these are important in how we go on to grow and develop too.

More recent research has also claimed that specific genes are linked to other aspects of our development, such as sexual orientation, intelligence and the chance of suffering from depression. The links here are much less clear, and have yet to be proved.

Just checking

1. Identify three human physical features that are determined by our genes.
2. Why do identical twins look exactly the same?
3. Identify three illnesses that are linked to genetic inheritance.

Think about it

Huntington's disease affects the brain and is inherited. It can lead to uncontrolled movements, emotional upsets and a loss of intellectual capability.

In the USA it is estimated that there are 25,000 people who live with the disease and 100,000 people who live with uncertainty that they may develop the disease at a later stage in their lives. Many people in the UK face the same situation.

Research the different ways in which Huntington's disease may affect the lives of individuals who have the disease and their close relatives.

Find out how many people in the UK have the disease and how many live with the uncertainty that they may develop the illness.

Heredity – the transmission of a particular quality or trait from parent to offspring through their genes

Genes – DNA ribbons that control a hereditary characteristic

Chromosome – a thread-like piece of DNA that contains genes and transmits hereditary information

Dominant – having the most influence or control

Huntington's disease – a hereditary disorder affecting the central nervous system causing abnormal body movements; also known as Huntington's Chorea

Made this way?

In this topic, you will learn how family, friends and culture can influence growth and development. It is the combination of this group of factors that influences the sort of people we become.

How we grow and develop is influenced as much by the environment we live in and the things that happen to us as by the genes we inherit from our parents. This is known as the influence of nurture.

Family

The family you live in and the way it nurtures you have a powerful effect on your physical, intellectual, emotional and social development. A 'family' comes in many forms in the UK. Some people live in two-parent families; some live in one-parent families; some live in **extended families**; and some children live in care. However, it is not just the type of family that affects how an individual grows and develops – it is also the care they receive and the quality of family relationships they have.

Throughout history people have raised children in family units. It is now generally accepted that the family is the best environment for children to develop intellectually, emotionally and socially in.

A child's family teaches them the **customs** and traditions of the society they live in. As the UK is a multicultural society, a whole range of customs and traditions exist. People choose to dress according to the customs of their culture, according to their age and depending on which aspect of their life they are currently involved in. You probably dress very differently for school than

Your world

Ahmed takes his daughter Alina to visit her grandmother regularly. On a recent visit, Alina's grandmother told Ahmed and Alina about a newspaper story she had read, highlighting the importance of family and friends in helping teenagers achieve their best results in GCSE examinations.

In small groups, discuss what sort of help family and friends might be able to give teenagers as they prepare for GCSE examinations in Y10 and Y11.

Learning in families can take place in many different activities

when relaxing at home or going out to a special event with your friends. The family also teaches a child the **values** that need to be accepted in a society: for example, in our society we value honesty and trust.

The influence of the family on young people is known as **primary socialisation**. No two families are the same, and the particular influence young people receive from their family plays a role in determining what sort of adult they will become.

Friends

The influence of our friends is also important in shaping the sort of people we become. Friends tends to be in the same age group and in childhood and adolescence are often of the same gender. What our friends do, think and believe also tends to influence our own behaviour patterns. We look at friendship in more detail on pages 34–5.

Culture

There is no one **culture** in the UK: we live in a **multicultural** society. The UK encompasses many different ethnic groups, each with its own customs and traditions.

Many of the values we have are common across all ethnic groups: for example, nearly everybody believes that theft is wrong. However, one of the most interesting aspects of our society is its diversity, created by the bringing together of the different traditions and customs of so many ethnic groups. Being multicultural has brought a range of festivals, celebrations, music and more to our society, as well as the chance to enjoy all sorts of types of food!

The variety of lifestyles among different groups in our society affects the way individuals grow and develop. For example, the emphasis on hard work and the value placed on education in Indian culture is one reason why individuals from this group are often so successful educationally.

Think about it

In pairs, list the most important values for young people to learn to help them be effective members of society in adulthood. Share these with the class and then collectively come to an agreement about which five values are the most important.

Do you think people in later adulthood have different values than people in adolescence?

Activity

Alina has a close group of friends at school. They all have high ambitions to work in the health and social care sector in the future, possibly as doctors, nurses and social workers.

In what ways will it benefit Alina's intellectual development to mix with friends who all have high ambitions for careers in the future?

Extended family – a family that includes more than just parents and children: for example, with grandparents, uncles and aunts, and so on
Custom – a practice or way of acting that is a habit or usual
Values – set of principles by which people lead their lives
Primary socialisation – the influence of carers on values, attitudes and behaviour
Culture – distinctive patterns of human activity and ways of life in a group
Multicultural – including a range of ethnic and cultural groups

Just checking

1. Identify two different festivals associated with different cultures and explain what they involve.
2. Draw a diagram to illustrate your own extended family.
3. In what ways can friends influence each other's behaviour?

White wedding or civil ceremony?

In this topic, you will learn how growth and development can be influenced by sexual orientation and by going through marriage or a civil ceremony, and separation or divorce.

Forming permanent relationships

In adolescence and early adulthood, people become more certain about their **sexuality** and **sexual orientation**. This is also the time when they are likely to form permanent sexual and intimate relationships.

Sexual and intimate relationships are some of the most important relationships we have in our lives. Being close to another person can make you feel valued and loved. It can also create a sense of security, as you know that another person feels you are special and wants you to be a part of their life. Some of these relationships will last a lifetime, but others may last for just a limited period of time.

Successful intimate relationships affect all aspects of our physical intellectual, emotional and social development. People often choose to start a family and experience the fulfilment this can bring. For some, coming to terms with their sexuality may involve the realisation that they are gay or bisexual. How others respond to this can have significant effects on the person's growth and development. Being happy and contented in a relationship can allow you to focus on your work and intellectual development; if an intimate relationship is going through a difficult patch, this can have a negative effect on many aspects of your life.

Marriages and civil ceremonies

Deciding to marry or make a commitment to another person through a **civil ceremony** is one of the biggest decisions people make during their lives. As well as being a legal commitment, it is a

Your world

Emma, Lewis and Felicity are discussing whether they will ever get married and whether marriage is old-fashioned these days.

Design a questionnaire to use with your class to find out if marriage is still popular with young people today. Include some questions about the benefits of being married for the people who choose to marry.

Activity

Ben and Nicola live together in a flat on The Green. They share this flat with their friends Mike and Colin.

Create a table to show the possible emotional and social benefits for Ben and Nicola of having an intimate relationship with each other.

statement about an emotional attachment to another person. In our culture, people traditionally choose who they will marry, usually based on love and attraction. In other cultures, **arranged marriages** can be common.

After marrying, it usually takes a while to adapt to a new way of living. The two people now have responsibilities towards each other and have to consider the other person's needs as well as their own. These new bonds may bring with them a number of emotional and social benefits, but married life is not always easy. As the saying goes: 'Falling in love is easy; the difficulty part is making it last.'

All relationships need to be worked at, through good times and bad, if they are to succeed.

Separation and divorce

In deciding to make the commitment of marriage, people become legally joined together. If one partner wants to end the relationship, they will have to go through a **divorce**. In the UK, it is only possible to be married or connected by a civil ceremony to one person at any one time.

Separation and divorce are among the most stressful life events a person can go through. As well as the emotional and social issues caused by the split, there are often complicated financial issues to be sorted too. If the family has children, decisions will need to be made over **custody** arrangements.

Although difficult, divorce can be the right decision for all concerned if the relationship has permanently broken down. After the divorce is complete, the people affected by the change can move on with their lives.

Just checking

1. Explain two benefits for an individual of getting married or having a civil ceremony.
2. List three reasons why people may choose to have a civil ceremony rather than a church wedding.
3. Describe two ways in which a teenager's growth and development could be affected by the realisation that they are gay.

Activity

Interview a family member or friend about their wedding. Make sure you find out:

- the type of wedding it was
- where it took place – church or registry office
- what they enjoyed about the day
- what problems and stresses occurred which were not planned for.

From the information you have collected, design a leaflet for young people called 'Planning for a successful wedding day – important things to bear in mind.'

Sexuality – sense of emotional, sexual and affectional attraction to others
Sexual orientation – the direction someone's sexuality takes: for example, towards men or women
Civil ceremony – a legal ceremony with no religious elements, conducted by a registrar, having the same legal validity as a traditional marriage
Arranged marriage – a marriage arranged by a person other than the person getting married
Divorce – the legal ending of a marriage
Custody – the legal arrangements about who is responsible for a child after a divorce

Money makes the world go round

This topic explains how growth and development can be influenced by work, wealth and poverty, income and social class.

Work

Most people spend a large part of their adult life working. This gives them the income to buy the goods and services they need, for themselves and their family. The types of work people choose to do and the relationships they build with people at work affect their growth and development.

Jobs can be **manual** or **non-manual**. Manual jobs – 'hands-on' work such as working in the building trade, or being a hospital porter or a farmhand – can be very physically tiring. Some can have short-term and long-term effects on the body at different life stages. Non-manual jobs – such as a receptionist or a manager – require people to use their minds, rather than their bodies. Sometimes non-manual jobs can be stressful, and the work may involve little exercise, leading to a type of lifestyle that is linked to high blood pressure and heart disease.

All jobs have both positive and negative effects, and these will affect the growth and development of the person doing that job.

You will look at work relationships in more detail on page 38.

Wealth and income

In the UK, **wealth** and **income** are not distributed evenly. Some people come from wealthy backgrounds and eventually inherit wealth from their families. This wealth may be 'old money', where the family has been rich for many generations, or 'new money', where the most recent generation is the first to have acquired it: for example, the Queen has 'old money', while Victoria and David Beckham's children will benefit from a great deal of 'new money'!

Your world

Does money make people happy?

With a partner, pick a wealthy celebrity who often appears in the media. Discuss the possible benefits and problems for them of having such a high level of income.

Be prepared to feedback at least three benefits and problems for a whole-class discussion.

Manual work – work that requires the use of physical skills

Non-manual work – work that depends primarily on mental skills

Wealth – being rich, and having a plentiful supply of goods and money

Income – money earned over a given period of time

Poverty – despite benefits, having insufficient money to afford essentials to live

However, most people's money comes from the income they earn for the work they do. The level of income a person earns is linked to the skills, qualifications and talents they have, how hard they work, and the area of work that they are in. Some people are born with a talent that will earn them a high level of income, or enter a field of work where wages are high. For most people, their level of income is largely set by their qualifications and skills and the amount that they work.

The way a person's wealth and income affect their growth and development is not straightforward. Wealth may mean that people can buy private education for their children, get private healthcare for their families, and have more material possessions in their lives than others. However, wealth and a high income do not guarantee health and wellbeing.

Having a low level of income and wealth makes life more difficult. When income is limited, people can find it hard to meet even their most basic needs (see Maslow's Hierarchy of Needs on page 67). There are still a large number of people in the UK who live in **poverty** on a daily basis. Poverty can have profound negative effects on a person's physical, intellectual, emotional and social development. On top of this, we live in a society where people are measured by the possessions they have. Many teenagers are concerned to have the most fashionable designer clothing and the latest gadgets – but all of this costs money.

Social class

One of the ways of making sense of how society works is to use measures of social class, which are usually based on occupation and income. The more educated a person is and the higher the income they earn, the higher up the social class scale they appear. For example, doctors and lawyers are well educated and earn a high income, so they appear at the top of most measures of social class. It is quite common to talk about upper, middle and lower social classes, but in reality the divide is much more detailed than this.

Looking at society, you can see how social class affects the way people grow and develop. For example, people from the upper classes tend to get better qualifications and live longer than those from working-class backgrounds; and people often marry others from a similar social class to their own. Thinking in these terms can help you understand the society we live in.

Activity

Steven and Joy both live on The Green. Steven is a personal trainer and Joy is an occupational therapist at the local medical centre.

Choose either Steven or Joy. Create a table to show the possible physical, intellectual, emotional and social effects of the work they do on their personal growth and development.

Just checking

1. What are the main differences between manual and non-manual work?
2. How might having a low level of wealth and income positively affect a person's growth and development?
3. Why might the children of carers who earn a high level of income be at an advantage at school compared to children from families with a limited income?

Town or country?

Here you will learn how human growth and development can be influenced by where we choose to live, the housing conditions we live in and the effects of the environment around the area we live in.

Town or country living

Where you live affects many aspects of your health, wellbeing and quality of life, so choosing where to live is a major life decision. In the UK, which is quite densely populated, there are many types of places to live: some people live in **cities**, some live in large **towns** and others live in **rural** areas.

City living and rural living have their own benefits, and will appeal to different sorts of people.

Benefits of city living	Benefits of rural living
Employment opportunities	Steady pace of life
Wide range of social activity opportunities for all ages	Less pollution – air quality, sanitation, cleaner living environment
Multicultural living	Less risk – a safer place to live and raise a family
Fast pace of life	Sense of community
Good transport links	Green space

Your world

The people who live on The Green live in the **suburbs** of a big city. Draw a spider diagram to show the possible benefits for the residents of The Green of living in this sort of area.

City – a large densely populated urban area, traditionally one with a cathedral, though city status is now granted by the Queen

Town – an urban area that is smaller than a city and has a fixed boundary

Rural – in an area with a population of fewer than 2,500 people

Suburb – a residential area round the edges of a major city

Many people in early adulthood are attracted to city living. It gives them the chance to develop a career and meet different sorts of people. Most big cities offer us a wide range of opportunities to develop our social lives. For example, cities have large venues that attract famous performers, musicians and theatre companies for people to enjoy, have all sorts of bars, clubs and social centres, and are the first places to show popular movies – all easily accessible thanks to good transport links. Sporting opportunities are available to meet almost every type of interest, which can support the physical growth and development of people of all ages.

However, many people are born in rural areas, or choose to live there. Often, people living in the city want to move out into more rural areas as they move into the later life stages. Starting a family can lead people to make the decision to move outside the city, as the quality of education and health facilities may be better.

Types of housing

Once people have selected an area where they wish to settle, they need to decide on the type of accommodation they are going to live in. Housing conditions have a big impact on the health and well-being of individuals. Some people are lucky that they live in houses with plenty of space and all the children in the household have their own bedrooms. This can help physical health, but also helps with intellectual development in childhood and adolescence as children have a quiet space to concentrate on work.

People sometimes have to live in conditions which are not ideal, and the type of housing a person or family has can affect a person's physical health and development. If a person suffers from asthma, cold and damp housing conditions can make this condition worse.

Does modern housing help people's development and wellbeing?

Just checking

1. Identify three reasons why people in later adulthood might be more attracted to living in a rural area.

2. Explain why people in adolescence might be attracted to city living.

3. What different types of pollution do people living in cities face during their everyday lives? How might this pollution affect their physical health?

Activity

There are many different families, groups and individuals who live on The Green. Although The Green has an area with grass, trees and benches to sit on, it is in a built-up area. The residents face a range of problems associated with living in the suburbs of a big city. It can be noisy; there is often a lot of litter; and many of the locals complain that the quality of services they get from council has declined. Refuse is collected only once every two weeks.

Some of the residents are meeting to try to come up with some plans to improve the local area and, as a result, their own quality of life.

1. Working in a small group, come up with some proposals of your own to present at one of the meetings. For each, explain how it might affect the residents' physical, intellectual, emotional and social development.
2. Present your ideas to the class as a whole.
3. Create a table to show the possible disadvantages of living in a city and in a rural area.

Think about it

How would life be different for you if you lived in Hong Kong? Hong Kong is a very densely populated city where most people live in high-rise multi-storey flats and apartments. Do some research to find out what life is like for people who live in this city.

Who am I?

In this topic, you will learn how the factors that affect our growth and development influence how we see and value ourselves.

Do you ever wonder how other people see you and what they think of you? Do you sometimes feel you're having a bad day, but cannot quite work out why it is happening? If you have these sorts of feelings from time to time, you are just like everybody else in the world.

Self-concept

As you pass through life, a range of factors and events help to shape your ideas about who you are. Going to school, getting a job, settling into a long-term relationship and retiring all have a deep effect on your emotional and social development. You create what is known as a self-concept – a set of ideas, feelings and attitudes that a person has about who they are, and their worth, capabilities and limitations. Your self-concept develops and changes as you go through life.

To help understand self-concept, we sometimes split it into two parts:

- self-image
- self-esteem.

Self-image

Self-image is how you see yourself. It is your own mental picture of who you are.

You may see yourself as attractive, intelligent, and as a really talented athlete. Your self-image may be greatly influenced by how you think other people see you. This is shown to you by what people say to you, what they say about you and how they behave towards you.

People can have a positive or negative self-image, which can change daily. Some teenagers have a poor self-image in adolescence as they go through puberty, as it is a time when people can feel very self-conscious and open to comparing themselves to others. For example,

Your world

Work with a small group of people in your class who you know quite well. Each person is to write down one positive feature about each member of the group. Each person then listens to what the others have chosen to say about them.

How does listening to these comments make you feel? Discuss as a group.

Activity

George is 90 years of age and lives on The Green. He is a war veteran and spent a large part of his life in the army. He has a number of medals, which he is proud of. He is still very fit, and exercises every day. He has a good set of friends and cooks his own food daily from fresh ingredients. He says that this is what keeps him so fit and active.

Identify and explain the factors that may lead to George having a positive self-concept.

getting spots or acne can make a teenager feel bad, not just about they way they look, but about who they are.

Self-esteem

Self-esteem is how much you like, accept and respect yourself as a person – often talked about in terms of how much you 'value' yourself.

Some people have a tendency towards high self-esteem, and others towards low self-esteem. People who compare themselves to others in a negative way tend to have low self-esteem; people who are not so concerned about what others say tend to have high self-esteem.

However, events and experiences can change your self-esteem considerably. For example, if a student achieves all their target exam grades, their self-esteem will go up. Your self-esteem can even change several times within the course of a day. You may wake up not feeling good in the morning but, if you walk past a friend who tells you how nice you look today, it can make a significant difference to your self-esteem.

The self-concept equation

When we put self-image and self-esteem together; this gives us what we call our self-concept:

Self-image + Self-esteem = Self-concept

Good self-image and high self-esteem usually lead to a positive self-concept; poor self-image and low self-esteem usually lead to a negative self-concept.

You will explore how self-concept is influenced by a range of factors in Unit 4 (see pages 206–213).

Dear Lindy

I am writing to you in the hope that you can help me sort out my life! I am a 24-year-old man and have been dating my girlfriend since I was 16. She has just told me that she no longer finds me attractive and has been seeing someone else for six months. Should I leave her at this stage, even though I still love her? If I do, will anybody else ever find me attractive? I feel I am not as good looking and attractive as most of the blokes I know.

Hoping you can help me,

Tony

Self-image – how you see yourself
Self-esteem – how you value yourself
Self-concept – a combination of self-image and self-esteem

Just checking

1. Identify three factors that might lead to a teenager having a positive self-image.
2. Explain why self-esteem may change on a daily basis.
3. What is meant by a positive self-concept?

Now you see me, now you don't

In this topic, you will learn more about the factors that can affect our self-image, self-esteem and self-concept.

Do any members of your family or friends have a positive self-image and good self-esteem? Have you ever wondered what sorts of factors have contributed to them feeling positive about themselves?

Here we will look at some of the factors that contribute to the way people see and value themselves.

Factors that affect self-concept

Every person is different, and individuals are affected in different ways by a range of factors and events that happen in their lives.

It is important to realise that one factor can affect two people in very different ways. A passing comment to a person such as 'you look attractive today' could make one person feel really good about themselves, whereas another person might think that this comment was meant as a put down. The effect can depend on who makes the comment and how an individual interprets it.

Age	Appearance	Gender	Social class	Ethnicity/culture
Education	Relationships with others	Sexual orientation	Emotional development	Life experiences

Factors that affect self-concept

How these factors affect self-concept varies according to the individuals concerned, but it is important that you understand how these factors could positively or negatively affect the different parts of an individual's self-concept. To remind you, the self-concept equation is:

$$\text{Self-image} + \text{Self-esteem} = \text{Self-concept}$$

Your world

Joy is an occupational therapist and Steven is a fitness instructor. They believe the work they do is important in helping other people to develop themselves, to become the sort of person they are truly capable of being. Many of the people they meet are unhappy with their lives and the way they presently look.

Working with a partner, list the sort of activities Joy and Steven could do with their clients to help them build their self-esteem, change their self-image and improve their self-concept.

Activity

Ahmed is married and has two children, Aaron and Alina. They live in an apartment on The Green. The family is of Arabic descent and came to the UK from Iran. The family still keeps many of the traditional family practices that are part of Iranian culture.

- Identify ways in which the culture and beliefs of Ahmed's family may be different from mainstream UK culture.
- Explain how having a distinct culture may have a positive effect on the self-concept of the family members.

Activity

Working as part of a group, look carefully at the people used as models in a range of magazines. (You might all want to bring in your favourite magazine into the classroom for this activity).

Construct a table for the six life stages to show which life stage the models who appear in the magazine see to fit into.

Explain what your results tell you about how people are portrayed in magazines.

In Unit 4, each of these factors will be developed in much more detail, so here we just look at two of the most important: appearance and age.

Appearance and age

The way we actually look and how we think we look are often very different. Both are an important influence on self-concept.

Over the last 30 to 40 years, people have become more concerned with appearance and whether they measure up to society's expectations. Youth and looking young appear to be much stronger values than they ever were. In the past, women have had more concerns about appearance, but in the 21st century this affects both sexes more equally.

A person's self-image is partially created by how they see themselves against the '**blueprint**' expectation of society. This is particularly important in adolescence, when young people are creating their own individual identity, and appearance is important. If a person feels that they do not match up to society's expectations, this may negatively affect their self-image and self-esteem.

As people pass through the life course, their appearance changes and they experience the effects of ageing. Some people accept the ageing process well, and easily come to terms with ageing and the advantages it might bring. However, other people may find getting older a challenge, and the process could negatively affect their self-esteem and self-image.

It is important to realise that we are all different. The images we see in the media are just the views of a few people about how we should look.

Did you know?

A recent survey discovered that 54% of women aged 25–45 intended to have cosmetic surgery. The most common reason for having surgery was that they felt it would make them feel more confident. Cosmetic surgery is also now becoming much more popular among men who often want to look like the male role models they see in the media.

Blueprint – an accepted model

Just checking

1. Explain how a serious injury resulting in a person becoming wheelchair bound may affect that person's self-concept.

2. In what ways may self-image and self-esteem change if a person finds that their boyfriend or girlfriend has been unfaithful?

3. Explain how positive feedback in a school report may affect a person's self-concept.

Nature, nurture or both?

In this topic, you will learn how genetic and environmental factors (nature and nurture) combine to affect the way we grow and develop.

How does it work?

Both nature and nurture affect the way we grow and develop, but how do the different factors come together? Understanding human growth and development patterns is never easy. Two people may have very similar skills and qualities in childhood but grow and develop into very different people in adult life.

Using physical skills

We are all born with differing levels of physical skill and talent.

Some people are born with the natural ability to sing or dance and their future success is often determined by the physical attributes they have, which are determined by our genes. However, what we make of physical attributes we have is dependent on nurture. A person may have the capability to be successful in singing but they will need to have the support to achieve their potential.

The successful artists we see on television programmes who have been blessed with a raw talent will have a whole range of other people to thank for their achievements as well.

As you move through life, it is important that you make the most of the abilities nature has given you. Exercising on a regular basis has many positive benefits for your growth and development, helping you to:

- maintain a body that functions well into later adulthood
- relieve the stresses and strains of everyday life
- meet new people
- combat illness and lessen the effects of **degenerative diseases**.

Your world

Ben, Nicola, Mike and Colin share a flat on The Green. They are all good friends and are discussing whether Colin was born gay. He says he has always known he was gay for as long as he can remember. He was too scared to admit it until he was 19 because of what other people might think.

Discuss in a small group whether you think people are born gay.

Activity

Mike is a top-class footballer who lives on The Green. His aim is to compete in the 2012 London Olympics for the UK.

Draw a spider diagram to show the possible influences that will determine whether Mike is successful.

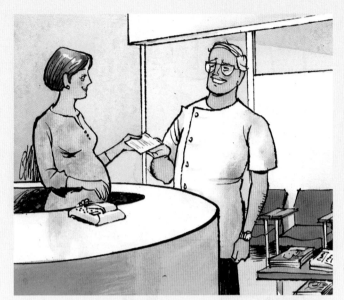

Case study

David and Carol went to the same junior school. They always achieved similar results, and were seen to be of the same academic ability. After junior school, Carol's parents moved to a new area, so they went to different secondary schools.

Prepare a presentation for the class about the possible effects the following factors may have had on David and Carol's development:

- intelligence
- family support
- friendships
- type of school.

Using intellectual skills

Different people are born with differing levels of intellectual ability, or cognitive intelligence. The use people make of their intellectual ability and the way it develops is strongly influenced by nurturing factors. Two people can have the same level of intellectual ability, but take very different paths in their lives. No two schools offer exactly the same quality of education, and no two sets of carers influence their children in exactly the same way. People are also influenced by their experiences and the people they meet in their lives.

Social and emotional intelligence

As well as having cognitive intelligence, people can also develop their **social intelligence** and **emotional intelligence**. As we progress through life, we learn how to manage our feelings and relationships better. A child has to learn that they cannot do what they want to do all the time; after a while they learn how to discuss things, and have the ability to come up with compromises. In the first serious intimate relationship a teenager has with another person, they are bound to make mistakes in the way they handle events and situations; as they get older and experience more, they develop a better understanding of their own emotions and those of others, work out how to act in certain situations, and learn how to deal with people in a more sophisticated way.

Having social and emotional intelligence benefits people's working lives too: people who are socially and emotionally intelligent can 'read' people better, so are often good at managing people and dealing with work-related issues.

Degenerative disease – a disease where tissues and organs gradually deteriorate or break down

Social intelligence – the ability to act wisely in relationships

Emotional intelligence – the ability to manage one's own emotions and those of others well

Just checking

1. Identify and describe the influence of two factors that might affect a person's growth and development in middle adulthood.

2. Using an example, explain the meaning of social intelligence.

3. How important are genetic factors in determining how long a person is likely to live?

It's a family affair

Here you will learn about how the family and the various relationships between members of the family affect personal growth and development.

Family

What does the word **family** mean to you? People all around the world live in family groupings of various types, but no two families are exactly the same.

Most people will live in a family unit at some stage in their lives. There are many different types of family arrangement the UK. Some people live in a two-parent family, others in one-parent families, and some in extended family groupings. Many people see the family as crucial in keeping society safe, stable and functioning, as it is the family unit that plays the greatest role in **socialising** the children.

The adult members of the family provide for the physical needs of family members. Young children need to have most of their needs provided for, and many families provide significant support for older relatives, who might live within the family unit or near by. This support could involve simple things such as cleaning, or helping with washing, dressing and cooking.

Members of the family also provide emotional support to each other. In infancy, as you have seen, bonding is a key process for development. Older family members often support each other through their problems and crises, listening, giving advice, and offering 'a shoulder to cry on'.

Because family members spend a lot of time together, and often share social activities, the family unit plays an important part in the process of social development. It is the first place where people learn how to interact with others, where children learn how to play with others and build relationships. This experience often provides the blueprint for relationships in later life stages. Many families form strong bonds, and remain close even when children have established their own family units.

Your world

Carol, the receptionist at the dentist on The Green, is expecting twins. Carol and her husband are really pleased. They have been trying to have children for over two years.

Discuss with a partner the positive effects of starting a family. What do you think are the benefits of having twins?

Family – a group of people connected through blood relations, marriage and co-residence

Socialise – bring into society, train or guide to be part of a social group

Bereavement – when someone dies, the period of loss during which grief takes place

---

Activity

There is debate in the media about the best way for carers to spend time with children. Should carers spend quality time with children, doing activities together? Should children spend so much time alone with computer games and using social chat sites? Discuss with a partner how you view these issues.

Intimate relationships and marriage

When children develop into adults, they often settle into stable, permanent relationships (see page 36). Although divorce and separation are common in the UK, about half of those who settle in a permanent relationship will remain with that person throughout their life.

Being in a permanent relationship can have significant effects on growth and development, and in shaping self-concept (see pages 26–27).

Parenthood

Many people who settle into permanent relationships choose to have children or adopt. Having children is a happy event for most, but brings major new responsibilities. Looking after children is tiring and can be stressful, and many new parents find this difficult to adapt to. Managing a social life is not as easy as before; money may be more limited; and the children need to be looked after and supported around the clock.

Many young people choose to have children in the later part of early adulthood so that they can enjoy their independence before they settle into the responsibilities of parenthood.

Dear Lindy

I am 35-year-old single mum with three young children. Our family has been rocked recently by the death of my father after a car accident. It has left my mother desperately upset, and my children are lost without their grandad. He was a really important part of our lives.

What advice would you give us to help get through the next few months and move on with our lives?

Jenny

Separation and divorce

Sometimes relationships break down, temporarily or permanently. This can lead to separation and divorce (see page 21). This process is a difficult time for the family, and affects all aspects of a person's growth and development. Relationships between family members are under strain, people are emotionally upset and sometimes down and depressed – a person's self-esteem may well go down. Divorce or separation can even affect a person's everyday eating habits and their physical health.

Bereavement

During anyone's life, they will inevitably face the death of family members. Having a parent or child die is one of the most painful events people have to cope with. In later adulthood, people lose their life-partners – sometimes people they have been with for over 50 years – and how they respond to this can have a huge impact on how they go on to live the rest of their lives.

Just checking

1. What different types of family arrangement are there in the UK?

2. In what ways may older relatives depend on their children and grandchildren?

3. How can divorce and separation affect self-esteem?

Friends united

In this topic, you will learn how friends and friendship groups affect personal growth and development.

Friendship

Do you spend a lot of time thinking about your friends? In adolescence, friendship patterns change quickly. Some people can be the best of friends one day, and not speaking the next. Does this happen to you?

However much they change, friendship groups are important throughout life. As we grow and develop, we gradually learn how to mix with others and form relationships. Through this sort of socialising in childhood and adolescence, we learn the social skills we need to form fulfilling relationships in later life – and some of the friendships we form in our early years may even continue throughout our lives.

Through being with friends, we also learn the main values we need to feel part of our culture, such as trust and honesty. As we interact with others, our own unique personality is formed, and we become individuals.

Friendship at different life stages

Having friends is an important part of life. We socialise with our friends and share our lives and the events that happen to us with them. Friends offer support in difficult situations and, if a person is a close friend, their viewpoint is often worth listening to.

In adolescence, friendships become closer than in childhood, and teenagers are better able to form friendships with people of the opposite sex, as well as their own. The types of friends you choose in adolescence can have an effect on your intellectual development. For example, if you mix with a wide circle of friends, you will have a wider range of experiences to draw on in life, which may promote further intellectual development. People tend to conform to **peer group pressure**. When people disagree with friends or end

Your world

Paul is in a band and lives in a ground floor apartment on The Green. He has a wide circle of friends who he meets regularly. Most of his current friends he met through work, but he still keeps in contact with a couple of friends he made at school.

List five qualities you look for in a friend.

Compare these with another member of your group. Are the things you have written similar? Do you think all people look for the same things when they make new friends?

What benefits do you think Paul might get from remaining in close contact with some of the friends he had at school?

Activity

Select a person in adulthood or later adulthood to interview about friendship. Ask this person about a long-term friend they already have, and what it is that has kept them so close (you may wish to design some questions before you conduct your interview). List the qualities of friendship they mention and write this up in a table.

friendships, this can affect all aspects of personal growth and development.

As we progress into early adulthood our network of friends may widen, as many people leave the area in which they were born to go to college or get a job. The new friends we make can bring different dimensions to our lives and further our experiences. They can change and influence our views and opinions on anything from dress sense to religion.

In middle adulthood, friendships may be deeper and even more settled: people who have known each for a long time often feel they can trust and understand each other very well. The life events people go through together often create friendship bonds that last forever. As their children grow up and leave home, parents may have more time to spend with friends. It can be a time when friendship groups are expanded and new activities undertaken.

Later adulthood can be an exciting time for friendships.

People who have retired may have a lot of time to socialise. If a person is fit and healthy, they can share new activities and experiences with friends. People in later adulthood often join social and leisure clubs and make new friends. However, people in later adulthood will have to deal with the death of friends too, and this can be difficult if the person has been a friend for a long time. Some people feel isolated in later adulthood, as they may not have the physical capability to leave home and socialise with others.

> ### Think about it
>
> What sort of new and exciting activities are available to older people, which could involve meeting new and different people?

> **Peer group pressure** – the influence of the social group you belong to

Just checking

1. Explain why friendship is so important in adolescence.
2. In what ways can friends offer support in later adulthood?
3. Describe how peer group pressure might affect intellectual development.

Up close and personal

In this topic, you will learn how intimate, personal and sexual relationships can affect an individual's growth and development.

Relationships

When was the last time you told someone close to you that you loved them? Do you find it difficult to express your feelings to those who are important in your life? You will not be alone in facing these sorts of problem in adolescence.

All individuals need to know that they are valued and cared for by others: we do this through what we say and how we behave. How valued and cared for we feel will affect the way we grow and develop.

We all have a range of different relationships in our lives. These include those with members of our family, the people we choose to be our friends and the people we work with. We may interact with many different people on a daily basis, but our relationships will be closer and more **intimate** with some than others. During our lives, we will feel attracted to some people, and some of our relationships will be **sexual** in nature.

Your world

Ben and his girlfriend Nicola live together and have a very good relationship. However, like any other couple, they have times when they don't get on and have disagreements. Nicola always knows when there is a problem because Ben tends to go quiet and she has to make the effort to get him to express what he is thinking. Ben admits he finds this difficult to do.

Discuss with a partner why you think Ben finds it difficult to talk about personal problems.

Do you think this is mainly a male problem, or is it the same for both sexes?

Be prepared to feed back your thoughts to a whole-class discussion.

Relationships in infancy and childhood

During infancy and childhood, social and emotional development is rapid. Our experiences during this period are crucial to our future development, and the bonding process between carers and infants or children is key. Young children need to receive love and to be encouraged to express their own feelings openly. This happens almost automatically from the infant's perspective, but how the carer responds to the emotions of the infant is crucial: the infant will read the messages from the people it interacts with and learn from them how to express feelings and how to behave emotionally.

In our culture, it has been traditional for women to be the ones who care for children and who discuss issues involving emotions and feelings with them. Boys have often received the message – whether openly expressed or hidden – that they should keep their feelings inside, and that being able to express emotions is a feminine trait.

> **Intimate relationship** – a close relationship
>
> **Sexual relationship** – a relationship involving sex

This situation is gradually changing as males see the benefits of being able to express emotions freely.

Relationships in adolescence

The most significant change in relationships during adolescence is the development of the feelings of physical attraction to others. This happens to individuals at different times, and people can be attracted to the opposite sex, the same sex or both. This new aspect to relationships is one of the most exciting parts about growing up, but can be hard to handle too.

The relationships people have with their friends can be very different in adolescence. Friendships between girls tend to be more personal and intimate, with many discussions about feelings and emotions. Friendships between males tend not to be so close, and they tend to discuss feelings less. It might be said that relationships for men are more straightforward than for girls in adolescence. However, this may not always be for the best if men do not share their feelings and keep them 'bottled up' inside.

The importance of expressing feelings

Expressing your feelings helps you deal with the events that happen in your daily life. It is healthy to have close and intimate relationships with others and to be able to show everyday human emotions, such as happiness, sadness or anger. Health problems such as high blood pressure have been linked to stress levels, but talking to others about your problems can help reduce stress, and lessen your risk of getting ill.

Adult relationships

In adult life, people have usually become more experienced in handling relationships and are more comfortable with their own sexuality – they are more emotionally mature. People settle into longer-lasting close relationships with other adults, and many start a family of their own. Having a family brings more responsibility, and it is helpful to have someone close and intimate to share family issues with.

For many people, adult life is also the time when they have most responsibility at work, and may face unexpected life events. You will look at this in detail in the next topic.

Dear Lindy

I am facing one of the most difficult decisions in my life at the moment. I have been going out with my girlfriend for over two years and really love her. We have a good relationship and can talk about nearly anything. The problem I face is that one of my closest male friends at college has told me he is gay and finds me attractive. I have to admit that I do find him attractive and feel confused. Part of me wants to ignore these feelings, but part of me wants to explore them further. Should I allow myself to become even closer to my friend?

What should I do?

Jack

Just checking

1. Explain why the bonding process with infants and children is so important for relationships in adulthood.
2. Why is it important that fathers express their feelings and emotions to their children?
3. What are the benefits of having a close and intimate relationship with a friend who you can tell anything to?

We're working on it

In this topic, you will look at how working relationships affect human growth and development.

Working relationships

Do you already know what sort of work you want to do when you leave school or full-time education? Are you happy to work away from home during the week, and not see your friends and family? Would you be prepared to commute over two hours a day to and from home to work?

These are some of the issues you might have to face in your working life.

Why work?

Almost all people spend a large part of their adult life working. Paid employment provides people with an income to purchase the goods and services they need to survive and to lead a comfortable, contented life. Most people would like to have a well-paid job and not have to worry about money, but usually the more money we earn, the more stressful the work is.

Types of work relationship

At work, we develop formal and informal relationships. Formal relationships involve those with people who manage us or whom we manage. A person usually responds to their manager in a formal way when they are discussing issues. We also meet and work with other people who are sometimes known as **colleagues**. We work alongside these people and they may become close friends. These relationships are called informal work relationships. Many people meet their future life partners through work, and make many close and personal relationships with others that last throughout life.

Promotion

As people become more experienced in their work, they may well apply for and achieve a **promotion**. Promotion is usually linked with a rise in income, which can have a positive effect on personal growth

Your world

David has built his dentist's business up over the last ten years and it now successful. He has a waiting list of people who want to come to his practice. He works five days a week and on Saturdays till 1.00pm.

David is really worried that his work life is affecting his relationship with his wife and children. He does not see them as much as he would like.

Draw a spider diagram to show the changes David could make at work to help improve his relationships with his family.

Select one of these changes and prepare to feed back to the class on how this might improve the situation.

Colleague – person you work with

Promotion – when a person secures a more responsible job at a higher level of responsibility within the same company or organisation

and development. The effects of promotion on growth and development are looked at later in this unit (see page 44)

Work/life balance

As people take on more responsibility or take on extra hours, they need to measure the benefits they will gain from the work against the costs in other areas of their lives – this is call the work/life balance.

If someone is working very long hours on a regular basis, they may miss out on family life, and their relationships outside work may suffer. For example, for someone with a young family, one of the pleasures should be being able to spend time with them and seeing them grow and develop; if the person is working too hard, they may miss out on this crucial part of family life.

A stressful job may also affect a person's physical health and wellbeing. It is not good to skip meals and have to spend large amounts of time worrying about work issues.

Redundancy

Sometimes people are made redundant from work. Redundancy happens when the employer no longer needs the person to work for the organisation, usually because the job is no longer needed. Redundancy is different from being fired: people may be fired because they are not effective in their work, but redundancy occurs for organisational rather than personal reasons.

Retirement

At the end of middle adulthood, most people retire from full-time work. With retirement, the individual will have more time for family and friends. However, some people may feel they are no longer productive and valued members of society. How retirement affects a person depends on how they prepare for retirement and accept this change.

Activity

Julie is the dental hygienist at the surgery on The Green. She has enjoyed her work, but is now planning for a happy retirement.

Construct a table to show the possible benefits and challenges Julie will face when she retires from full-time employment.

Just checking

1. Explain why it is important to have a good work/life balance.
2. Describe three effects that redundancy might have on a person's growth and development
3. Explain the difference between formal and informal work relationships.

Planned for that!

In this topic, you will learn how expected life events affect growth and development.

Life events

Are you the sort of person who likes to plan what is going to happen? Do you think you are flexible when unplanned things happen quickly in your life? Do you cope with change easily?

As we pass through life, some of the events that affect our growth and development are **expected** and predictable, while others are **unexpected** and unpredictable. Most people expect to start full-time employment at some stage, but people do not expect to be involved in a serious car accident.

Expected life events

Here are just some of the events you might expect to happen in your life.

Expected life events
Starting nursery
Starting school
Starting work
Getting married
Parenthood
Retirement
Menopause

The effect of different life events on an individual's growth and development can be complex, and hard to measure. Most life events have both positive and negative effects on the individual concerned. Often, when events change in our lives – whatever the change is – we experience stress, and it takes us a while to adapt to the new circumstances we find ourselves in.

Expected life events tend to happen at particular life stages. Starting school happens in childhood, starting full-time work usually

Your world

Sabah is chatting with her friend about Aaron starting nursery soon. She has decided that he is ready for the change, and that this will help promote his growth and development.

Working in pairs, identify possible benefits for Aaron's growth and development of starting nursery. How might Sabah help prepare Aaron for this change?

Ask at home how you were prepared for starting at nursery or primary school.

Think about it

Few people these days think of their job as a 'job for life'. How do you think the world of work has changed over the past 100 years? Has the rise of new technology made work easier, or more stressful?

happens in late adolescence or early adulthood, and the menopause normally happens in middle adulthood.

Starting work

Securing full-time paid employment is a major, life-changing event for most people. It means that the person concerned is more likely to become independent and have more freedom. Their self-concept changes from being dependent on others to becoming a self-supporting adult. They can provide for their own physical needs, as they now have an income. New relationships and friendships will form too – starting work often leads to new social development.

However, the change is unlikely to happen without a level of stress and insecurity. The person may feel insecure for a while and anxious about the expectations other people have of them – a completely natural emotional response. Employment is also likely to lead to new learning and intellectual development as the person comes to terms with the tasks that need to be done.

People often need to be flexible in how they work as well. This can be in terms of the hours they work, working away from home or even working from home all the time. New technology is having a massive impact on the working world and this impacts on the sorts of relationships people have.

As starting work is an expected life event, people can prepare and plan for the changes that are likely to happen. This can make the process easier.

Getting married

Deciding to marry is almost always an expected life event! Many people set a date for their marriage more than a year in advance. There are different customs surrounding marriages in different cultures within the UK. Some couples prepare for their marriage by living together first, to see if they are compatible, while others wait until they are married to share the same home.

Marriage affects all aspects of growth and development, and most marriages involve each partner making a lot of adjustments to their lifestyle.

Starting a family

Most people want to start a family at some stage in their lives. This is usually an expected life event. People plan for this to happen. However, there has been an increasing number of unplanned pregnancies over the last 20 to 30 years in the UK, and we now have one of the highest teenage pregnancy rates in Europe.

Expected life event – a predictable event that happens during the life course and affects future development

Unexpected life event – an unpredictable event that happens during the life course and affects future development

Activity

You have been asked to write an article for a local magazine about the effects of having children on the growth and development of the parents.

Research and write your article, making sure that you cover both the positive and negative effects of this life-changing event. Remember to use PIES to help you.

Just checking

1. Explain why parenthood is usually an expected life event.
2. Describe three positive effects of starting full-time schooling.
3. Explain why planned and expected life events can still be stressful.

A nasty shock

In this topic, you will learn how unexpected life events can affect growth and development.

Unexpected life events

Sometimes life seems to be going just fine – as the saying goes, 'everything in the garden is rosy'. However, without warning, events can happen that will change our lives for ever.

Unexpected life events are those that we do not know are going to happen, so cannot plan for. They can be particularly difficult to handle, and the long-term consequences may take a lot more coming to terms with than expected life events. It is probably only after a good period of time that we can look back and see how events like these have affected our lives, in good ways as well as bad.

It is now commonly accepted that the most significant learning in our lives can come from dealing with difficult issues like those that arise with unexpected life events.

Here are just some of the unexpected life events that might happen in your life.

Your world

Maud divorced her husband recently after their relationship broke down. She discovered he had been seeing another woman for more than 18 months, and felt betrayed.

With a partner, discuss the likely effects of the relationship breakdown and divorce on Maud's growth and development.

Unexpected life events
Serious injury
Relationship breakdown
Divorce
Bereavement
Serious illness
Inheriting an unexpected sum of money

Activity

Mike, the professional football player who lives on The Green, could not play at all last season as he had torn his Achilles heel in training. He is now fully recovered. Mike says that this event had a huge impact on his life. Prepare a presentation about the possible effects Mike's injury may have had on his growth and development.

Serious illness

Most illnesses we have during our lives only have short-term effects, and we recover relatively quickly. For example, if you have a cold or the flu, you might feel unwell for a short time, but your illness has no effect on your growth and development in the long run.

However, people can have serious illnesses at any life stage, and these can have an impact on the rest of their lives. Life-threatening illnesses occur most often in middle and later adulthood, as the ageing process takes effect, but they can also happen in infancy and childhood.

Some illnesses may have a genetic link, while others are contracted through infection. The way we lead our lives can also cause serious illness. For example, repeated exposure to the sun can cause skin cancer – an increasingly common problem among people in early adulthood.

Although serious illness is linked to physical growth, the consequences may affect all aspects of a person's development. Serious heart disease may affect our intellectual and social development: for example, a person may be too ill to work or socialise with friends, and handling the illness can be difficult to come to terms with emotionally.

Bereavement

Having a loved one die is difficult to handle at any stage of life. In infancy and childhood, the loss of a parent or **sibling** may have serious effects on growth and development.

A child who loses a parent may find they have to change their lifestyle completely, with a new carer, a different home, an unfamiliar school or very different living patterns and responsibilities – and this all takes time to adapt to. Similarly, it is difficult for a parent to come to terms with the death of one of their own children. The process of dealing with death is known as bereavement and can last for a number of years. People never forget the death of a loved one, but most find they can eventually come to terms with the event.

In middle and later adulthood, it is more common for people to have to deal with the death of life-partners, family and friends. The range of support available to help handle these sorts of events is explored in the topics that follow in this unit.

Did you know?

Rates of obesity, with all the long-term problems it brings, are growing among adolescents in the UK. Serious heart disease is expected to be the highest it has ever been in 2020 for the age group 30–35 as a result of adolescents being so overweight. By 2035, it is projected that coronary heart disease (CHD) will have increased from its current rate of 5% to 16% of all young adults.

Siblings – children who share at least one biological or adopted parent

Just checking

1. Explain why unexpected life events are difficult to handle.
2. How might a serious illness in childhood affect a person's growth and development?
3. Explain why the death of a life partner after 40 years of marriage may have a serious effect on a person's social and emotional development.

What works for you?

Here you will learn how unexpected life events at work such as promotion, redundancy and unemployment can affect growth and development.

A world of work

How do you think you would feel if you were unemployed and could not find work? How would you handle the chance of a promotion with a pay increase if you felt you were not ready for the challenge? What would it be like if you had two job offers, and didn't know which to take? In today's world of work, people face these sorts of issues every day.

Promotion

Promotion is usually seen as a positive life-changing event. Often it is unexpected, though in some work situations people can plan ahead and prepare themselves for promotion.

Being promoted affects a person's self-esteem and self-concept: they may see themselves in a more positive way. Promotion usually results in a pay rise, and the extra income can affect a person's growth and development. If people do not have family commitments, some people may use the extra money to develop their social lives; if they do, they may use the money to provide for the needs of the family as a whole.

However, being promoted usually means more responsibility, a greater workload and possibly an increase in stress levels. This may affect a person's private and social life in a negative way. Deciding to accept a promotion is not always as straightforward as it sounds!

Redundancy

Being made redundant will usually have a negative effect on a person's growth and development. A person's self-esteem and self-concept may change, they will no longer have a regular income

Your world

Ben lives on The Green and is a chef. He is fully qualified. He has recently had a meeting with his manager who has offered him a promotion. The new job will give Ben a significant pay rise but he will have a lot more responsibility. He will now be expected to manage other workers and organise their work.

Design a table to show the possible positive and negative effects this life change could have on Ben's growth and development. If you were in Ben's position, what would you do?

Did you know?

When a business wants to encourage a person to take redundancy, they often offer them a 'golden handshake'. This is usually a substantial sum of money to encourage them to leave. The opposite of this, when a business wants someone to stay rather than leave, is called 'golden handcuffs'.

Connotations – ideas and values that go with something

and they will be classed as unemployed – a description that has negative **connotations** for many people.

People who are made redundant may get a financial settlement from their employer. The amount usually depends on how long the person has been employed and their salary.

Sometimes people take voluntary redundancy. This means that they offer to be made redundant if a business needs to reduce its workforce. This can be a positive step for a person who is near retirement age and would welcome the opportunity to retire early, especially with an unexpected redundancy settlement.

The process of being made redundant will probably affect all aspects of the person's growth and development, and will affect their family too. It is likely to be a time of insecurity and confused feelings, as well as a time of change.

Unemployment

Having a job and earning an income is central to most people's lives, so being or becoming unemployed is hard for most people to handle.

A job gives the person an income so that they can meet their physical needs and those of their family. Although money alone is not always what makes a person feel contented, life is usually harder without a regular income. If a person loses their job, it is likely to affect their self-esteem as they no longer feel they are a valued and productive member of society; being classed as unemployed can affect their self-concept. Being unemployed can also limit a person's social development, as income is tight and the social opportunities presented by work are suddenly cut off.

However, unemployment may promote new intellectual development, as people find themselves having to train and prepare for new job opportunities, or moving into areas of work they may not have foreseen.

The support available to help people who are made redundant or who are unemployed will be explored later in this Unit (see pages 50–51).

Just checking

1. What sorts of reason cause people to be made redundant by their employers?
2. Explain how being unable to secure a job after leaving full-time education may affect a person's growth and development.
3. How might a promotion at work affect a person's self-esteem?

Think about it

Can you imagine what it must be like to be unemployed?

Discuss with a partner what you would do if you became unemployed for a period of time in the future. What steps would you take to improve your future employment prospects?

Dear Lindy,

I have just passed my 53rd birthday and have worked for my present employer for over 30 years. The business is facing hard times – the products we make are not selling well due to competition from other firms. Last week, the business asked if any workers would consider voluntary redundancy. I had not planned to leave work until I was 60, but I am tempted by the good redundancy package.

What sort of things should I be considering in reaching this really important decision in my life?

Derek

Family comes first

Here you will learn how partners and family can help people handle expected and unexpected life events, and help manage the effects of these changes on their growth and development.

Family support

If you had a problem to handle in your life, who would you turn to first to ask for support and advice? Why do people often listen closely to what members of their own family have to say about important issues?

The family plays an important role in supporting people through the expected and unexpected life events they face. Family members can offer **informal support** to each other, and usually feel a responsibility to do so.

In infancy and childhood, the family is central to a person's growth and development. Parents support their children, and siblings support each other. In some cultures, people live in extended family groupings and support is available across the generations within one household. As we progress into adult life, family support is still important, even though people become more independent.

People often like to discuss issues with family members as they have a great deal of shared experience, and trust their opinions – there is the feeling that people in your own family 'get you', and know you better than anyone else. In later adulthood, the tables may turn: as older people face the issues that arise through the ageing process, they may now find themselves looking to their own children for support.

Physical support

At particular times in our lives, we all need physical support from others. To survive, we need food, water, clothing and protection from the physical environment. In infancy, a baby is unable to meet any of its own physical needs and is totally dependent on its carers –

Your world

George is 90 and lives in a flat on The Green. He is in good health, and is frequently visited by members of his family, which he really appreciates. He still leads a very independent lifestyle.

With a partner, discuss the sorts of physical support George's family could give him to help him maintain his independence. Remember to use PIES to help structure your thoughts. Be prepared to feedback your ideas to a whole-class discussion.

Did you know?

Research has shown that the physical development of an infant's brain is closely linked to the nurture they receive from carers. So spending time with an infant really can help promote their intellectual development.

without this support, the baby would die. As we move through life, most people become independent – usually in early adulthood – and can meet their own physical needs.

Some people with disabilities may never be able to be totally independent and may need support to meet their physical needs throughout their life.

In later adulthood, it is likely that all people will eventually need physical support as the effects of ageing take place.

Families are often central in providing for the physical needs of other relatives. This is done informally; people do it because they want to help each other, out of love and a sense of family obligation.

Intellectual support

Family members can be a great help in promoting each other's intellectual development. This is most apparent in infancy, childhood and adolescence. Carers have a major role to play in language development and early years education, when children learn through structured play and modelling. Research shows that the support given by carers at this stage will have a major effect on progress and intellectual development in adolescence. Carers who show an interest and enthusiasm for learning are likely to pass this interest on to their own children.

Emotional support

For many people, the family is their main source of emotional support. Family members share problems and frequently help others through unexpected events. For example, if a child has a serious accident, the medical services would deal with the physical problems that arise, but it would probably be the family who would help the parents and child deal with their feelings about the accident.

Social support

Families often spend time socialising and bonding together. Parents and children may be involved in a range of social activities, and children often play together. The bonds formed between siblings may well extend into adult life. They will often support each other in adult life financially, socially and emotionally. If there is a serious illness in the family, it is not uncommon for brothers or sisters to look after their nieces and nephews for a period of time.

Activity

Ahmed and Sabah have two children. Alina attends a secondary school. Aaron is in infancy and is soon going to nursery. The family all value education and see it as a way forward to achieve success in later life.

Design a table to show the sorts of support Ahmed and Sabah might give their two children to support them in their intellectual development.

Informal support – support offered by others that is not paid for, and is not done as part of an organisation

Just checking

1. Use examples to explain what is meant by informal family support.
2. Describe two sorts of social support grandchildren may offer grandparents.
3. What advantages might living in extended family groupings offer if an unexpected life event occurs?

A little help from your friends

Here you will learn how friends can help people to handle expected and unexpected life events, and to manage the effects of these changes on growth and development.

We will focus on adolescence and later adulthood in this section to illustrate how important friendships are, though they are also important in other life stages.

Support from friends

Can you talk to your friends about almost anything? Do you discuss things with your friends that you wouldn't discuss with your parents, carers, brothers or sisters?

For many people this is the case, especially in adolescence. Friends offer each other good support, and their friendship is built around a range of different qualities.

Your world

Emma shares a flat with Lewis and Felicity on The Green. She is a professional dancer and has recently badly injured her ankle in practice. She has a cast on her ankle and will be unable to dance for at least eight weeks.

Identify the different aspects of Emma's life that will be affected by her injury. How might Emma's friends support her to get through this difficult time?

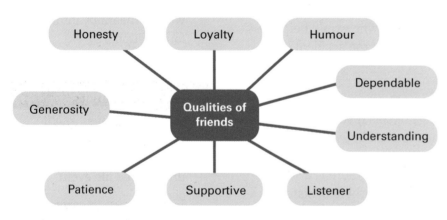

Qualities of friends

People usually have a range of very different friends. Some are close, and you may see them almost every day – they may be referred to as 'best friends'; others may be less close, and you may see them less often.

Activity

For each of the following situations, identify the sort of support a friend might offer:

- leaving school
- the birth of a child
- the death of a friend
- being promoted.

As we pass through life, friendships become more firmly established: people are bonded together by a shared history of events and experiences. Supporting each other through relationship problems, accidents and sometimes bereavement brings people closer together.

By middle and later adulthood some friendships may have lasted for 30 or 40 years. The people we form friendships with, even during childhood, may stay friends throughout our lives.

In adolescence

The people we have in our lives help us cope with the range of events we experience. They share the good times, and help us handle the difficult times – sometimes just by being there for us and listening.

Some of the best times in our lives are those that we have shared with others. In adolescence, teenagers like to socialise in larger groups and experience events together. Going bowling or skating, to the movies or into town, is often best done with a group of friends, as it makes the event even more fun. Friends can often help each other with schoolwork, share interests and support each other's intellectual development too.

In later adulthood

In later adulthood, most people have retired from full-time employment and have more time on their hands. If a person is fit and healthy they can develop existing friendships, establish new ones and spend more time with the people they are close to.

In the UK, there are now more people over the age of 65 than there are under the age of 16. This has led to a growing 'silver sector' in certain industries: for example, gyms and leisure centres often have special sessions for people in later adulthood, which can be some of the busiest times of the day. These sorts of change have given new opportunities for older people to support each other through the life changes they are experiencing.

Physical support may be needed in later adulthood, as people's energy levels and physical health may start to decline. Some older people may not be able to get out of the house as much as they used to, and some may even become **housebound**. Having a group of friends who visit regularly may be the only opportunity that person has to share their feelings and socialise with others. Older people may not have other family members living in the area, so may depend on the support of friendship groups.

Later adulthood may also be a time when people lose their life partners. Having friends to offer support through this experience – and who may have been through it themselves – may help the person come to terms with what they have been through.

Activity

Identify a family member or neighbour who lives near to you who is in later adulthood.

Design a questionnaire to assess how important friendship is. Ask the family member or neighbour and a member of your class to answer the questionnaire.

Compare the similarities and differences in the results you received.

Housebound – unable to leave the house

Just checking

1. Describe three qualities that you would look for in a close friend.
2. How could close friends help a person in early adulthood going through a relationship breakdown?
3. What types of support do friends usually offer each other?

Let's get professional

In this topic you will learn about the role of professional support in helping people to handle expected and unexpected life events.

Professional support

When was the last time you visited the doctor for advice with a health problem? Would you visit a financial adviser if you were considering buying your first home? We all need professional advice at certain key points in our lives.

When life-changing events happen, such as serious injury or relationship breakdown, people often need professional support. Professional supporters are trained and qualified to deal with complex or difficult situations in specific areas. These people have a lot more knowledge and expertise than the members of a person's family or their friends.

As professionals have wide experience of dealing with particular situations, they can offer sound advice and pass on useful information. They may also know how to access further types of support: for example, a GP will know where someone can get help with any mental health issues they have.

Through the support of professionals, people can learn and benefit from the experiences others have had. Getting support from professionals should be not be seen as a sign of weakness, but as a sign of strength.

Health support

As we pass through life, it is likely that we will all access many professional health services – usually starting on the maternity ward! We are all likely to need the support of the doctor to help us deal with common illnesses like chickenpox, or common problems like broken bones. Some of us will experience life-changing illnesses or serious accidents that need prolonged professional help and support. Stress is another factor of modern life with which

Your world

The residents of The Green are fortunate to have a health centre, Social Services department and hospital close by. List five professional services the residents of The Green will be able access from these organisations. Briefly describe the sorts of service these professionals would provide for local residents.

List three professional services you have used recently.

Did you know?

The second most common reason for absence from work in the UK is stress.

professionals can help, through counselling sessions, health advice and alternative therapies.

In the UK, we have a National Health Service to meet people's everyday health needs. Some people choose to pay for private medical treatment. You will look at these services in more depth in Unit 2.

Social support

People access various types of professional social support at different times in their lives, and for different reasons. Support is available to help children, adults, people with disabilities and those facing life-limiting illnesses.

Older people who have been independent all their lives may prefer to have social support so that they can stay in their own home, rather than moving into residential care. People usually access this sort of social support through their local Social Services department, although they can also turn to the private sector. There are many types of private residential home for people in later adulthood who need, or decide they would prefer, to have more constant support and care.

Social services organisations are not the only sources of professional social support. If someone is thinking about buying a flat or house, they may ask for financial advice from a bank or building society. People having problems with their neighbours might find they need to get support from a solicitor. If there are high levels of noise or antisocial behaviour, environmental health officers or the police may be called in to handle the situation. Everyday situations like this can all impact on people's health and wellbeing.

Many hands

Here you will learn how charity, community, voluntary and faith-based organisations help people handle the expected and unexpected life events that affect their growth and development.

Supporting others

Have you ever considered giving some of your time voluntarily to a local group or charity to help others? People can find themselves in difficult situations when unexpected life events happen. As you have seen earlier in the unit, these can affect all aspects of a person's life.

The voluntary sector has always played a big part in supporting people dealing with difficult situations in their lives. Voluntary groups include:

- charity/community groups – Samaritans
- voluntary groups – RSPCC, Citizens Advice Bureau
- faith-based groups – Salvation Army.

The voluntary sector

Before the National Health Service and Social Services were established, **voluntary sector** organisations were the main providers of support to others. Many voluntary organisations are registered charities and get most of their money from public fundraising. Some of the bigger organisations hold high-profile national fundraising events. For example, in 2008 Cancer Research UK held 260 sponsored 'Race for Life' runs throughout the country, and raised thousands of pounds for its work.

Most voluntary organisations have some paid staff, but rely on volunteers who give their time for free. Many of these organisations and their volunteers help people deal with the physical, intellectual, emotional and social consequences of the events that shape people's lives.

Faith-based organisations

Religious organisations have traditionally played an important part in helping people deal with the life events that affect them. A strong religious faith can be a big help in handling life events. At

Your world

Maud lives on The Green. She is a member of her local church and attends services and other church events about three times a week. Maud has a strong belief in helping others and works in a local cancer charity shop two afternoons a week.

In a small group, discuss the types of voluntary organisation there are in your local area that help others facing difficult life events.

Choose one of these organisations and describe the types of support it provides.

Voluntary sector – organisations that carry out activities other than for profit

Community group – a group of people who come together with a common purpose in the interests of people in the community

Floods in Doncaster

In 2007, parts of Doncaster were severely flooded. Some people were not able to return to their own homes for over a year. During this time, the local community worked together in volunteering to help others less fortunate than themselves. Local radio and television channels coordinated community appeals and many people donated unwanted cookers and washing machines to help those in need. Some people volunteered to support their neighbours by sharing housing for short periods. Local churches also coordinated support for those who needed food and shelter.

emotionally difficult times, such as bereavement, faith can help someone come to terms with their position, see it in context, and feel able to move beyond it. The support of the people who are also active in the religious organisation can help people as they adapt to their new circumstances.

Many religious organisations take an active role in supporting less fortunate members of their community. For example, visits to older people who are housebound can be a real support and offer people a better quality of life. Many religious groups raise funds for different causes, and can offer practical help by providing food, clothing and shelter for people who homeless.

Community groups

Across the UK, **community groups** exist to support people who are experiencing challenging life events.

In areas where traditional industry has declined and unemployment is high, community groups have become part of the fabric of life. People may be going through emotional times, finding it difficult to socialise with friends and struggling to pay the bills. Parents may not have the money to be able to fully support their children's intellectual development. These communities often experience a decline and crime rates rise.

In the Dearne Valley, an ex-mining area near Barnsley, local people set up a Safer Neighbourhood Scheme. Unemployment meant that crime rates were high and many people did not feel safe in their own community. The Safer Neighbourhood Scheme:

- worked with police to make neighbourhoods more safe
- removed graffiti
- established activities for young unemployed people to engage in
- set up afternoon clubs for older people who felt unsafe at night.

This scheme has been successful in reducing the levels of crime in the area. People in later adulthood now feel more secure, and everyone can socialise without fear.

Activity

Citizens Advice Bureau can be found in most areas of the country and offer practical advice and support for people with a range of issues. These might involve practical problems such as how to handle noisy neighbours or managing finances.

Pick an unexpected life event and identify three ways in which this event may affect a person's growth and development. How might the Citizens Advice Bureau be able to support a person through this life event?

Just checking

1. Describe three ways in which members of a church may support people in later adulthood in the community.
2. Where do most voluntary organisations get the money from to fund their activities?
3. Describe three activities that a community group might be involved with in an area of high unemployment.

Assessment for Unit 1

Welcome

Are you looking forward to being able to show the examiners what you learned in Health and Social Care? You should be if you are well prepared. Are you worried that you might find some of the questions hard and you may not be able to show all that you have learned and can do? Well don't! The examinations are designed to let you prove what you do know and can do. Your examination board, Edexcel, has spent a lot of time and effort to make sure that the examinations you sit are fair and that you can understand the questions you are asked.

How Unit 1 is examined

Key things you need to know

- The examination is 75 minutes long and you can get a maximum mark of 70. If you manage this, you will be awarded an A star. Some people will, so let's try to make sure it is you!
- Examiners work on a principle of 'a mark a minute', with 15 minutes extra to let you **read** the questions, **think** about them, **plan** your answers, **write** your answers and **review** what you have written, to check that it does actually answer the question set.
- The examination paper for Unit 1 will consist of a range of types of questions. There are some multiple-choice – 15 on each paper. Other questions are based around short case studies or scenarios and can range in marks from two to ten. Split your time carefully in the examination.
- The shorter questions do require short and to-the-point answers. If you write too much, you are wasting valuable time. The longer questions require you to think about what you have to do and construct an answer that does exactly what you are asked.
- A range of 'command words' will be used in the examination. We will explore what they are and what they mean later.
- Some marks are awarded for the quality of your written English. You need to show that you can write in a sensible and structured way.

> **Remember:**
>
> R = read
> T = think
> P = plan
> W = write
> R = review

Approaches to revision

Every person has their own approach to revision, but research shows certain things can help.

- Split your revision into timed 'chunks'. It is unlikely that you will be able to concentrate for more than one hour at once, so take breaks.

Top tips for preparing

Make sure:

- **you have covered all the content you need to**, as set out in the examination board's **Specification for GCSE Health and Social Care.** Your teacher will have this in booklet form, or you can look it up for yourself on the internet.
- **you have revised.** Don't leave all the revision for the days just before the examination. Make a revision plan for the weeks before the examination.
- **you know how to answer the different types of questions** that will appear on the examination. We will practice this later.
- **you know what the different 'command' words used by examiners mean** and how these guide you to write accurate and detailed answers.
- **you have practiced** doing all the different types of questions regularly well before the examination.

If you do all of these things, you are likely to be able to show what you know, what you can do and what you have learned.

- Revise actively. You could shorten your notes, design mind maps, or create 'flash cards 'of important information.
- Build in variety and your revision will be more interesting.
- Some people find background music helps them focus; others find it distracting. The choice is up to you, but be honest with yourself!

Top tips for revision

- Cover all parts of the specification equally well. The examination will test all areas of the specification.
- Pay particular attention to the parts you find hard. It's not a good use of time to revise what you already know well.
- Design a revision plan to cover the weeks running up to the examination so that each topic is covered at least twice.
- Incorporate times for practicing questions and mark them.
- Write some answers for common questions such as 'How might promotion affect a person's growth and development?'
- On the night before the examination, spend time checking out your knowledge and understanding.

Revision

Design a revision plan for the six weeks before your examination date, including:

- coverage of all the topics in Unit 1
- time for topics you find difficult
- time set aside each week to practice doing questions
- at least one week just before the examination to do a final check on your learning.

Just checking

1. How long is the examination?
2. What type of questions will you face
3. In completing the examination what are the five things you must remember to do? (Hint: R, T, P, W, R.)

Completing multiple-choice questions

Fifteen multiple-choice questions will start off the Unit 1 examination. There are two different types of questions you may be set.

1. The first will test what you know, understand and have learned about the unit. There will be one correct answer.

2. The second will see if you can think more deeply and recognise that more than one answer is correct.

Let's look at two examples.

1. What life stage is referred to as infancy?

a. First six months of life   **c.** First year of life
b. First two years of life   **d.** First nine months of life

This is a straightforward knowledge and understanding type of multiple-choice question. If you have revised, you will know the answer is **b**. You spot the right answer and then move on to the next question. If you are unsure, you must think sensibly and follow a route to getting to the most likely right answer. Rule out the answers you know to be wrong, and then make a reasoned decision. The odds are then greater that you might get the question right. Whatever you do, don't just guess: think about your decision first.

2. Which <u>two</u> of the following are unexpected life events?
A Sudden disability; **B** Birth of a baby; **C** Starting school; **D** Sudden illness

a. **A&B**   **c.** **C&D**
b. **B&C**   **d.** **A&D**

This sort of question is more demanding but, if you follow a plan, you should get to the correct answer. Firstly, see if you know the correct answers from what you have learned and revised. If you do, the answer will stand out straight away. If you don't, see if you know that **one** of the answers is correct. If, for example you knew that **D** Sudden illness was correct, then you know that there are only two possible answers: **C&D** or **A&D**. You then need to look at statements **A** and **C** very carefully. If you then know that starting school is an expected life event, the answer must be **d: A&D**.

These sorts of questions are a little more difficult to do but with practice you will get to grips with them. It is unlikely that more than five out of the 15 questions will be of this type.

Practice multiple-choice questions

1. What is the name of the hormone responsible for the sexual changes in males during puberty?

   a. oestrogen
   b. testosterone
   c. thyroxin
   d. growth hormone

2. What is the name given to the time in middle adulthood in which a monthly bleeding cycle stops?

   a. menstruation
   b. menopause
   c. menstrual
   d. maturation

3. What term is given to the process by which people learn behaviour during early years within the family?

   a. primary socialisation
   b. infancy
   c. early learning
   d. personal development

4. A peer group refers to:

   a. a friendship group.
   b. a family group.
   c. a religious group.
   d. an intimate sexual relationship.

5. Which two of the following are examples of gross motor skills?

   A knitting **B** running **C** jumping **D** using a computer keyboard.

   a. A&B
   b. B&C
   c. C&D
   d. A&D

The answers to these questions are on page 63.

You will need to practice doing these types of questions regularly before you sit your examination. Your teacher will be able to supply you with some questions from past examination papers and sample questions from the examination board. Also ask to look at the practice questions in the support pack your teacher should have.

Just checking

1. Describe the two different types of multiple-choice questions used in the Unit 1 examination.

2. Why is it a poor tactic to just guess the answer of a multiple-choice question if you are not sure of the correct answer?

Understanding the longer questions

Being able to show the examiner what you know, understand and can do is really important – and to do this, you have to be able to unpick each question. The key to doing this is to know what the 'command words' mean and what the examiner wants you to do in your answers.

Students often think that it is the student with the most knowledge who will get the highest mark in the examination. In reality, the student who achieves the highest marks is the one with good knowledge and understanding, who knows what the questions are asking.

The command words are used regularly throughout the paper so the better you get to grips with them, the better you will be able to answer the questions you are set.

You may wish to look at the assessment section for Unit 4 in this book. Here you will find more examples of questions and the sorts of answers students produce. This will help you to understand the common mistakes students make.

Command words

The table on the next page shows you the command words that are likely to be used in your examination for Unit 1, with examples of how they may be used. Shorter questions tend to use 'identify', 'describe' and 'define', and are worth one to four marks. Medium-length questions use words such as 'explain' and 'explain, using examples', and tend to have marks between four and six. Longer questions use the words 'examine', 'discuss' and 'assess', and tend to have marks between six and ten. There will probably only be a couple of these longer questions on the Unit 1 paper.

> **Command words** – words that tell a student writing an answer what they have to do

The 'command words'

Identify	You only need to list your points. On some occasions, they may be one-word answers. Example: Identify two life stages.
Describe	Write a sentence or two about something the examiner asks you. Example: Describe two ways retirement may affect a person's development.
Define	State the meaning of something. Example: Define 'peer group'.
Explain	Write a few sentences to show you understand a particular idea or concept in the question. Example: Explain the meaning of 'self-concept'.
Explain with examples	Write a few sentences to show you understand a particular idea or concept in a question. You will need to include examples in your answer. Example: Explain, using examples, the difference between gross and fine motor skills.
Assess	Consider an issue in some depth and come to a conclusion. Example: Assess the importance of family relationships on growth and development.
Examine	Consider a question or statement from different points of view. Example: Examine the possible effects of starting school on a child's emotional development.
Discuss	Consider a question and look at it from different viewpoints. This often involves coming to a reasoned conclusion and seeing things from different viewpoints. Example: Discuss the effect of income and wealth on development.

What the examiners thought

Working with a partner, see if you can work out how many marks the examiners can give to each of the following questions. The answers are on page 63.

1. Mike is 43. Identify Mike's life stage.
2. Define what is meant by self-image.
3. Describe how a change like the menopause may affect an individual's self-image.
4. Explain how having little money may affect a person's health and wellbeing.
5. Discuss the importance of education and training for an individual's development.
6. Examine the possible effects of promotion at work on a person's health and wellbeing.

Just checking

1. Explain why is it important to read the command words at the start of a question with the utmost care.
2. Explain why it is a good move to spend some time planning your answers to the longer six– to ten-mark questions.
3. Why is it important to look at both sides of an issue in a 'discuss 'or 'examine' question?

Answering the longer questions

The key to answering longer questions is having a number of skills. We will look at some of the skills here and develop them. This will be reinforced in the assessment section for Unit 4. Make sure you take a look at this as well.

The skills you will need to develop are:

- understanding what the question is asking you to do – command words.
- looking at the marks attached to the question. Remember the rule of 'a mark a minute'? A ten-mark question will require you to write for ten minutes, after you have done some thinking and planning!
- knowing how your answer will be marked by the examiners. The people who mark your answer mark it in line with a mark scheme. If you know how this scheme is applied, you can learn how to access all the marks.

Sample question

Let's get to grips with a sample question. Look at the background information, right. This is the sort of information the examination board will give you at the start of a section of questions. It is important that you **read** this carefully and **refer** to it as you try to answer the questions. The background information is a stimulus to get you thinking and to help you access the questions set. It also gives you clues as to what might be relevant to your answers.

> Dean has a positive self-concept. Identify and explain two possible factors that may account for this. (6 marks)

This is a typical question you may face. So how is it marked? Well, here is a mark scheme for you to look at carefully.

- 1 x 2 marks – for the correct identification of two factors that may lead Dean to have a positive self-concept.
- 2 x 2 marks – for explaining how each of the two factors selected may help Dean to have a positive self-concept.

Background information

Dean is 22 years of age and works as a part-time gym instructor. He is currently at university finishing his degree in Sports Studies. He enjoys his work at the gym and has ambitions of one day owning his own gym. Dean and his girlfriend, Jo, have decided to go travelling for a year when he finishes his degree.

Shaping an answer

The candidate is likely to use some of the following ideas from the background information:

- Dean has a part-time job that he enjoys
- Dean has money and an income
- Dean has a girlfriend/stable relationship
- Dean is academically successful
- Dean is studying a programme that he enjoys
- Dean has ambitions and plans for the future.

Answers

What's your answer?

With a partner, try to apply the mark scheme to each of these answers. What mark would you give each answer?

Sample answer 1

Dean has a positive self-concept because he goes to university and he is a gym instructor. This makes him feel good about himself as he may get a good job in the future. He also has a girlfriend and she probably makes him enjoy his life more as all boys want to have a girlfriend.

Sample answer 2

Dean goes to university and is studying for a degree. This means he was probably successful in his school examinations, which will have given Dean good self-esteem and a positive self-image. These together could explain why he has a positive self-concept now.

Dean also has a long-term relationship with Jo. They are planning to travel for a year together after he finishes his university course. Having a stable relationship with Jo probably makes Dean feel loved and valued. This will also help him have a positive self-image and good self-esteem.

Adding these together, we can see why Dean has a positive self-concept.

The two answers are very different in terms of the knowledge and understanding shown and how the information given is used and developed by the candidates.

What the examiners thought

Marks for sample answer 1

This candidate was given 2/6.

- x 2 marks for identification. The candidate correctly identified that Dean goes to university and has a girlfriend

The problem for this candidate is that they do not really go on to develop their answer very much and do not show the examiner that they can explain the points they make. A reference is made to the factors making Dean feel good. There is no real reference to self-image or self-esteem as you would expect from a student who really understands self-concept. No marks were awarded for explanation.

Marks for sample answer 2

This candidate was given 6/6.

- x 2 for identification. The candidate correctly identifies that Dean is academically successful and in a stable relationship.
- x 2 for explanation. The candidate fully develops both of the points identified and 'explains' how they contribute to a positive self-concept. To an examiner, it is obvious that this person fully understands self-concept as they talk about the two parts that add together lead to form it: self-image + self-esteem.

Last-minute preparation

As the examination approaches, it is useful to go through practice questions, to test that you can shape answers for each type of question. With a partner, test each other to see how well you do!

You might want your notes or textbook with you at the first try. As you get closer to the examination, see if you can do them from memory.

Basics

1. What does PIES stand for?
2. List the different life stages.
3. Identify the growth, development and changes that take place in each life stage.
4. List the life stages in order and the ages attached to each life stage.
5. Identify four factors that affect human growth and development.
6. Identify two factors people choose in their lives that affect their growth and development.
7. Identify two factors that affect growth and development as people pass through the life course.
8. Identify two changes that happen in puberty to:
   - girls only
   - boys only
   - both girls and boys.
9. Identify the different types of relationships people have in their lives.
10. What are self-image, self-esteem and self-concept?

Short written questions

Check that you can put your knowledge into words. The answers to these questions earn 1–3 marks. You may not need full sentences: some may need just one- or two-word answers.

1. George is 60 years of age. Identify the four life stages he has passed through and put them in the correct order.
2. Identify two physical characteristics linked to George's life stage.
3. Identify two physical characteristics associated with George's next life stage.
4. Jane is 38 years of age and earns a high income. Identify three positive effects of having a good income on health and wellbeing.
5. Identify two negative effects of having a hard, stressful job.
6. Nathan is 22 years of age. Identify three physical changes Nathan would have experienced in his **previous** life stage.

Questions using background information

Make sure you look for 'clues' in the background information as to what the examiner wants. Check the number of marks awarded when deciding how long to spend on each question.

1. Explain the difference between growth and development. (4 marks)
2. Identify and explain **one** source of **support** Abby could use to help her achieve a healthier lifestyle. (3 marks)
3. Explain the difference between self-image and self-esteem. (4 marks)
4. Using the background information, explain why Abby may have a negative self-image at present. (4 marks)
5. Explain how Abby's wellbeing may be negatively affected by her present lifestyle. (6 marks)

7. Tina is 55 years of age and going through the menopause. Identify two physical characteristics associated with the menopause.
8. Describe how the menopause may affect a person's self-image.
9. Melissa is 15 years of age. Identify which type of relationship is most important to adolescents at this life stage.
10. Which sort of relationship would have been most important to Melissa in her previous life stage?

Longer written questions

Here you will need to write in full sentences. The questions tend to focus on 'explanation', 'difference between' or 'the effect' of something. Remember the general rule of 'a mark a minute'!

1. Explain the meaning of the term 'emotional development'.
2. Explain, using examples, how friends may support a person going through a divorce of relationship breakdown.
3. Explain what is meant by 'bonding'.
4. Explain how diet may affect may affect physical health.
5. Explain, using examples, how moving to a town from the countryside may affect a person's social development.

Background information

Abby is 47 years of age and a single parent. She has two children, Barrie and Charlene. Abby works for a catering company and has just been promoted to manager. Now she works longer hours, has more stress and sees less of her family. Abby smokes heavily and has put on weight, as she does not always eat properly and skips meals. Charlene is encouraging her to adopt a healthier lifestyle.

Answers

Multiple-choice (page 57)

1 = **b**

2 = **b**

3 = **a**

4 = **a**

5 = **b**

Don't expect there to be an equal numbers of a, b, c and d answers — it doesn't work that way. Have confidence in your own judgement.

How many marks (page 58)

1. 1 mark
2. 1 mark
3. 2 marks
4. 4 marks
5. 8 or 10 marks
6. 8 or 10 marks

Other than 1-mark questions, the examiners rarely ask questions with an odd number of marks.

Unit 2: Exploring Health, Social Care and Early Years Provision

Your world

Guess how many different health, social care and early years services you have used since you were born. Now write down as many as you can remember, or know about because your family has told you. Were you right in your original guess?

Learning objectives

- The type of care needs of major service user groups
- The types of services that exist to meet service user needs
- How services have developed and how they are organised
- The ways in which people can obtain care services and the barriers that could prevent service users gaining access to those care services
- The main roles and skills of people providing health, social care and early years services
- The principles of care and values that underpin all care work with service users

Health and social care provision can be given at any age

Introduction

This unit is about the range of care needs of major service-user groups and the services that exist to meet these needs.

Care needs of major service-user groups

All people have health needs, which, as you read in Unit 1, can be divided into physical needs (to do with the body), intellectual needs (to do with the brain), emotional needs (to do with feelings) and social needs (to do with getting on with other people).

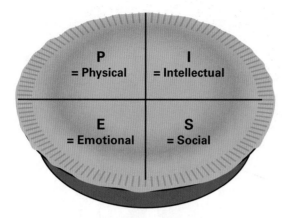

Take the first letter of each of the health needs and it spells PIES

Services to meet service user needs

The main areas covered in this qualification are health, social care and early years. Early years services are part of the children and young people's sector.

Health sector

The role of a health worker is to help people stay healthy and to treat and cope with the symptoms if they become ill, be it physically or mentally. Health workers include doctors, nurses, dentists, opticians, pharmacists, and more.

Social care sector

The role of a social worker is to help people live more successfully within their local communities by helping them find solutions to their problems. Social workers not only work with an individual but also build relationships with their families and friends, as well as working closely with other organisations involved with the individual, such as the police, health service, schools and housing.

Children and young people sector, including early years

The role of a worker with children and young people is to help them receive the services to which they are entitled. These workers include social workers who help keep families together. This sector also covers education services, adoption and foster care and children's homes. It aims to help all children and young people develop and reach their full potential by providing all the services they need to do so. Early years covers children up to the age of eight years old.

Sector – one of a number of parts of a society that focus on a similar thing: for example, the care industry is divided into sectors that are responsible for different aspects of the care of people

How you will be assessed

You will produce a report based on an investigation of the needs of one service user, on how these needs are met by service providers and care practitioners. It must contain evidence of the range of care needs of the service user, the types of services offered and how they are organised, the ways your person can obtain these services and any barriers that might stop them using them. It must also show the main roles and skills of the people providing the services and the principles of care and values that underpin their work. This report will be completed in controlled conditions.

Your world

Look at the picture. Identify people from each of the six different age groups. Can you remember the correct names of each of the age groups you learned about in Unit 1? If not, look at the list (left) and remind yourself of them. Which age groups are hardest to identify just by looking at a picture?

At your service

In this topic, you will look again at the different age groups of service users and start to understand the range of their needs.

The different groups

People can be divided up according to age groups:

- Infants (0 to 2 years)
- Early childhood (3 to 8 years)
- Adolescence (9 to 18 years)
- Early adulthood (19 to 45 years)
- Middle adulthood (46 to 65 years)
- Later adulthood (65+ years).

People from all ages can also fall into a group of people with specific needs: they may have some form of physical or intellectual disability, have a very high ability in a certain area or have a medical condition. All these groups, and others with other sets of specific needs, need

Did you know?

Maslow was the eldest of seven children and was a Jewish boy growing up in a non-Jewish neighbourhood in Brooklyn, New York. He spent his rather unhappy childhood in libraries, surrounded by books and with no friends, and studied people he considered to be exemplary, such as Albert Einstein and Eleanor Roosevelt, to come up with his theories.

services that allow them to be as independent as possible and reach their full potential, whatever age they are.

The physical, intellectual, emotional and social needs of service users

Maslow's Hierarchy of Needs

Our basic health needs do not change as we pass through the various stages of our lives, but different people will need different kinds of support from services depending on their particular situation or life stage.

Psychologist Abraham Maslow designed a **hierarchy** of needs in the 1930s. This is shown as a pyramid of human needs, with the most important at the bottom and the most complicated at the top. If we do not have food, water, oxygen, sleep and warmth, we will die – so without these, we cannot hope to have the needs on the next level of the pyramid met, such as feeling safe and secure, protected from danger and financially secure.

People at different life stages have different views of their needs. For example, children left on their own, even with their basic physical needs met, may feel frightened and unsafe, but adults might be very happy to have some time to themselves to relax.

Maslow's Hierarchy of Needs: How far from the bottom would you put yourself?

Failure to meet these needs

Failure to meet some of the needs in Maslow's hierarchy can have serious consequences. People who live in a dirty, cold house on an unbalanced diet are less likely to feel safe and secure and are more likely to become ill. Similarly, people whose social needs are not met, who lack love and affection, will find it harder to develop relationships with others and will have poor self-esteem. They will be lacking in confidence and will be less likely to succeed in their education and in life generally.

Hierarchy – list of things or people arranged in order

Activity

1. Look at Maslow's Hierarchy of Needs. Are all your basic needs being met? Are your safety and security needs being met? Write down where you feel you come at the moment, with level 1 being the bottom and level 5 being the top. You will not have to show anyone else, so be honest.

2. Write down all the different things that affect how you feel about yourself. Then write down how you feel about yourself overall at the moment, with 1 being feeling bad about yourself and 5 feeling very good. How does this level compare with the level you think you are on the pyramid?

3. Write a list of three things you are going to try to do to move you up to at least the next level.

Just checking

1. What do we mean by saying someone has a specific need? Give three examples.

2. What are the five levels of need identified by Maslow in the 1930s?

3. Why are basic physical needs at the bottom of the Maslow's pyramid?

Starting out

This topic looks at the range of physical, intellectual, emotional and social needs of infants, children and adolescents.

Infants

Although there are certain needs all groups have, as shown in Maslow's Hierarchy, other needs vary. Generally, only infants need to be fed and have their nappies changed, and form attachment relationships (bonding) with their parents and main carers, so these are needs specific to this group.

Children

The PIES of children are shown in the table below. As you can see, there is very little difference in physical needs, some difference in intellectual and social needs, and the most difference in emotional needs as infants develop into children.

Physical needs	Intellectual needs	Emotional needs	Social needs
Warmth	Play	Respect	Develop routines
Shelter	Stimulation	Love	Meet other people
Balanced diet	More advanced toys	Encouragement	Play and learn with others
Protection	New experiences	Laughter	Explore their own environment
Good hygiene	Books	Be valued	Use social facilities
Sleep	Television	Dignity	
Exercise	Education	Learn independence	
Fresh air	Role modelling	Self-esteem	

The PIES for children aged 3 to 8 years old

Your world

The needs of toddlers are shown in the spider diagram opposite. Draw a table with four columns headed physical, intellectual, emotional and social needs, and write each need in the correct column.

Activity

1. Look through old magazines or catalogues. Cut out pictures of activities children take part in, such as eating a meal with their family, horse riding, dancing, sports, playing games and playing with toys. Stick each picture in your book and identify which one or more of the PIES are being met by the activity: for example, stimulation. Write this by the picture. Remember, childhood is from three to eight years old so do not use pictures of infants or adolescents!

2. By each picture describe how the activity is helping the child's physical, intellectual, emotional and/or social development.

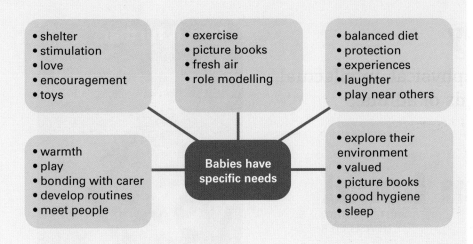

- shelter
- stimulation
- love
- encouragement
- toys

- exercise
- picture books
- fresh air
- role modelling

- balanced diet
- protection
- experiences
- laughter
- play near others

- warmth
- play
- bonding with carer
- develop routines
- meet people

Babies have specific needs

- explore their environment
- valued
- picture books
- good hygiene
- sleep

Take it further

1. Use the table for children to see how to present this task. Make a similar table for yourself as an adolescent. Don't forget needs such as learning to be assertive, taking responsibility for others and learning about sex and sexuality.
2. Which of these PIES are you finding hardest to cope with? Write a letter to The Green Local expressing your feelings about being an adolescent and explaining what adults such as parents and teachers can do to make things easier for you.

Adolescents

Adolescence is one of the most difficult life stages for many individuals. It is when you usually go through puberty and start to change into an adult. Your reproductive organs start to function and changes in hormone level mean that emotions become confused and you may feel under a lot of stress.

Just checking

1. Which three needs are specific to infancy?
2. Which area of need changes most between infancy and childhood?
3. Why is adolescence the most difficult life stage for many people?

Girls	Boys
Gain weight	Gain weight
Grow body hair, mainly underarm and pubic	Grow body hair, mainly underarm, chest, face and pubic
Grow taller	Grow taller
Breasts develop	Penis develops
Hips widen ready for child bearing	Testicles drop
Periods start (menstruation)	Voice breaks
	Shoulders broaden

The major changes in puberty for boys and girls

As time goes by

This topic covers the key physical, intellectual, emotional and social needs of adults.

The Green Local

**WINTER EDITION
NEWSLETTER**

Lea signs up to play for United

Mike Lea, aged 20, puts his success down to the fact that he has worked hard at both his studies and his sport. He allows himself a night out a week, with his friends, when he enjoys a drink, but the rest of the week he trains hard, goes out shopping with his girlfriend and plays football games on a games console with his mate Ben.

Identify Mike's needs and how they are being met.

Adulthood

Adulthood is the stage of life when most people start to feel that they understand and accept themselves and begin to feel more settled. Although they never stop learning new skills and acquiring knowledge, this happens more slowly than for younger people. Adults tend to spend a lot of time making decisions, such as where to live, who to live with, whether to get married, have children, what job to do, when to retire … the list is endless.

In any age group the importance of different health needs changes with time but, because the different stages of adulthood are longer, adults have more varying needs within each of them. Health and social care workers need to understand these needs so they can help service users as the need arises.

Early and middle adulthood

Physical needs	Intellectual needs	Emotional needs	Social needs
Warmth	Stimulating work	Respect	Money to access activities
Shelter	Learn new skills for home, work and leisure	Love	Opportunities to meet other people
Balanced diet	Conversation	Encouragement	Learn with others
Safe surroundings	New experiences	Laughter	Travel
Good hygiene	Books	Feel valued	Leisure facilities
Sleep	Media	Dignity	Free time
Exercise	Education	Independence	Information about available activities
Fresh air	Role models	Self-esteem and self-awareness	
Health facilities	Job security	Stable relationships	
Menopause		Preparation for parenthood, children leaving home, retirement, death of loved ones	
		Financial security	

The PIES for adulthood

Later adulthood

Inevitably, with age, people's bodies gradually change and start to wear out a little. They will have more needs as they get older, such as access to convenient health and leisure facilities, practical help as they become less mobile, and support in times of distress. However, later adulthood can now be at least as long as early or middle adulthood, and many people look forward to this stage of their lives. They can retire from work and their children have usually moved out so they can spend their days doing the things they have always wanted to do, provided they remain healthy and have saved for retirement.

Just checking

1. List three needs of adults for each of the PIES.
2. Why is it important to meet new people as you get older?
3. Why do you think it is right to call people over 65 years of age older people instead of old or elderly?

Meeting the demand

Here you will find out about how health, social care and early years services respond to the needs and demands of the different groups including universal services and targeted services. This topic also covers how services meet social policy goals and assess needs.

Think about it

Unintentional 999 calls are putting increased pressure on the emergency services. The number of people ringing the number by mistake has risen, as more people now have mobile phones. There are about two million 999 calls a year in London, and some 80,000 are unintentional calls from mobile phones. What are the possible consequences of this to someone who genuinely needs help?

Your world

Look at the picture of Felicity, who has fallen over and badly damaged her ankle while jogging round the park near The Green. Write down the different services Felicity will be involved with over the next few weeks.

Responding to the needs and demands of service users

Service providers respond to the needs and demands of the different groups who are referred to them. This might be at the request of the user, a family member, a friend or a professional, such as a doctor (see on pages 88–89). The request might also be made by a stranger, such as at the scene of an accident, when a passer-by might dial 999 to summon medical help.

Activity

With a partner, research social policy goals on obesity on the internet, and find out how services in your area are trying to meet these goals. Pick one of these goals and produce a leaflet to put on display locally, explaining:

- what the particular goal is that you have picked
- why this goal has been set
- how local services are trying to meet it.

Most services work in partnership to provide a better, more all-round service to meet the needs of a service user. How they do so will be covered on pages 86–87.

Universal services

Some services are available to everyone, and these are known as universal services. These include, for example, the NHS, Social Services and Early Years Education.

Targeted services

Other services are targeted at specific groups of people with a specific set of needs. Examples include the Alzheimer's Society, which helps those who have Alzheimer's disease themselves or whose lives are affected by it, and Asthma UK, which aims to improve the health and wellbeing of people with asthma.

Meeting social policy goals

When the government **commission** a group of people to look into a problem facing our society, such as homelessness, child poverty or drug abuse, that group of people will report back on what they have found out. Based on that report, a **policy** may be written to help tackle the problem and targets may be set to **implement** the policy. These targets are known as social policy goals.

One example is the goal set by the Government in September 2007 to reduce the proportion of overweight and obese children to the level it was at in 2000. This aims to reverse the rising tide of **obesity** in the population by making sure that all individuals can maintain a healthy weight. The goal forms part of the Government's Public Service Agreement to improve the health and wellbeing of children and young people under the age of 11. The Department of Health and the Department for Children, Schools and Families are jointly responsible for delivering this, and have sent guidance as to how to meet this social policy goal to all Primary Care Trusts and local authorities.

Assessing the needs of the population

In order to identify likely service demand and provide services that meet needs within a local area, the health services and local authorities assess those needs. For example, the CYPS (Children and Young People's Service) collects a wide range of information – such as the percentage of children who go to school without any breakfast – so that they can target support where it will be most effective – for example, by making sure that schools run breakfast clubs so that children can get breakfast before school starts.

Commission – to instruct or give authority to a group of people to do a particular task
Implement – put into action
Policy – a piece of legislation or legal writing, to which service providers have to refer to find out how to deal with particular situations
Obesity – being unhealthily overweight

Just checking

1. What is the difference between a universal service and a targeted service?

2. What is a social policy goal?

3. How do service providers assess the needs of the population? Give an example to illustrate your answer.

Why provide services?

This topic looks at why individuals may need to access services.

Why individuals use health, social care and early years services

Services are provided either because individuals want and need them, or because the Government feels they need to be provided to overcome a problem by meeting social policy goals: for example, a service might be developed to help people stop smoking, because treating smoking-related illnesses costs the country a lot of money.

Some individuals will use services because they have a temporary need – for example, they need treatment for an ingrowing toenail – while some individuals need treatment for a permanent need, such as Down's syndrome, which is a **chronic** condition.

Individuals use health, social care and early years services because they may need one or more of: care, support, advice and medical treatment.

How many services has George used in his life?

Your world

List as many different services as you can that George might have used from when he was just an embryo in his mother's womb to now, at the age of 90. Look at your list for when he was younger. Are there any you have put on the list because you used them, but in fact would not have existed 90 years ago? Use the internet to help you.

Care

Everyone needs someone to look after them in some way at different points in their lives. For example, a preschool child might go to a nursery, where children are cared for and at the same time learn new skills: how to interact with others, how to express themselves and how the world works. Childminders, day-care centres for children or older adults, schools, residential homes, community groups, hospitals, hospices and many other services provide care.

Support

People also need different kinds of help, such as money, help to get around or even encouragement to solve their own problems. For example, if you have had a stroke and recovered as much as possible, but have been left disabled, the support you need could include rehabilitation, where you would learn to use your limbs again, occupational therapy to learn how to do simple tasks around

Think about it

The first of 152 GP health centres in England was opened in November 2008. The new centres will open between 8 am and 8 pm for seven days a week. Any member of the public can use them for a range of services, which include minor surgery. How will this help you and your family access the services they want?

Case study Sunita

Sunita is an older Muslim woman whose husband died six months ago. She has moved from her home into sheltered accommodation after falling and dislocating her hip – she could no longer manage to get upstairs to bed and the bathroom. She used to see her friends regularly and visit the local mosque, but now she is too far away and cannot walk there. Her hip is still causing her pain, and she is becoming less mobile because she takes no exercise. Her family do not visit her very often, because her daughter lives 70 miles away with her young family, and her son is too busy enjoying a hectic social life. The warden of the sheltered accommodation notices that Sunita seems very sad and lonely. He is a very caring man and is determined to help her have a happier life.

1. Write down all Sunita's needs.
2. What do you suggest the warden does to get Sunita (a) care (b) support (c) advice (d) medical treatment?
3. Which of these will most improve Sunita's quality of life?

the home with a disability, and help to get money to have a car adapted for your new needs.

Advice

At some stage in their lives, all people will also need to be given an opinion or information as to what to do in a particular situation. It might be that you suspect someone is being abused and you ask advice as to what to do to help him or her. You could ask services such as Social Services, a teacher at school or the Citizens Advice Bureau. Other sources of advice are available on a whole range of issues, including helplines such as Childline and NHS Direct, church or voluntary groups, and medical services.

Medical treatment

Everyone also needs medical treatment from time to time, to have a medical problem dealt with. It might be at the doctor's for a condition such as flu, or at the walk-in centre for a sprained wrist, or at a hospital for treatment for more serious conditions, such as appendicitis, cancer or heart disease. Some residential care homes also give medical treatment, as do dentists, opticians, community nurses and midwives, and many other service providers.

All services are provided to meet people's needs, be they physical, intellectual, emotional or social. Their main aim is to help people be as independent, healthy and happy as possible, so that they can reach their full potential.

Chronic – something that persists for a long time

Just checking

1. What are the four main reasons that people need to use health, social care or early years services?

2. Give three examples of where a child might be cared for.

3. Give three examples of where you could go for advice for a social care problem, giving a different example for each place of the type of problem you might need advice on.

When you're young

This topic talks about the range of health, social care and early years services available to infants, children and adolescents. There are far too many to be mentioned here, so this only gives some examples.

Healthcare

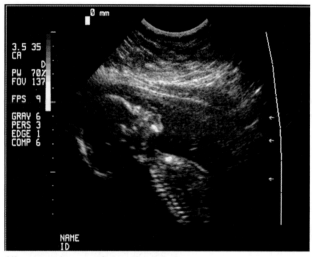

Ultrasound scan of an unborn baby

You have been looked after by healthcare providers all your life – and even before you were born, with careful monitoring while you were still inside your mother's womb.

Every family with children under five has a health visitor who supports them by visiting the home to give advice on issues such as feeding and sleeping. The mother is encouraged to attend postnatal clinics too, at their GP's surgery or at hospital, for further monitoring for herself and her baby. The baby's height and weight are checked regularly to check whether the baby is growing at the expected rate.

Children continue to be monitored throughout their early years, with their height and weight, their eyes and teeth checked regularly. A child with a condition such as asthma will attend a clinic for that condition at the GP's surgery or local hospital, where it will be monitored by nurses and doctors who will give support, advice and treatment. The health visitor will continue to give support if needed, on issues such as growth and development, everyday difficulties such as teething and behaviour and where to find additional support, such as toddler groups, playgroups and day nurseries.

Young people are also given various **immunisations**, from when they are babies to the age of 18 years.

Young people access healthcare by visiting the doctor, dentist, optician, Brook (a service that offers free and confidential advice on sex and contraception), hospital and many other services as the need arises.

Social care

What sorts of needs do you think the social care sector would cover?

One example is early childhood intervention. If a child experiences a developmental delay, such as a delay in starting to talk, this can be made worse over time. Early intervention comes in the form of the provision of services to provide appropriate therapies for such children and their families. These services aim to lessen the effects of the condition by minimising the delays and maximising the child's chances of reaching each normal step of development.

Another example is if a young person is suspected of being abused. Such suspicions can be brought to the attention of Social Services in a number of ways – for example, through a family member, teacher or friend. At this point, a social worker is assigned to the young person and they are taken to a place of safety while an investigation is carried out. Here Social Services help not only the young person but also their family to deal with the problem.

Early years

The Children and Young People's Service (CYPS) provides monitoring and support, and children and young people use many of their different services throughout their childhood and adolescence. These range from those used by nearly all children and young people – such as education or health – to those needed by some children and young people at some time in these life stages – such as Children's Social Services.

CYPS consists of council departments that have formed partnerships to bring together all services that work to improve the lives of children and young people. They cover issues ranging from dental health to mental health to teenage pregnancies. All have visions for their children and young people based on the five aims of *Every Child Matters*, which are being healthy, staying safe, enjoying and achieving, making a positive contribution and achieving economic wellbeing.

Immunisation – an injection or dose of a drug to help fight diseases that can kill or cause lasting damage

Activity

1. Think about yourself at school. On a big piece of paper, write 'I matter' in the middle and draw five branches outwards, evenly spaced. Along each branch, write one of the *Every Child Matters* aims (given on this page). At the end of each branch, write down all the ways in which the staff at school meet each aim for you.
2. Now write down (honestly!) what else you could do to help the school help you to achieve these aims.

Just checking

1. Name three places where you could go to get help with a medical problem.
2. What are the five aims of *Every Child Matters*?
3. What is meant by early childhood intervention?

All grown up

In this topic, you will learn about some of the wide range of health, social care and early years services available to adults.

Healthcare

Most healthcare in the UK is provided by the National Health Service (NHS). Adults access a wide range of health services, including all those used by younger people, such as hospitals, dentists, opticians, GP surgeries and community nurses, but also ones adults are usually more likely to use, such as chiropodists, heart specialists, sex specialists, and even plastic surgeons.

Some medical conditions and needs are much more likely to occur in adulthood, such as osteoporosis (brittle bone disease), hip and knee replacements due to wear, hysterectomies, physiotherapy after accidents and strokes, alopecia (hair loss), insomnia, diabetes due to weight problems and problems such as snoring. Also, more adults than younger people have mental health problems.

Complementary services such as reflexology, osteopathy, aromatherapy and chiropraxy are now used alongside more conventional treatments. Doctors often refer adults to these services, which are run privately outside the NHS.

Social care

Social services provided for adults include voluntary and community services, such as refuges for adults at risk of violence, homelessness services, support services such as the Samaritans, and advice services such as the Citizen's Advice Bureau. Some, such as Relate, are provided because adults are having problems with relationships.

Your world

Write a list of all the different services you think will be available to Daisy, who lives in the residential home near The Green. Share your ideas with three others in your group. Then go online to look at the services available at a local care home. Are there any you missed? Are there any you are surprised to find offered? Why are you surprised?

Complementary – running alongside and supporting other services so as to form a complete whole or to enhance each other

Prognosis – the likely outcome

As adults get older, they are more likely to need services like those in the diagram below. They can access them at places such as residential care homes, sheltered accommodation and day-care centres.

Help available to older adults

You will know from the previous topic that the main role of the social care sector is to assess needs and provide access to services required to meet those needs, for people of all ages.

If, for example, an older adult decides that he can no longer manage to live on his own and would prefer to move into a residential care home with people of his own age, he or his family would contact Social Services. A social worker would visit him to find out certain information, such as how mobile he is, what his general state of health is, his medical history, family details and (if it is decided his need is such that he should be given a place in a home) how much money he has available to contribute toward his care. The social worker would then help him find a home that both he and his family felt was right for him, and help him apply for a place and for any grants he is entitled to, to help him pay for his care. The interview between the social worker and the service user is part of the monitoring process, helping him get a suitable place he can afford.

Early years

Adults will need early years services when they become parents. These range from antenatal and postnatal care to services provided by midwives, nurseries and schools.

Activity

1. You may not have heard of some of the conditions mentioned here, or may know little about them. In your group, each pick a different condition to research and produce your own 'Key word' boxes, describing in one sentence what each of them is.
2. For the condition you researched, produce a factsheet to explain to others:
   - what the symptoms are
   - which services are needed for treatment
   - what the **prognosis** is
   - how to prevent the condition occurring or returning.

Just checking

1. Name three services that adults will use, but younger people are unlikely to.
2. Give three examples of what social services will do to monitor and support an older person.
3. Why do middle adults need different services from when they were young adults? Give three examples to explain your answer.

Can we help you?

In this topic, you will learn about the different providers of health, social care and early years support.

Types of provider

Statutory provision is funded and provided by the Government. These services must be offered because Parliament has passed a law that requires them to be provided, and all UK citizens have a legal right to receive these. They include:

- **NHS Trusts** Trusts are **autonomous** organisations set up to do a specific job. For example, there are 23 Ambulance Trusts in England, with others in Scotland, Ireland and Wales, which run the ambulance services; similarly, the Hospital Trusts oversee NHS hospitals and specialist care centres.
- **integrated children's services** CYPS brings together all services in an area for children and young people from birth to the age of 19, to ensure that they work and communicate together to meet the needs of children, young people and their families or carers. With some vulnerable groups, the age can be extended to 25. Integrated children's services include Sure Start and Connexions, and support *Every Child Matters* (see pages 76–77).
- **extended services** Extended schools work with the local authority, local providers and other schools to provide access to a core of integrated services, such as study support, sport, music clubs, childcare at primary schools, parenting and family support and easy access to targeted and specialist support, such as through Sure Start Children's Centres. They also allow access to facilities such as ICT and adult and family learning. They are provided beyond the school day, not necessarily by teachers or on the school site.
- **local authority services** These are the local council bodies that undertake an estimated 700 different tasks. These include running education, leisure and social services, as well as environmental health, planning, surveying, accountancy and legal work.

Private provision is made by businesses that make a profit. Examples include:

- **private companies** These run organisations such as private hospitals and residential care homes.

Your world

Write down all the different nurseries near where you live. You can find the names of most of them in the Yellow Pages, or on yell.com. Using the internet, find out how each of them is funded.

Activity

Think of a local health, social care or early years charity or support group in your area. Do some research on it, including what it does with money raised, its logo and how you as a school can help it. Produce a PowerPoint™ presentation to persuade others in your group why they should raise money to help that charity or support group.

Take it further

Have a more detailed discussion about how your group could raise some money for the charity. Have a go at putting your plans into action and, if you are successful, invite someone from the charity to come and receive the money. You could also ask them to give a talk to your group on the work of the charity.

- **self-employed practitioners** These are people who set up in business on their own to make money for themselves, such as private physiotherapists.
- **outsourced indirect care services** 'Outsourcing' means bringing in companies that are not directly involved in health, social care and early years services to provide a service for those who are, such as hospital catering.

Voluntary provision is provided by charities or community groups that do not make a profit. Without these, the statutory services would not be able to cope because they would not be able to afford all the other services. They include:

- **charities** These raise money to help others, doing things such as relieving poverty and advancing health or education. Age Concern and the British Heart Foundation are examples of charities.
- **local support groups** These are set up to help people with a physical, social or emotional condition that some one might need help with, such as support groups for carers looking after people with mental health problems.
- **non-profit organisations** These are often run by paid employees with volunteer help, and are set up so that they make only enough money to pay the employees and do whatever they are set up to do, without making any profit. Examples are Childline, the Samaritans and hospices.

Charities are all examples of non-profit organisations. However, not all non-profit organisations are charities, such as some housing associations.

Informal provision is when care is provided free by family, friends and neighbours.

Autonomous – self-governing
Indirect care – people who provide a service to the **direct carers** that will ultimately benefit the service user: for example, a day-care centre manager
Direct care – people who provide care directly to the service user: for example, a doctor

Just checking

1. What is meant by statutory provision? Pick one example and explain it fully to illustrate your answer.
2. What do local authorities do?
3. How are voluntary organisations funded? Give three examples of voluntary organisations and explain how each one is funded.

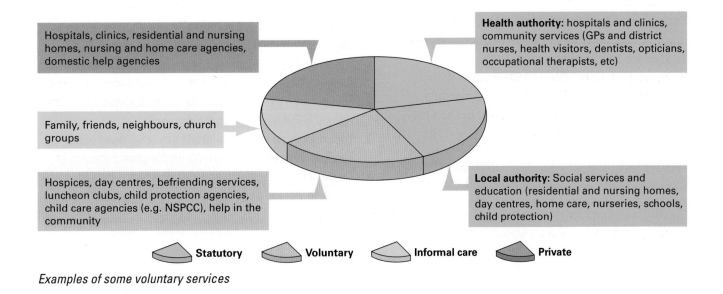

Hospitals, clinics, residential and nursing homes, nursing and home care agencies, domestic help agencies

Health authority: hospitals and clinics, community services (GPs and district nurses, health visitors, dentists, opticians, occupational therapists, etc)

Family, friends, neighbours, church groups

Hospices, day centres, befriending services, luncheon clubs, child protection agencies, child care agencies (e.g. NSPCC), help in the community

Local authority: Social services and education (residential and nursing homes, day centres, home care, nurseries, schools, child protection)

Statutory   Voluntary   Informal care   Private

Examples of some voluntary services

Here's to your health

82

Here you will learn how national and local health care services are organised, including the relationship between the different organisations within the framework.

National provision

The NHS was created in 1948 by the Health Minister Aneurin Bevan, to create free healthcare for all. There have been many changes since that time, as technology and our population and health needs have changed. The NHS is now run nationally by Parliament, via the Department of Health (DoH), which is a government department headed by the Secretary of State for Health. The DoH plans the overall direction of the NHS and sets and monitors national healthcare standards, such as reducing waiting lists for appointments. It also funds the NHS.

Local provision

Each of the 28 administrative areas of the country has a Strategic Health Authority (SHA), headed by an NHS Executive. These have the responsibility to implement DoH policies and manage local health services, by monitoring performance and planning strategy in the area.

In addition to this, a number of Special Health Authorities provide specialist services across England. These include the National Blood Authority, which organises blood donations and distribution.

Your world

Who runs a school?

Think about how a school is run. Try to draw a 'family tree' diagram to show how you think your school is managed and organised, starting with the head teacher at the top. Can you imagine how hard it is to draw a similar diagram for the structure of the health service?

Activity

1. Try to draw a 'family tree' diagram or flow chart on a large piece of paper to show the structure of the health service in England. The relevant organisations are mentioned in the text to help you. Add any more services you can think of – there are lots more!
2. Find out who the Secretary of State for Health is and include his or her name on the diagram.
3. Look back at pages 78–9 and add any other health care services, such as voluntary ones, in the correct place.
4. On the internet, research how this structure differs in Scotland, Ireland and Wales. Draw new diagrams for each.

Healthcare is divided into three areas: primary, secondary and tertiary care.

Primary care

Primary care refers to the health services that are the first point of contact for people who have a health problem. The bodies responsible for this are Primary Care Trusts (PCTs), which are large, local organisations at the centre of the NHS. They control 80 per cent of the NHS budget, and are responsible for managing health services in your area. Primary care includes GPs, dentists, opticians, pharmacists, NHS Direct and walk-in centres.

Secondary care

Patients who need care that cannot be provided by primary care services are referred to secondary care services, such as hospitals run by NHS Hospital Trusts (which are in turn supported by Ambulance Trusts), Mental Health Trusts, and social care services. Patients are either referred by a doctor or taken there in an emergency.

Tertiary care

This sort of care is provided by more specialised departments or hospitals, which are often linked to medical schools or are teaching hospitals. They treat people who have conditions that need more specialised doctors. Hospital doctors refer patients to tertiary care if needed.

Hospices, which treat people with terminal illnesses, are an example of tertiary care.

Take it further

Find out more about:

- Mental Health Trusts
- NHS Direct
- Walk-in Centres

Produce a factsheet on each.

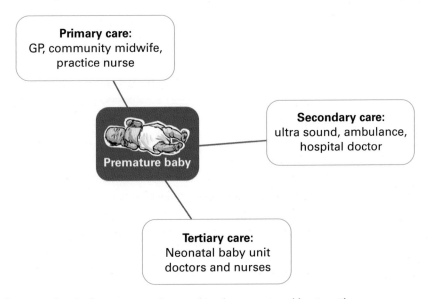

An example of primary, secondary and tertiary care working together

Primary care:
GP, community midwife, practice nurse

Premature baby

Secondary care:
ultra sound, ambulance, hospital doctor

Tertiary care:
Neonatal baby unit doctors and nurses

Just checking

1. What do the following stand for? DoH, NHS, SHA, PCT.
2. Explain what is meant by the expressions primary care, secondary care and tertiary care.
3. Give five examples each of primary care, secondary care and tertiary care services, and explain briefly what they do.

Who does what?

This topic looks at the structure of social care and early years services, including the relationship between different organisations within the framework.

Social care

National provision

The provision of social care also comes under the responsibility of Parliament, via the Secretary of State for Health and the DoH. The DoH aims to provide policy and guidance for the delivery of a social care system that provides care equally for all, while enabling people to keep their independence and dignity. To do this, the DoH have set up a separate department, the Social Care, Local Government and Care Partnerships Directorate, with its own Director, within the DoH. There is a separate public body, which is not part of the Government, called the General Social Care Council (GSCC), which makes sure that all social care workers are properly trained and follow high professional standards.

Local provision

The DoH does not have direct responsibility for delivering social care services, but rather it funds local authorities and provides legal and policy frameworks to enable them to provide an effective social service. Local authorities retain their statutory responsibility for providing and funding social services, but they commission public, private and voluntary sector providers to deliver day-to-day social services that meet local needs, some of which fall in to the health or early years sectors.

Social workers are employed to assess the needs of people such as children and families with difficulties, people with disabilities or housing problems, or older people who need help. Once they have completed their assessment reports and identified a genuine need, funds are allocated and services provided. Some local authorities work together to provide some services that they couldn't afford on their own.

Early years (0–8 years)

National provision

The children and young people's sector, of which early years is a part, has a large overlap with social and health care. Parliament has

Activity

1. Repeat the activity from the previous topic, but for Social Services. Can your new diagram be joined to the one from the previous topic at any point? If so, join them up.
2. Repeat it again for the children and young people's sector using the information below.

Re-engaging – making someone interested in something again
Disaffected – having lost interest in, or resenting, something

Social care services

Case study Baby P

Read the report on Baby P on www.timesonline.co.uk dated 12 November 2008. Be warned: it is upsetting to read, but it really happened.

1. Identify all the different services at both national and local level which should have helped Baby P.
2. What do you think each service could have done differently?
3. Do you think any of the workers involved should be punished in any way? Explain your answer.

a Secretary of State for Education who heads the Department for Children, Schools and Families (DCSF). It aims to enable all children and young people to reach their full potential by raising standards, lifting more children out of poverty and **re-engaging disaffected** young people. The Early Years, Extended Schools and Special Needs group, which is part of the DCSF, is responsible for delivering Sure Start, a Government programme to deliver the best start in life for every child. It brings together early education, childcare, health and family support. Ofsted, a public body, has the responsibility of inspecting schools to make sure they reach the required standard.

Local provision

Local authorities have the responsibility of bringing together all agencies that work to improve the lives of children and young people (see pages 76–77). Early years services include childcare, childminding, free education places for all eligible three- and four-year-olds and advice and guidance.

Just checking

1. What does the Social Care, Local Government and Care Partnerships Directorate do?

2. Who is responsible for the funding of social services at a local level?

3. How is Early Years connected to the children and young people's sector? What kind of advice and guidance might a parent want from an early years service? Give three examples.

What a team!

This topic looks at partnership and multi-agency working, how the different service providers work together to meet client needs and how these services are integrated.

Working in partnership

As you will have realised, health, social care and early years professionals rarely work alone. They are more likely to work as part of a team.

Service providers from any of the sectors will meet at case conferences, usually with the client and their family, and work together to provide the right care. This **collaboration** of multi-agents leads to a **holistic** approach to care, so that the client's needs are more likely to be met.

Working collaboratively like this is a move away from the traditional structure of services based on professional discipline: for example, health care services working together and social care services working together, but each sector working separately from the other. The Childcare Act of 2006 is one example of how the Government reinforced what local authorities were already doing – working in partnership with the private and voluntary sectors.

Now you will learn about some good examples of working in partnership.

Sure Start Children's Centres

These are 'service hubs' – central points from which children under the age of five and their families can access integrated services and information. The idea is that this will help make sure that every child gets the best start in life. By 2010, every community (a settlement of 3,500 people) will have such a centre.

The services offered may vary between centres, but could include early education and childcare with a qualified teacher, advice on parenting, and help for parents to get work, linking with the local Jobcentre Plus and training. The centres aim to enable families with children to access good, affordable childcare, so that every child can fulfil their potential.

The Virtual Ward

The Virtual Ward is a free website, set up by the Care Services Improvement Partnership (CSIP) with the National Institute for Mental Health in England, where staff and people who use mental

---

Your world

In a group, write down all the agencies you can think of who come into school to work with teachers to help you as students. How do you think these agencies improve your life as part of a community of students?

Collaboration – working together
Holistic – looking at all the different needs of the client
Advocate – someone who speaks on someone else's behalf

Did you know?

By June 2008, almost 3,000 centres around the UK were offering services to over two million young children and their families.

Activity

Go on the Virtual Ward website. Go onto the Partnerships page and draw a mind map of the various partnerships shown.

Case study **Edward**

Edward is 45 years old and has lost his job as an accountant in a large company, due to cutbacks rather than any fault of his own. He is depressed: there are few jobs available at his level, and he will have to look after the children, because his wife has found a job to make ends meet. He starts to drink too much and becomes aggressive towards his wife and children, who are three, six and eight years old. He feels it is his role to support his family, and he now feels worthless.

1. What services can the family call on to help them through this situation?
2. How will these services work together to give the best possible support to the family?
3. How will Edward feel about calling on outside agencies to help him and his family?
4. How must the service providers approach the situation so as not to make Edward feel even worse about his situation?

health services can share good practice. Everyone can access information about positive and innovative practice, read supporting policy and use examples of training underpinning those examples. There is an editorial board, where people share ideas, discuss innovations and review resources. The most useful resources are moved across into the Virtual Ward.

If you knew someone with mental health problems or were working in mental health, you could use this online resource to get help and advice.

Multi-agency disability team/key workers

A person who has a disability may be involved with a range of care providers, who will form a team to manage her care so that she can live as independently as possible.

- The local Primary Care Trust will look after her if she falls ill, and will see to routine needs such as sight tests or dental work, as well as helping if she needs more specialist help, such as speech therapy.
- Social services will be responsible for needs such as housing and financial entitlements.
- She will also have a key worker, who will act as an **advocate** to help her keep in touch with her family, and with things such as collecting medication and money. The key worker will also arrange for her to attend various programmes to teach her how to live on her own, so that she can live in safety in the community. The key worker has responsibility for communicating with the rest of the team, to make sure she receives all the support and care services she needs.

Local authority extended services provision

These services, which play an important part in overall provision, were covered on pages 80–81.

The Virtual Ward homepage
(www.virtualward.org.uk)

Just checking

1. Why do different services work together to provide care?

2. Why have Sure Start Children's Centres been set up across the country?

3. What is a key worker and what do they do?

Access issues

Here you will learn about the different ways in which people can access health, social care and early years services, and that there are sometimes barriers to accessing services.

Methods of referral

Whenever you use a care service, such as going to the dentist, you are accessing that service. To access a service, you need to be referred – even if you refer yourself. There are three methods of referral.

Self-referral

This is when someone chooses to use a service for themselves, and is the main way people access services. A person might decide to go to the doctor's with a cold, go to a day-care centre or take a cycling proficiency course. If a parent asks for a place for her child at a nursery, this is still self-referral because the client is the parent, not the child.

Professional referral

This is when a care provider puts a person in touch with another service provider that offers a more specialised service, such as a doctor referring someone to an outpatients clinic at the hospital, a residential home worker asking a chiropodist to come to treat a service user, or a teacher referring a child to the behaviour support service.

Third-party referral

This is when someone puts a person who needs service in contact with that service because they cannot do so themselves. A person might ring the doctor to make an appointment for an older relative, a teacher might contact Social Services because they suspect a child is being abused, or a care worker might make a dental appointment for someone who has learning difficulties.

Barriers to access

Most of us find it easy to access the services we need but, for a variety of reasons, some people find it hard. The different reasons for this are known as barriers to access. You will find out more about these in the next two topics.

Legislation

Removing barriers **empowers** an individual to take control of his or her life, rather than relying on other people, and allows them to be

Your world

Imagine you need an appointment:

- with a doctor because you have flu
- at the hospital because you need an X-ray
- with the school nurse because you want confidential advice.

How do you make each of these appointments?

Did you know?

In September 2006, GPs referred 2,338,430 patients to a first outpatient appointment with a consultant in England – a figure that, by June 2008, had risen to 2,740, 616. That's a lot of appointments!

Case study **Mohammed**

Mohammed lives alone in a small ground-floor flat just off The Green, where he has been since his wife died two years ago. He is in a wheelchair, is partially sighted and cannot clean and cook very well for himself. His next-door neighbour tries to help as much as she can, by cooking an extra portion each meal time and taking it round for him. He cannot communicate his needs to her very well because he doesn't speak good English. Yesterday, she noticed that he didn't look well and didn't seem hungry. Today he was coughing and out of breath. She called the doctor. Mohammed's cough developed into pneumonia, and he had to spend some time in hospital.

1. What sort of referral is this?
2. Now healthcare services have become involved, what other sorts of referral might there be? Give examples of some of the services Mohammed might get referred to, to explain your answer.
3. What problems does Mohammed normally have when he needs to access health and social care services? List as many as possible, then suggest what can be done to improve on all these problem areas.

The barriers to referral

as independent as possible. **Legislation** exists to protect the individual's right to access services, including:

- the Children's Act 2004, which aims to improve the lives of children, including being able to access all the services they need
- the Discrimination Act 2005, which actively promotes the rights, including access to services, of people with disabilities
- the Health and Social Care Act, 2008, which seeks to modernise and integrate health and social care, and creates the Care Quality Commission to regulate these areas. The Act will help reduce barriers, such as fear of going to hospital in case of contacting a super bug (psychological), worry about a husband or wife having to pay towards a spouse's care (financial), and access to advocates (cultural/psychological).

Empower – help create the circumstances that mean someone can do something for themselves, such as make decisions

Legislation – a law or group of laws passed by Parliament

Just checking

1. What is meant by referral?
2. Name the three types of referral and give three examples of each.
3. Why is it important to remove as many barriers to access of services as possible?

Mind over matter

This topic looks at the physical, psychological and financial barriers that prevent some people accessing the services they need.

Physical barriers

When people think of barriers, they usually think of physical ones. These can include inadequate access to buildings or within buildings for service users with poor mobility or low strength, for wheelchair users, or for young children in buggies.

Making **adaptations** to existing and planned buildings can help service users. Installing ramps, lifts and stair lifts can reduce barriers, as can making sure that areas such as corridors are wide and uncluttered, so there is space to move around. Doing this would also help those who are blind or partially sighted.

To create good physical access, waiting areas should have seats that are well spaced out, doors should be wide and automatic, and any buttons on doors or intercoms should be low enough to allow those in wheelchairs to reach them easily. Similarly, reception desks should have an area that is lower, so that a receptionist does not have to lean over and speak down to someone in a wheelchair. Any transport provided needs to be adapted with ramps that lower at the back, and space and seatbelts for those in wheelchairs. Disabled toilet facilities should also be provided, as should smaller toilets for younger service users.

Psychological barriers

Psychological barriers are not physical, but come as a result of a service user being too scared or worried to use a service. This could be fear of coming into contact with a super bug, of losing independence or of not wanting to be looked after. Others might be too proud to ask for help or too scared of what they will hear is

Your world

The walk-in centre at The Green hospital

Write down any measures that have been taken to improve access to the walk-in service as shown in the illustration of The Green hospital. Can you think of any changes that would help more people access the walk-in centre?

Adaptation – changing something, such as a device or mechanism, so that it becomes suitable for a new or special application or situation

Stigma – a symbol of disgrace, something to be ashamed of

Means test – an investigation by a body such as a local authority to find out whether an individual or family is eligible to receive certain benefits, by seeing how much money they have or haven't got

wrong with them. Some people also think there is a social **stigma** associated with some services, such as mental health. Reading leaflets, posters and articles on the internet, designed to put people's minds at rest, could help reduce these problems. Those who are reluctant to travel to services can use NHS Direct or one of the many helplines available for a whole array of problems. Asking for help from a pharmacist can be less threatening than going to see the doctor. Finding someone to go with can also help. Care workers and doctors will also go to people's houses and encourage them to visit an appropriate service if necessary.

Someone with a mobility problem might worry about getting into the building, be embarrassed at having to travel across a large open-plan area in full view of everyone so feeling they are on show, or at having the receptionist and others leaning over to talk to them. If someone has an embarrassing problem, such as a sexually transmitted disease, obesity or alcoholism, a private waiting area would help.

Once contact has been made, service providers will use their training to explain carefully, clearly and kindly and so make it easier for them to overcome their fears to go next time.

Financial barriers

Charges and fees exclude and put off those who do not have money to pay for the services they need, such as disability aids, prescriptions and healthcare not provided by the NHS. Having to pay for transport or childcare to allow a person to attend a service can be a problem. Many dentists no longer offer dental care on the NHS and some services are not available locally.

Some services are **means tested**, and the results of means testing are not always as clear as you might think. For example, although a couple may earn a reasonable sum of money, this may be committed to paying the mortgage and other bills, so there may not be enough left to pay for a service that those means-testing them think they should be able to afford. Another couple may have plenty left to pay for the service because they have savings, so each case has to be considered fully on the facts of that individual case.

Activity

1. Do some research on the internet, look at leaflets or visit somewhere like the Citizen's Advice Bureau, to find out which health, social care and early years services in your local area are free to someone of your age and which you would have to pay for. Now do the same for someone your parent's or carer's age.
2. Find out if there are any benefits to help those who cannot pay, such as Child Care Tax Benefit.
3. Put your findings together with those of others in your group. Together, produce a booklet to help people with financial difficulties to overcome financial barriers to services.

Just checking

1. List five physical barriers and how they can be overcome.
2. List five psychological barriers and how they can be overcome.
3. List three services that people with financial difficulties would not be able to access, and explain why.

Open to all?

In this topic, you will learn about the other three types of barrier to people accessing services: geographical, cultural/language and resource barriers.

Geographical barriers

Geographical barriers are problems caused by where people and resources physically are. For example, when a service user lives in a rural area and has to travel a long way to access a service, there may not be suitable transport available, the transport links might not be convenient or they may cost too much. Alternatively, there may be too many people living in a particular area for the service to cope with, so people are sent to services further away. In some areas, hospitals will send an ambulance to collect a person who has no transport if they have, for example, mobility problems.

More problems can now be dealt with at health centres, by pharmacists or on helplines, avoiding travel to a hospital.

Cultural and language barriers

Cultural and language barriers arise when people are of a different culture, speak a different language, or don't understand the way things are expressed because of **jargon**, **slang** or **dialect**.

Did you know?

NHS Direct offers help to people 24 hours a day, every day of the year. You can ring them on 0845 4647 or contact them on their website, www.nhsdirect.ns.uk. They also have a digital TV service. They not only offer help to patients but also to GPs and dental services.

Activity

1. Look back at the activity you did about Mohammed on page 89. Now you have learned about the different barriers, are there any you missed in your answer?

2. Look at the community of people living at The Green and their environment at the start of this book. For each person, list the likely barriers, if any, to them accessing services.

Case study **Emergency Department to close**

The people of Edmonsonfield, which has a high level of people who are on low incomes, have reacted angrily to the news that the local emergency department is to close down. The nearest one will then be 10 miles away, at The Green hospital.

Why do you think they have reacted like this? List all your reasons.

Cultural barriers

The UK is a culturally diverse society, with people from a wide range of religious and **ethnic** backgrounds who have their own beliefs about who should provide care and how illness and social problems should be dealt with. It is important that cultural and language barriers are broken down, because such difficulties can deter members of some communities from using services that they need or are entitled to.

Cultural barriers can be there in simple, everyday things. For example, white middle-class people expect other people to look them in the eye, but in some cultures looking down or away is a sign of respect. Some cultures are not used to dealing with women of professional status and will be embarrassed and feel awkward with female workers.

Language barriers

Language difficulties can be overcome by having information on posters, signs and leaflets in a number of languages. Any information source should avoid slang, dialect or jargon to make sure it gets its message across. For example, someone told they are **NBM** before an operation will need to be told that it stands for 'nil by mouth' and they should not eat anything on the day of the operation. It is not possible to overcome all language problems as every receptionist cannot be expected to know a range of different languages.

People with a sight or hearing impairment will need information on tape, in Braille, in large print or via videos, sign language or a hearing loop.

Resource barriers

These sorts of barriers can arise when there are staff shortages, leading maybe to a shortage of beds on a maternity ward because there are not enough nurses on duty. You may have heard of the expression 'postcode lottery', where two people living in neighbouring streets, or even neighbouring houses, may find that one of them is entitled to an expensive, life-saving drug on the NHS, while the other has to pay for it because their postcode places them in a local area that has a lack of funding. Alternatively, someone might not be able to access a service they need for many months because there are so many people in the area using the same service.

Poor integration of services, lack of information and limited opening hours can also create resource barriers.

Jargon – words and phrases that relate to a certain profession or group, either technical words or shorthand ways of saying things

Slang – informal words and expressions that are not considered to be a standard part of the language

Dialect – a variety of language or speech pattern specific to the area lived in

Ethnic – relating to a distinct group with the same ancestry, culture or religious beliefs

NBM – nil by mouth, allowed nothing to eat or drink

Just checking

1. Name three reasons why people might have geographical barriers to accessing services.

2. Give three reasons why people might be reluctant to use a service due to their culture or speaking a different language.

3. You might not realise it but we all use jargon. Write an explanation of the various forms of text 'jargon' you use, such as 'lol', for an elderly relative who has never used a mobile phone. Then give three examples of how using jargon might be a barrier to a patient seeking medical help.

Health direct

This topic looks at the skills, qualities and qualifications needed to deliver all services effectively and then looks specifically at workers in healthcare who work directly with service users, on a face-to-face basis.

Working in care

There are many different settings and job roles for working on health, social care and early years.

In any setting, it is important that staff have the **skills** that are specific to that job: for example, a nurse needs to be able to measure blood pressure. It is also important to have skills such as literacy (in order to write reports and complete other paperwork) numeracy (to be able to do any task involving numbers), ICT and **interpersonal skills**. Workers also need **qualifications** depending on the job and **qualities** (see the table below).

Your world

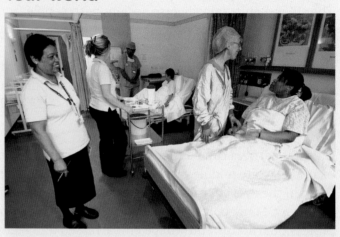

With a partner, think about a recent episode of a programme such as *Holby City* or *Casualty*, or a time you visited someone in hospital. Write down as many different jobs in a hospital as you can. Now put a tick by those who work directly with the patients, as opposed to those who provide a service but hardly come into contact with the patients at all, such as the cooks.

Qualities	Patient, get on with people, co-operative, tactful, sensitive, energetic, trustworthy, kind, reliable, adaptable, committed, calm, caring, respectful, observant, cope under stress, outgoing, assertive, flexible, dependable, sincere, motivated, friendly, good sense of humour, optimistic, cheerful, open-minded, punctual, understanding
Interpersonal skills	Communication (listening, speaking, other methods), negotiating, team work/leadership/work on own, time management/meet deadlines, prioritise, problem solving, accept responsibility, advocacy, organise, plan

Qualities and interpersonal skills needed in all jobs in the care sectors

Skill – the ability to do something well, coming from knowledge, practice, aptitude, etc.: for example, literacy

Interpersonal skills – skills that allow us to interact successfully with others: for example, being a good listener

Qualification – an accomplishment that fits a person for a job or some other task: for example, an NVQ

Quality – a distinctive personality trait: for example, being trustworthy

Service providers also follow a care value base, which you will learn about in Unit 3.

Kay, practice nurse

Most GP surgeries have at least one practice nurse; some have nurse practitioners (NPs) and healthcare assistants (HCAs) as well. Who does what in your practice, though, will depend on your nurse's/HCA's qualifications and skills; the receptionist can advise when a nurse, rather than a doctor, can help.

As well as taking blood, checking blood pressure and testing urine, Kay is often responsible for wound care, immunisations, contraception, and taking cervical smears. She can also provide health information including travel advice, or refer people to other health professionals, such as diabetic liaison nurses.

Kay is qualified to monitor chronic disease, such as diabetes, raised blood pressure, asthma and heart disease, working to agreed procedures. However, general practice is very much about teamwork so Kay can always ask one of the doctors for advice if necessary, and vice versa. She is also qualified to prescribe drugs, suggest changes to treatment plans, or provide phone consultations. Kay is involved in monitoring standards, training, and developing practice services. She is a good practice nurse, who offers a real choice for patients, and reduces pressure on doctor appointments.

Direct carers in health care

Above is a snapshot of the main job roles for Kay, a practice nurse at the GP surgery on The Green. The diagram below shows some other common direct care roles.

Direct carers in health care

Activity

1. Pick three of the carers shown in the diagram. For each, investigate the job role, the qualifications and the skills they need. Then, on a computer, produce a job card for each, to print out and give to others in your group so that you all end up with a full set. A useful website is www.learndirect-advice.co.uk.

2. Which of these jobs would you most like to do if you had to pick one? Write a letter of application saying why you feel you would be good at that job.

3. Have you any evidence of having any of the skills or qualities shown on this page on your CV? If not, plan how you can get such evidence for your Progress File.

Just checking

1. Why is it important to have skills such as literacy, numeracy and ICT?

2. List five jobs that a practice nurse does.

3. Name five interpersonal skills. Why are they necessary for care work? Try to rank your five in order of importance, giving reasons for the order you choose.

Social care direct

This topic looks specifically at the skills, qualities and qualifications needed by workers in social care who work directly with service users, on a face-to-face basis.

Care assistant

Care assistants provide care to those who need help with everyday activities. They work in people's homes, residential homes or day-care centres. The role may involve helping with dressing, meals, cleaning, washing, letter writing, managing money and bills and sitting having a chat. In a residential home or day care centre they might also organise activities, such a games and trips out.

The skills a care assistant needs include domestic skills such as cooking and cleaning, as well as interpersonal skills such as being a good listener. He or she will particularly need to be patient.

There is no requirement for any specific qualification to be a care assistant, although GCSEs in Maths and English, NVQ in Care Level 2 or BTEC First in Health and Social Care would be good to have on your CV when applying for such a job.

Occupational therapist

Occupational therapists help people to overcome difficulties that may be the result of a physical or mental illness, an accident or simply getting older. They try to help people recover as fully as possible and teach them new skills to cope with any disability or difficulty: for example, by helping them learn to walk again. They help clients to lead as full and independent lives as possible. The job often involves working one-to-one with a client and adapting treatment programmes to suit each person's needs and abilities.

The skills an occupational therapist needs include keeping records, counselling (not only for the client, but also for families and carers) and interpersonal skills such as relating and communicating well.

Your world

A 'meals on wheels' service helps older people to stay independent for longer. Write down as many different jobs as you can think of where people help others to cope with living independently in their own homes or with family problems.

Activity

1. George, from The Green, sometimes goes to the local day-care centre. How will Maud, who fills in some of her time as a care assistant, help meet George's physical, intellectual, emotional and social needs?

2. Mohammed, from a flat round the corner from The Green, needs occupational therapy after his pneumonia left him very weak. Joy visits him at home for a few weeks. What can she do to help him meet his physical, intellectual, emotional and social needs?

Direct carers in social care

To become an occupational therapist you need a at least five GCSEs (A* – C), two or three A levels with at least one science subject (such as biology) and a degree or postgraduate (after doing a different degree) course in occupational therapy.

Family support worker

Being a family support worker involves providing emotional and practical help and advice to families who are experiencing short- or long-term problems. Family support workers aim to help children remain with their families, rather than being taken into care. A social worker would refer a family support worker to the family. It could be for a wide range of problems, such as a family member being in prison, having a disability, or marital or financial difficulties. You would be working to address the family's needs, perhaps by helping them improve their parenting skills or getting a family member onto a programme to cope with an addiction, such as alcohol or drugs.

The skills you would need to be a family support worker would include record keeping and the ability to communicate with a team of other health and social care professionals. You would also need some experience, either paid or voluntary, of working with children and families.

There are a variety of relevant qualifications, such as NVQ Levels 2, 3 and 4 in Children's Care, Learning and Development or in Health and Social Care or CACHE or BTEC national certificates or Diplomas.

Palliative – for people who have an incurable condition or illness, or who are dying

Just checking

1. What are the skills you need to be an occupational therapist?

2. List at least five tasks you might be tackling as a care assistant.

3. What is the aim of a family support worker? Give three examples of how a family support worker would achieve this aim when working with a family of immigrants who do not speak English.

Early Years direct

In this topic, you will learn about the skills, qualities and qualifications needed by workers in early years who work directly with service users, on a face-to-face basis.

There are many jobs in this sector. Here you will learn about two of these as examples: nursery nurse and portage worker.

Nursery nurse

A nursery nurse cares for children aged eight or under and can work in a wide range of settings such as nurseries, schools, crèches, hospitals, residential homes, day nurseries and the child's own home. If they are working with babies, nursery nurses will spend a lot of time feeding, dressing and changing them, but older children will need more advanced play activities and stories to help them learn and develop.

Typical qualifications, skills and qualities are shown in the advert to the right.

Portage worker

A portage worker provides a home-visiting service for preschool children who have developmental, learning or physical difficulties or other special needs. As a portage worker, your job would be to try to help the child develop by suggesting activities and routines so that he or she is not too far behind when reaching school age. You would work in a team with professional such as health visitors, social workers, physiotherapists and speech therapists.

Your world

A children's playgroup

Can you think of many jobs working directly with children up to the age of eight? Pool your ideas with a partner and see how many you can come up with between you.

Little People's Nursery

We are looking for a dedicated nursery nurse to join our team in delivering the highest possible quality childcare to our little people. The successful candidate will have a childcare qualification at level 2 or 3 and a thorough knowledge of 'Birth to 3' issues and the Foundation Stage.

We are looking for someone who:

- is a warm, committed individual with initiative
- has a desire to enhance the lives of children
- can be flexible, works well as part of a team and is highly motivated
- is positive and sensitive
- is literate and numerate
- has a current first-aid qualification

If you would like to apply please send a CV and a covering letter to Miss Little, Little People's Nursery, The Green, Littledon, London, SW111 6TJ

Rates of pay will depend on experience and qualifications. Closing date is 20th August 2008.

Job advert for a nursery nurse

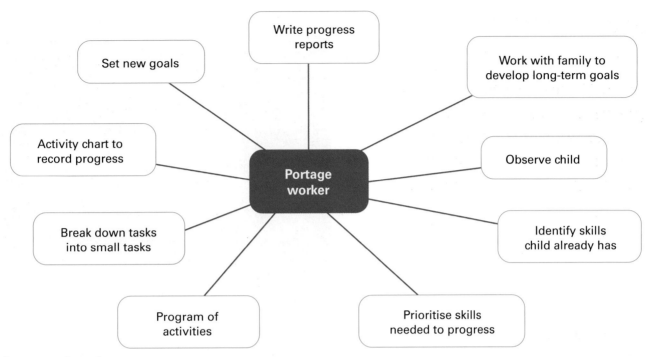

Portage worker role

To be a portage worker, you need experience of working with children under the age of five and an understanding of child development. Relevant qualifications are any in teaching, nursery nursing, social work or nursing or a Level 3 early years qualification such as NVQ Level 3 in Early Years Care and Education.

Other direct care early years jobs include child development workers, nannies, au pairs, childminders, education psychologists, early years practitioners and social workers. You can find out about these jobs on websites such as http://careersadvice.direct.gov.uk.

Take it further

Write job cards for all the jobs described so far, to match those you did in the activity on page 95.

Just checking

1. What are the skills needed to be a nursery nurse?
2. Why would you need good communication skills and patience to be a portage worker?
3. Do you have to have more previous experience to be a nursery nurse or a portage worker? Why do you think this is the case?

Activity

1. Look at the diagram and read the description of the portage worker's job. What skills and qualities do you think you would need to do the job?
2. Another direct care worker is a teacher, in this case of children up to the age of eight. Write down the skills and qualities you would need to teach children this young.
3. Find out on the internet what qualifications you need to teach young children.
4. Write a list of questions with your group so you can interview your teacher at school to find out the difference between teaching young children and teaching young people like you.

Managing it

In this topic, you move on to look at indirect jobs – where the carer does not work with the service users on a day-to-day, face-to-face basis – in management.

Management

Every organisation needs a manager, whether it is a nursery, a residential home or a day-care centre.

The managers of an organisation are in charge of its day-to-day running. They have to manage the budget. This includes working out how many staff they can afford to employ, working out how much to charge if it is a fee-paying service, buying furniture, other equipment and resources, buying in other services and paying bills. Managers also have to contact other services when necessary and deal with the family and friends of the service users. They will provide the resources for all activities and trips, and will organise most of those. They have to organise the other staff, and monitor them to make sure they are doing their jobs properly, as well as working out staff rotas. Managers have to write reports, policies and procedures, and must make sure that everyone is sticking to health and safety regulations. On top of this (and much more), managers have to make sure that service users and staff are happy with the service.

There are many different managerial jobs in the health and social care sector. As an example, you will look at the job of managing a medical or health centre or a GP's practice.

Practice manager

As a practice manager, you would be in charge of the business side of a medical or health centre or a GP surgery. Your duties would include:

- appointing and supervising medical secretaries and receptionists
- organising any necessary training for staff
- looking after accounts and budgets: for example paying wages

Your world

How is a service like this managed?

At a Citizens Advice Bureau, clients can come for advice and information on a wide range of problems and concerns. There are many different sorts of staff, and the building must be kept clean, safe and well maintained. Why do you think services like this need a manager? Write a list of the jobs the manager might do.

Think about it

'Those who can, do; those who can't, manage.'

Do you think this is fair? Do people who manage need to be able to do the jobs of those they manage too?

Case study **Care Home**

A care home manager is concerned that it is taking too long for his clients to be woken up, dressed, washed and given breakfast. Many of them have mobility problems, so use a portable toilet in their own rooms before being taken to the dining room for breakfast. He decides his staff will give clients their breakfast on a tray in their room, either on the portable toilet or in a chair, depending on how quickly they have been dressed and washed.

1. How would you feel if you were one of the clients?
2. Which physical, intellectual, emotional and social needs of the clients are and are not being met in this situation?
3. What are the hygiene issues?
4. Imagine you were a relative of a client. What opinion would you have of the manager? Is he a good manager? Which skills does he need to improve on?
5. Imagine you are a care worker in the home and you are upset about this because you think it is unacceptable. However, you need to keep your job and don't want to fall out with the manager. Write down exactly what you could say to him that makes the point tactfully so he can't take offence.

- drawing up duty rotas for doctors and other staff
- organising and monitoring the reception and the appointments system
- managing medical records systems, both manual and computerised
- controlling stocks, such as equipment, drugs and stationery
- making arrangements for cleaning and maintenance
- organising security
- organising and attending practice meetings
- monitoring prescription data.

You would have a great deal of contact with outside organisations such as local NHS Trusts and primary care groups, and with local authority social services departments.

What skills does it take to be a practice manager?

To be a practice manager, you would need good organisational and leadership skills as well as literacy, numeracy, ICT and interpersonal skills, such as team work and communication. You would also need to be a good motivator, be adaptable, pay attention to detail, be creative and be able to plan and to take the initiative. Have you got many of these skills yet?

Although there is no set qualification to become a practice manager, some experience in either management or administration is expected, preferably in a health or social care setting. There are various degrees and diplomas available in management, such as the Association of Medical Secretaries, Practice Managers, Administrators and Receptionists (AMSPAR), which would prove useful but are not essential to getting the job.

Just checking

1. Explain why a manager of a residential home is an indirect carer.
2. List five skills that all managers have to have.
3. What is the main purpose of being a practice manager?

Supporting cast

In this topic, you will continue to learn about indirect care jobs, including those that are outsourced to private companies.

You have probably been in touch with a medical receptionist at some point in your life, when you've been to the doctor's or dentist's. You'll look at this role first, as an example of a key indirect care job, then look at some other roles.

Medical receptionist

A medical receptionist works in a variety of health settings, such as a GP's surgery, a health centre, a dental practice or a hospital. The medical receptionist is an indirect carer because, although providing a crucial service, he or she does not actually deliver the medical or dental help that clients come there for. As a medical receptionist, you would check in patients, find their medical or dental records, make appointments, direct patients to their appointments, contact other service providers and do general clerical and administrative jobs, such as writing letters and keeping records up to date.

You would need good interpersonal skills, especially communication, as you would have to deal with people of different ages and cultures, some of whom do not speak much English, in person and on the telephone. Literacy and ICT skills are also important. You would have to be well organised and efficient.

There are no compulsory, specific qualifications for the job, but you would need at least GCSEs or the equivalent at most settings.

Your world

School staff are not all teachers…

Write down all the jobs done in your school by staff who are not teachers. How do they help you? How do they help teachers? How important do you think their jobs are? Do you treat them in the same way as you treat teachers? Explain your answer.

Activity

Research one of these roles and add it to your collection of job cards.

Outsourced – when a service is bought and brought in from a private company

Other indirect care roles

These include school reception staff, porters, cleaners, gardeners, laboratory assistants, drivers, and many more, all of which are very important to keeping services going. Catering is one common example – what would other services do without it?

Catering staff

Catering staff can be employed directly by the main service, as in a day-care centre, or can be **outsourced** to private companies. For example, most schools do not employ their own catering staff, but pay a private company to come in and do the catering.

Catering staff work as a team to provide a balanced diet and meet the varied dietary requirements of a range of clients. The head chef or cook is in charge of the whole kitchen, and as such is a manager. As a head chef, you would plan the menus, deal with suppliers while staying within budget, organise, monitor and pay the kitchen staff, and make sure that everyone works within hygiene, health and safety guidelines.

You would need good communication and leadership skills, the ability to work under pressure and in hot conditions and a good understanding of health and safety regulations.

To be a chef, the qualifications you would need are GCSEs in English and Maths and other work-based qualifications, such as a BTEC National Certificate or Diploma in Hospitality or Hospitality Supervision. Alternatively, you could work through an apprenticeship scheme.

Other catering staff include trainee (or commis) chef, people to wash up and prepare vegetables and serving staff – this might involve pushing a trolley round and giving out meals or drinks in a hospital. Although you would have to communicate pleasantly with people, you would not need any qualifications to do this.

Other outsourced indirect services

These include cleaners, security, portering and waste management.

Just checking

1. What are five jobs that a medical receptionist has to carry out?
2. Name three different services that are usually outsourced.
3. Name three different jobs you might have if you worked in catering in a hospital. Explain why each job is indirect. Is there any aspect of each job that is direct? Explain your answer.

Case study **Ben**

Ben lives in a flat on The Green with his mates: Mike, a footballer, and Colin, a plumber. Ben started his career at a company making sandwiches for vending machines in various companies including the hospital. He worked hard to get his NVQ Level 2 in Hospitality and Catering, and then moved on to be in charge of an area of the kitchen while working for his NVQ Level 3 Advanced apprenticeship in Hospitality and Supervision. When his assessor came to assess him for his Level 3, she said he had moved the business forward. He has now gone to work as chef at the restaurant round the corner from The Green. He is 23. His girlfriend Nicola has just moved into the flat with them. She is a beautician and they have been going out together for four years.

1. How has Ben's work and social life met his physical, intellectual, emotional and social needs?
2. What skills has Ben had to use to get to where he is today?
3. What are the demands to be met when preparing food for customers from a multicultural community? What additional demands would Ben face if he worked in the hospital kitchen?
4. Colin is sometimes asked to do some work at the hospital. He also sometimes works at the school. How do you think he would be expected to behave when working on a ward near patients, or in a school near children?

Be fair

The care value base is a set of values that all who work in health and social care base their work on. This means that service users know what sort of treatment they can expect to receive. In this topic you will learn about one of these values, promoting anti-discriminatory practice.

Your world

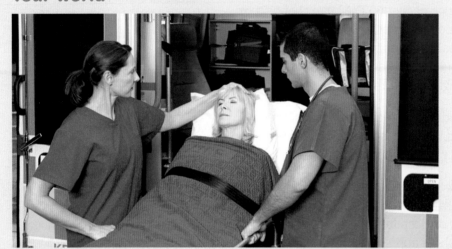

How are decisions made at a hospital emergency department?

Hospital emergency departments can be hectic places, where decisions need to be made quickly – and people's lives can depend on them. How do you think the staff should decide who to treat first? How do you think they should *not* decide who to treat first?

Values and principles

Workers in the care sectors share a set of care values, which form the care value base. To provide a high standard of care, service providers follow a set of **principles** based on these values.

Discrimination and prejudice

There are several kinds of **discrimination**. Someone might have a **prejudice** (a bias) against a person or a group of people for reasons such as age, gender, race, ethnicity, class, religion, sexual orientation, ability, health, disability, dress or appearance. They might then discriminate against that person or group and treat them differently.

There are four different forms of discrimination.

- **Unfair discrimination** is when a person is treated unfairly in comparison with somebody else. One example of such behaviour

Think about it

If you, as a student and so a service user, made a rude or racist comment to a teacher you would, quite rightly, be told off for this. An older adult in a residential home, who might have lost some of his mental capability so doesn't know any better, would also be told off if he made an unsuitable comment to a care assistant. Discuss why this is right.

is if someone is not being considered seriously for a job because they are older than another candidate, despite having the same qualifications and experience.

- **Direct discrimination** is when someone is rude, hostile or offensive to someone because they see them as being different: for example, when someone who is overweight is called names at school. This form of discrimination is easy to prove because it is heard or witnessed by other people.
- **Indirect discrimination** is harder to prove. Someone's boss may appear to be very supportive and friendly, but he may show he doesn't respect her ideas by dismissing them in a jokey way whenever she puts one forward.
- **Positive discrimination** is when a decision is made in a person's favour for the exact reason that there is something different about them: for example, advertising for Asian actors to appear in the musical *Miss Saigon*.

Promoting anti-discriminatory behaviour

Imagine someone from the medical profession arguing that people who are obese or who live in an area with a certain postcode should not receive the hospital treatment they need to save their lives. This would be discrimination against those people.

Service providers need to be actively anti-discriminatory in recognising and responding to the needs of service users. Discriminating against people can affect their health and wellbeing, causing stress, anxiety and a low feeling of self-worth, as well as a loss of confidence.

While service providers need to have the correct attitude, it is also right that service users treat the providers in an anti-discriminatory way. It might be that providers have to challenge the attitude of some of their service users.

There is a great deal of legislation to protect people from discrimination and to help people who feel they have been discriminated against. This includes the Sex Discrimination Act 1975 and the Race Relations Act 2000.

Stereotyping and labelling

People discriminate against others, knowingly or unknowingly, by stereotyping and labelling them.

An example of this is when people talk to older people slowly, loudly and patronisingly because they assume they are deaf and are intellectually less able. This is stereotyping behaviour.

Principle – a basic guide to follow about the right way to behave
Discrimination – treating a person or group differently from others, in a positive or a negative way
Prejudice – an unreasonable feeling against a person or group or people

Activity

1. Joy and Steven live in their flat on The Green. Everyone assumes they are a couple, but in fact Joy is gay. They don't tell people because they worry that this will scare Steven's personal training clients away. Do you think they are correct to do this?
2. Do you think there is a better course of action for Joy and Steven to take? If so, what – and why do you think it is better?

Just checking

1. What are the four main types of discrimination?
2. How can discrimination affect people? Give at least five ways.
3. What effects can discriminatory behaviour have on service users? What effect can it have on service providers?

It's your right

This topic covers another principle that service users follow: promoting and supporting each individual's right to health and safety, dignity, privacy and independence.

Rights and responsibilities

A right is something that a person feels is due to them, or something that person feels is fitting for them to do. A responsibility is a burden of obligation. People have the right to have their own beliefs and lifestyles, but no one has the right to damage the quality of other people's lives. This means that rights often go hand in hand with responsibilities towards other people.

The easiest way to understand this is to consider a specific example. An adult has the right to drink alcohol, even though there is a danger of it damaging their health and shortening their life. However, the drinker has a responsibility not to drive while under the influence of alcohol, so that he does not put other lives at risk. Some would argue that, if he has a family, he has a responsibility to them not to do anything that will shorten his life.

Health and safety

Health and safety issues affect both service providers and users. Both have the right to be in a safe environment, away from harm, and there is considerable legislation around this issue. It is now part of a worker's daily routine to assess the safety of all situations.

Dignity

Another important aspect of being a service provider is to help people maintain their dignity so that they keep their self-respect. For example, a child at primary school who accidentally wets herself will be embarrassed if this is pointed out to everyone else. A good nursery teacher will simply take the child somewhere private, reassure her and get her clothes sorted out. This allows the child to maintain her dignity, rather than feeling ashamed.

Privacy

In order to have dignity, a person often needs privacy. Privacy means being free from intrusion or disturbance in your private life or affairs. For example, a person who can no longer look after himself and is in a residential care home will feel upset if the carers walk into his room whenever they want to, without knocking first. Having

Your world

Paul, a musician, is having a drink with friends at the Green Man pub. but is too hot so he has popped outside for some fresh air. Due to the smoking ban, there are a lot of smokers outside, but Paul is not a smoker. What are the rights and the responsibilities of (a) Paul and (b) the smokers?

Think about it

Some rights are enforced by others: for example, it is now your right to be able to work, eat, drink, shop and travel in a smoke-free environment as no one has the right to smoke in an enclosed public place in England any more. This law that came into effect in July 2007. The law has enforced your rights. Do you think there are any rights that have no responsibilities with them? Discuss this in your group.

Independence – not having to rely on someone else to do things for you

Nuclear family – two parents living with their children and keeping themselves relatively separate from other family members.

been used to the privacy of his own home for many years, the constant disturbance and lack of privacy can undermine his self-esteem and make him feel he has lost his identity as an independent person, in control of himself and his own actions.

Independence

It is important people have control of their own lives, and workers in all care sectors aim to help people develop or maintain their **independence**. More people have fewer immediate family members living near by to help them now that more of us live in **nuclear families**, so there is an even greater demand on services to do this.

Just checking

1. When caring for someone, why is it important to allow a person to keep their dignity?
2. What part does privacy play in someone keeping his or her dignity?
3. What is the difference between a right and a responsibility? Explain this using the example of a pregnant young woman smoking.

Case study **Allegra**

Allegra is 84 years old and lives with her family above the Italian Restaurant on The Green. However, she is lonely because everyone else is busy in the restaurant, so she goes to a day-care centre twice a week, where she really enjoys the company. Because she is still physically fit, the care assistants let her take the tea trolley round to those who can only sit in a chair. She also helps wrap presents for other older people when they want to make a gift to a family member, and she helps lead games such as bingo. Recently she has had a fall and broken her ankle. She is expected to make a good recovery, but for the moment she cannot get around as well as she would like, and needs help going to the toilet and having a bath when at the centre.

1. Say how promoting and supporting are being applied to Allegra when she visits the day-care centre.
2. Explain how each of these will make her feel about herself.
3. Construct a spider diagram with Allegra in the centre. On the 'legs', write down the ways in which Allegra is being helped at the day-care centre. Next, add any suggestions you have of ways in which her family and friends can apply the same values as the service providers to help Allegra when she is not at the day-care centre.

Let's communicate and relate

Another part of the care value base is promoting effective communication and relationships, which you will learn about in this topic.

Communication

It is vital that service providers communicate effectively with service users. Good communication means that relationships can be formed to empower the users, so that they feel that their opinions about their care are valued, that they are respected and that they can take part in decisions that affect their own care.

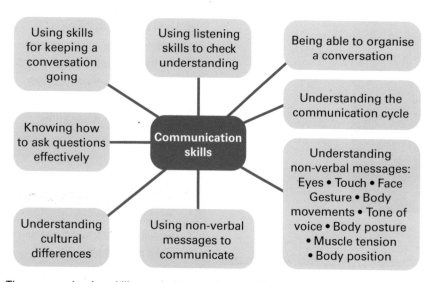

The communication skills needed by service providers

There are three main types of communication.

- *Verbal communication* is the ability to both explain and present your ideas clearly through the spoken word, and to listen carefully to other people.
- *Non-verbal communication* refers to the messages we send out to express ideas without talking, through the use of body language, facial expressions, gestures and tone of voice. Some of the most important body areas are shown here.
- *The written word* is central to the work of any service provider: for example, when keeping records and in writing reports. Different types of communication need different styles of writing, but all require literacy skills – the ability to be able to present the written word clearly and correctly.

Your world

Francesca is Enrico's daughter and she has been deaf from birth. One day, she is crossing the road by the restaurant when she is knocked over by a cyclist suddenly swerving to avoid a dog. How do you think the cyclist could try to communicate with her in order to reassure and help her?

Think about it

The teachers you like best at school are probably those who are fair with you and who talk to you and try to get to know you as a person, so developing a relationship with you. If you feel a teacher doesn't even know your name after the first half term of teaching you, how do you feel? How does it affect your attitude to that teacher and their lessons? What does that show you about the importance, for example, of a child in care having a good relationship with her carer?

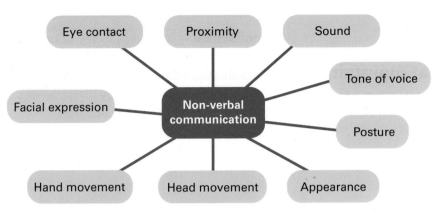

The main elements involved in non-verbal communication

Relationships

In establishing and maintaining a trusting relationship it is important to:

- **set boundaries** It is important in any relationship to establish boundaries and understand why they are needed. For example, a teacher may chat and joke with her students, but there is a line beyond which students are not allowed to go, such as not to be overfamiliar. By establishing boundaries and building good relationships, the teacher **enables** her students to talk to her when they have problems, and is in a position to notice signs of abuse in her students.

- **promote independence** No relationship should be such that it stifles independence, which is crucial to a person's wellbeing and self-esteem. For example, if a care worker asks the opinion of an elderly resident and allows him choice within the boundaries of the rules and other residents' needs, he will feel as though his views still matter and he will be more likely to trust the care worker.

- **support individuals with communication** It is important to establish ways of communication with individuals that not only enable them to understand you clearly, but also allow them to make their feelings and views clear to you and others.

- **be consistent and reliable** Being both consistent and reliable in a key part of establishing and maintaining trust.

- **help and enable** Any relationship – particularly where one person has to trust another to look after them – will be more successful if those concerned try to be as helpful as possible.

Other important factors in relationships include promoting a person's rights, being non-judgemental, maintaining a person's privacy and maintaining confidentiality, all of which are covered in other Topics.

Enable – supply with the means, knowledge, or opportunity; make a person able to do a certain task

Activity

1. Consider a trip to the dentist. Describe, using each of the factors listed above, how the dentist has established, and keeps, your trust, so that you will allow the dentist to inspect and treat your teeth.

2. Produce a leaflet to be given to a new and nervous patent to reassure him that the dentist can be trusted. Make sure it looks professional.

Just checking

1. Why is it important to build up trusting relationships if you are to look after, safeguard and protect an individual?

2. List eight factors that are important in establishing and maintaining a trusting relationship.

3. For three of these factors, give examples of a care setting where the factor is important and explain why. You can use examples from this Topic or use your own ideas.

That's a secret

In this topic, you will look at maintaining confidentiality of information – another important care value.

Confidential – to be kept secret, or used only within certain agreed limits.
Confidential information – information that has been entrusted only to the person to whom it has been communicated

Your world

Where does my son live?

Look at the picture of a scene in The Green's dental practice. Carol is dealing with a man who has come in asking for his son's address. He says it is very important that he contact his son with an urgent message. Carol has told him that she cannot give out details about any of the practice's clients, and the man has become very angry.

Why is it important that Carol the receptionist does not give out any information regarding the man's son?

Confidentiality

Maintaining the confidentiality of information communicated by a service user is very important in health, social care and early years.

Service providers have lots of information about a service user. Think about the information your doctor has about you. This not only includes basic facts but also personal details such as worries about your weight or an embarrassing problem, information about issues such as contraception, or even information about your family or friends. The information will vary depending on which service provider you are using, but each will know a lot of **confidential** information about you.

Imagine, then, the huge amount of information a provider has on someone who is older than you or is in some kind of residential care. It is crucial that service providers keep this secure.

Breaching or breaking confidentiality is inappropriate behaviour and can have many consequences, some of which are shown in this table.

Think about it

How do you feel when you have told someone you consider to be a friend a secret and they tell other people about it? Think about how you would feel if you had a condition that you had decided to keep a secret from the rest of your family for a certain reason, and the doctor told them anyway. How would you feel towards the doctor? How would it affect your future treatment by him?

Consequence	As a result, the service user might be ...
Loss of trust	Less likely to say how he really feels or share a problem
Lower self-esteem	Likely to feel unvalued and as though they don't matter
Risk	Feeling their property and personal safety threatened
Loss of professional reputation	Feeling the provider is unprofessional
Law breaking	Likely to sue the provider
Discrimination	Treated differently by others

The possible consequences of breaching confidentiality

Legislation on confidentiality

The Data Protection Act, 1998, protects people's rights to confidentiality, whether the data is stored on paper or electronically.

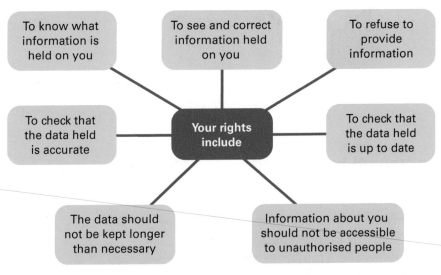

The Data Protection Act, 1998

Necessary breaches of confidentiality

There are times when it is appropriate to breach confidentiality. Examples include if service users are at risk because they might harm themselves in some way, if they are a risk to the safety of others, or if they have broken, or are about to break, the law. It is therefore inappropriate behaviour for a service provider to promise to keep everything confidential; they should explain that there will be times (such as those just mentioned) when it might be necessary to pass information on to an appropriate colleague or authority.

Activity

Explain the possible consequences of the following breaches of confidentiality.

1. A worker passes on information about when a person's family are going to be away on holiday to someone whose boyfriend is in prison.
2. A worker tells someone about a person who lives near him who has been mentally ill, but now has the illness totally under control.
3. A worker tells her daughter that a patient, who is the father of someone in her class at school, has cancer but has not told his family because he wants to see what the prognosis is first.

Just checking

1. What does 'breaching confidentiality' mean?
2. What are three possible consequences for service users if information about them is not kept confidential?
3. Give three reasons why it is sometimes necessary and acceptable to breach confidentiality.

What do you believe in?

This topic looks at the final part of the care value base: acknowledging individual personal beliefs and identity.

Your world

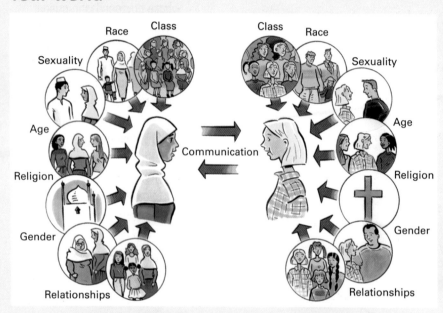

The groups that a person belongs to influence their beliefs and identity

Write down five things that you believe in. Compare them with the five things each of another two friends has written down. What topics have you covered between you?

Acknowledging individual personal beliefs and identity

... it sounds important, but what does it involve? To do this we have to show respect and treat people as individuals, by understanding their beliefs, valuing their diversity and treating them fairly.

Beliefs

A person's identity depends in part on their beliefs. Every person has beliefs. Beliefs are thoughts stored in the subconscious mind and are strongly held opinions that determine how a person sees life. Many people have not reflected on what they believe, but their beliefs will still show up in their daily lives, by influencing their thoughts, words, feelings and actions.

People have these beliefs because of events that happen in their lives, the influence of family and friends, and other factors that help shape a person's beliefs. Beliefs might be based on someone's religion or simply on the person's sense of self-worth.

If a person is constantly thinking that they are not good enough, it will affect everything that person does. Beliefs can even affect a person's health. A person who worries all the time will be more likely to have headaches and stomach problems.

A person's beliefs will also affect how they access services. If a person believes they are not very bright, they may not try hard at school, believing they can't do the work – so they may not access the education they deserve. If a person has religious beliefs that comfort him in times of trouble, he may be more able to cope and will have more confidence to seek help from services.

Diversity

Diversity means a variety or range of differences. To value diversity means to respect and value the cultures and beliefs of other people. If we are unwilling to accept that other people's beliefs and cultures may be different from ours, and so dismiss and ignore them, we will not be able to learn about them and so understand them.

A good service provider will get to know the people they work with, so will not make any assumptions about people. They will be open to other people's life experiences and differences, and value their diversity. They will form good relationships with their colleagues and the service users. A team of service providers who have different interests and skills is more likely to be able to tackle the range of tasks when helping a service user, and the team will enjoy working together.

Treating people as individuals

Everyone should receive a service of equal quality that meets his or her personal needs – but this is not the same as everyone receiving the same service.

For example, everyone should be able to register with a doctor, but some people will take up more of the doctor's time at certain times in their lives if they have an illness. Treating people as individuals, taking into account their different beliefs, abilities, and so on, is crucial to caring for others.

A service provider needs to acknowledge an individual's personal beliefs, even if he or she does not share those beliefs. For example, if Manny is Jewish and only eats kosher food at home, it is only right that he is given kosher meat, whether he is in prison or in hospital. This will make him feel that his identity has been valued and will help his sense of wellbeing, as well as his rehabilitation or recovery.

Do you care?

This last topic of Unit 2 looks at how the care values are reflected in the behaviour, attitudes and work of care practitioners.

Putting the care values into practice

To ensure that their behaviour, attitudes and work reflect the care values, care practitioners are provided with various rules and guidelines, which come in four main forms: legislation, codes of professional practice, policies and procedures to follow.

Your world

Imagine that you are distressed because others are challenging something you really believe in – something that says who you are as a person. You arrange to have a confidential chat with a teacher. Describe how you would expect the teacher to respond to you to make you feel reassured. Think about the place you meet, the teacher's body language, tone of voice, and so on. Role-play the situation with a partner.

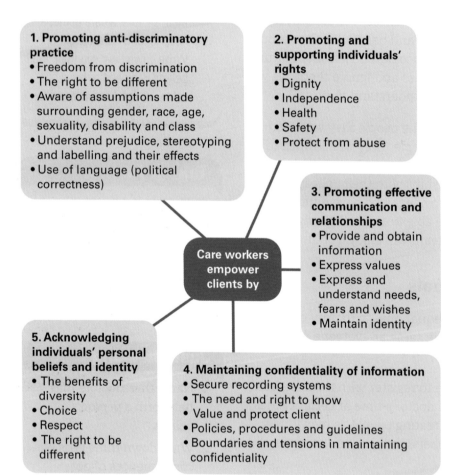

1. Promoting anti-discriminatory practice
- Freedom from discrimination
- The right to be different
- Aware of assumptions made surrounding gender, race, age, sexuality, disability and class
- Understand prejudice, stereotyping and labelling and their effects
- Use of language (political correctness)

2. Promoting and supporting individuals' rights
- Dignity
- Independence
- Health
- Safety
- Protect from abuse

Care workers empower clients by

3. Promoting effective communication and relationships
- Provide and obtain information
- Express values
- Express and understand needs, fears and wishes
- Maintain identity

5. Acknowledging individuals' personal beliefs and identity
- The benefits of diversity
- Choice
- Respect
- The right to be different

4. Maintaining confidentiality of information
- Secure recording systems
- The need and right to know
- Value and protect client
- Policies, procedures and guidelines
- Boundaries and tensions in maintaining confidentiality

The care values

Think about it

Having laws and codes of practice is all very well, but they have to be applied well to be effective. How do people working in the health and social care know what laws and guidelines they must follow? How much is it their employer's responsibility, and how much their own responsibility to know what they should do? Do people need to know the detail of every law that applies to them?

Case study Emma

Emma collapses and breaks her arm as she falls. She is rushed into hospital with appendicitis, where they operate to remove her appendix and set her arm in plaster. She is very upset when she comes round from the operation because she is a dancer, and she will miss an important audition for a London musical. She is self-employed and will not be able to earn her living while she is out of action – which means she will not be able to pay the rent on the flat she shares with Felicity and Lewis.

Look at the care values diagram. Describe how the nurses will treat Emma to help her recover while she is in hospital. Remember – she has physical, intellectual, emotional and social needs.

Legislation

If you do not adhere to the law, you are breaking it and can be charged with a crime. One example of legislation that every care practitioner must abide by is the Age Discrimination Act, 2006, which prohibits unjustified and indirect discrimination and all harassment and victimisation on grounds of age, of people of any age, young or old.

Codes of professional practice

All professional bodies and services should have a code of practice (sometimes called a code of conduct) with guidelines for people who work in that body or service to follow, to make sure they are adhering to the values of that profession. One example is shown here – the Nursing and Midwifery Council's Code of Practice.

Any code of practice advises service providers on how to behave, not only to promote the individual rights of the service users, but also to protect themselves. It will also set out the standards of practice and conduct that those who work in the sectors should meet.

Policies

A policy is different from a code of practice, in that it tells a service provider how to deal with a particular situation in his or her own workplace. Every service provider has its own policies, which depend on its specific role and situation. Service providers have policies that cover areas such as positive promotion of human rights, work practices, staff development and training, quality issues and confidentiality.

Procedures

A procedure is a list of steps for a service provider to follow to complete a particular task in a certain way, based on the value base. One example of a procedure that a nurse may follow is the procedure for a bed bath. This will be written so that, when followed correctly, the patient has as little embarrassment as possible.

Code of professional conduct

As a registered nurse, midwife or health visitor, you are personally accountable for your practice. In caring for patients and clients, you must:

- respect the patient or client as an individual
- protect confidential information
- co-operate with others in the team
- maintain your professional knowledge and competence
- be trustworthy
- act to identify and minimise risk to patients and clients.

These are the shared values of all the United Kingdom health care regulatory bodies.

Extract from the Nursing and Midwifery Council's Code of Practice

Just checking

1. What are the five care values?
2. Name the four types of rules and guidelines that care practitioners have to follow.
3. What is the aim of each of these? Describe using examples to explain what you mean.

Assessment for Unit 2

Welcome

Are you looking forward to your first piece of assignment assessment work in Health and Social Care? If you are following the single award, you will do this one piece of work; if you are doing the double award, you will have another to complete too.

Many students really enjoy the chance of showing what they can do in producing a big piece of work over a number of weeks. It certainly tests your determination and organisation skills. Some teachers call this 'assignment work', others call it 'portfolio work', but the new name for this type of work is '**controlled assessment**'.

> **controlled assessment** – a big piece of work produced over a number of weeks, previously called 'assignment work' or 'portfolio work'

How Unit 2 is assessed

Key things you need to know

- You will write a report for this piece of assessment.
- The task/s involved in the report will be set by Edexcel, your examination board.
- The report will be based on an investigation into the needs of one service user and how these needs are met.
- The report has to be written up over a 22.5 hour period of classroom-based work and is marked out of 50.
- The report will be written under controlled conditions. This may be completed in different ways. Your teacher will give you information about how this will be done in your school or college.
- You will be able to bring both the primary and secondary data you have collected to help you complete the tasks set.
- All written work, calculations and graphs must be completed in the lesson and supervised by your teacher.

What you will need to do

You will receive an Edexcel instruction sheet that sets the tasks to complete. These will require you to produce evidence, which will be assessed by your teacher against a mark grid. You will need to show:

- knowledge and understanding
- the ability to plan and carry out investigations
- analyse and evaluate information
- draw conclusions and make reasoned judgements.

In addition, the quality of your written work will be assessed.

You can choose a service user to base your work on, though Edexcel may ask you to select from **two or more** service-user groups.

Top tips for preparing

- Choose your service user carefully. The person you select will need to provide you with a lot of information. Make sure they can do this and are prepared to give you all you need.
- Select a person who has an interesting range of needs that are currently being met or partially met by service providers.
- Make sure you tell the service user that you will be keeping their information confidential and that you will not identify them by name in your work.
- Keep a copy of the questions you ask your service user as well as their answers as you can take these into the classroom to work from in your write-up.
- Collect a folder of information you will need to use in the writing up of your work in the classroom: for example, leaflets about services, job descriptions, etc.
- Decide how much time you are going to spend on the tasks set. Remember: you have twenty-two and a half hours. You do not want to spend fifteen of these hours on a task that only covers a small part of the evidence.

The range of material that the examination board will require to be evident in your report will show that you can:

- consider the care needs of service-user groups
- explore types of services that exist to meet service users' needs
- explain how the services are organised and have developed
- consider the ways people access the services they need and the barriers that stop them accessing the services they need
- consider the roles and skills of people who provide these services
- explore how care workers use the care values everyday.

The sort of tasks you might include as part of your report could be:

- a profile of a service user
- a case study of an individual you have selected
- an information booklet
- a presentation about an individual or a care professional
- a profile of a care worker and their role/work/skills/qualifications.

The importance of a good choice of person

The key to success in is the person you choose to base your study on. Make sure the person:

- has a good range of needs that need to be met. It would be good if some of these needs were social and emotional
- is involved with an organisation that is helping them significantly with meeting their needs
- uses a range of workers so that you can explore their work and find out the qualifications and skills needed to do it.

Good choice?

Identify a person you know and could possibly use for this report. The person must be from one of the following client groups:

- early years (0–8 years of age)
- people with health needs
- people with specific needs
- people in later adulthood (65+).

1. Describe the current needs of this person.
2. Identify the services they use to help meet their needs.

Just checking

1. How many hours will you have to write up the report?
2. Describe the sort of person that would be ideal to select to enable you to complete your report.
3. Why is organisation and planning so important in completing this report?

Writing your portfolio work

One of the skills you will have to show in producing your assessment work for Unit 2 is that you can produce a report and write at some length. You may choose to use a range of ways of presenting data and information using charts, graphs and tables. You will need to think about these approaches before you start your controlled assessment.

It is important that you develop the skills you need early in the course, and you will certainly need to develop them more if you intend to continue study on courses at post-16 level. In the world of work, you will also need to be able to write in an extended way to produce reports or summaries of events that have happened. It's a valuable skill to have.

In the longer questions, the assessors will also be looking at your 'QWC':

   QWC = Quality of Written Communication

You will need to show and use a number of general written skills that you will have been developing throughout your time at school or college. In the box to the right are some basic rules that are really simple, but are often forgotten.

As well as writing skills, you will also need to be able to 'use' the information and data you collect to help make your report detailed and show it is based on sound evidence. Below are some general skills you will need to have. Try to make sure you practice these before you actually start writing up your work in 'controlled' conditions; then you can be confident you can use them in the assessed write-up time, when you really need them. Remember, practice makes perfect.

Key skills you will need to develop are:

- writing questionnaires
- writing interview schedules
- conducting interviews
- collecting secondary data from a range of sources
- presenting information in appropriate graphs and tables
- understanding the graphs and tables you produce from your research
- drawing conclusions form the information you have presented.

Basic rules

- Use capital letters and full stops.
- Write in sentences.
- Use paragraphs to structure what you want to say.
- Include examples to show what you mean.
- Check what you have written and be sure it makes sense.

Ways to present your findings

Question asked to a service user with a serious, ongoing health issue: 'How many visits have you made to these health professionals in the last month?'

Results:

GP = 6   Nurse = 10
Specialist = 4   Chiropractitioner = 5
Total = 25

Here are some ways in which the same information could be presented. You will need to practice a range of different approaches and choose the best ones for your portfolio.

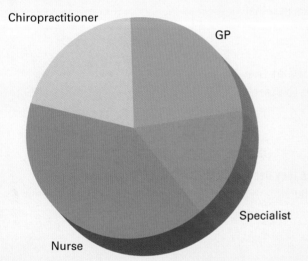

The same information shown on a pie chart

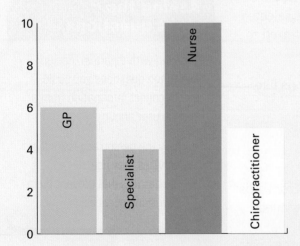

The same information shown on a graph

Interpreting data

1. Select one of the diagrams below to look at closely. Explain what it tells you about this person's use of health professionals in the last month.
2. Which health professional is visited most by the service user?
3. From the diagrams, is it possible to conclude which health professional is the most important to the service user?

Presenting information

Here is a tally chart of the number of times Chelsie, aged six, plays with particular types of toys during an hour's observation.

Pram	5
Cups and saucers	2
Fire engine	10
Bat and ball	3

1. Present this information in two different ways.
2. What does the information tell you about how Chelsie played during the hour?
3. Can you conclude that Chelsie's favourite toy is the fire engine?

Just checking

1. Why is it useful to present the results of some information you collect in graphs, diagrams or tables?
2. Why is it important to practice drawing these before you enter the 'controlled' report-writing sessions?
3. Why must you look carefully at information you present before you draw conclusions?

Examples of portfolio writing

Edexcel will set you a controlled assessment task. This will say clearly what you have to do. There may be a number of tasks to complete.

Sample question and answers

Here is an example of a controlled assessment task.

Produce a report based on an investigation into the needs of a service user that you have selected from an early years setting **OR** later adulthood.

Within this, there will be a number of tasks set. We will look at the first part of the first task set, to get a good idea about how to start!

Find out from your service user:

- how they accessed a service provider
- any barriers that may have prevented them accessing the service they used: for example, physical, psychological, financial, geographical, cultural/language and resource barriers.

Write up your findings as a case study of the service user.

Before writing up this work under controlled conditions, it would be useful to design a questionnaire or interview sheet for your selected service user. This could be taken into the classroom and referred to as you write up your case study.

The questionnaire/interview should NOT consist of questions like:

- Which services do you use?
- Were there any problems in accessing the service?

Instead, you might want questions that:

- are closed, and let the person just tick the right answer from a list
- are open, where you or the service user writes a more detailed answer, or you fill the sheet after listening to the person
- are about the services they use which are privately run, they pay for or are voluntary: for example, a social club, a private gym, etc.
- identify problems that people accessing services face and check whether the service user has faced them themselves.

Asking the right questions

Working with a partner, design five to ten questions you could use to collect information from a service user about:

- how the person accesses the services they use
- the barriers that prevent them accessing services.

Remember – it might be good to follow up some of your questions with open questions, which give you more detailed information.

Read these parts of two students' work carefully.

Student A

I am calling my service user X for confidentiality reasons. X uses the local health centre on a regular basis as they have a number of long-term health problems.

X regularly needs to use health services and to access them they will need some type of referral. In order to get care, a person must request and apply for it – or get a referral. There are five main types of referral: self-referral, third party referral, professional referral, compulsory referral, and emergency referral.

The student also explained in detail what each one of these referral methods was in detail.

X often makes a self-referral to the health centre when not feeling well. X has lung disease from long-term smoking and working in mining. They do this by phone. If X is too ill, family members make the appointment. This is third party referral. The doctor makes professional referrals to the hospital for X as necessary.

People often face problems accessing the services they need. The biggest problem X has is psychological. They have a fear of the doctors because they have a serious health problem and sometimes have been admitted to hospital so they put off going to the doctors sometimes. This is bad, as they sometimes make themselves even more ill by putting off the visit. X's family encourage them to go to the doctor when they know a visit is needed. The health centre knows the problem and does do home visits when X cannot get themselves there.

The student continued to write in this depth about other barriers such as financial, physical and geographical barriers.

Student B

My person has problems accessing the services they need from their health centre. This is because they live a long way from the centre. They don't like the doctors either. They think the doctors are rude. They usually refer themselves if they are ill and make an appointment. It is hard to get an appointment on the day you want it at the doctors, so what's the point of trying to make an appointment in the first place? The centre has wheelchair ramps which helps service users.

What the examiners thought

Student A

The student wrote well here and approached the task in an organised way. The student had a good level of knowledge and understanding. The evidence they present shows that they must have done some good research work before writing up the task. The student knew the ways in which people access services and related them to the person. This person wrote just as well for the other barriers that were linked to their selected person.

The student is probably working towards a grade A/B.

Student B

The student's work was limited and showed a lack of depth of knowledge and understanding. A number of points were made, but they were mixed up and in no logical order. The student does show information about accessing services and barriers, but there needs to be given a lot more depth of information.

The student is probably working towards a grade E.

Just checking

1. Why is it important to conduct a questionnaire or interview with a service user before you write up your work?

2. Explain why questions must be carefully put together.

3. Explain why it is important to plan the write-up of work before you begin it.

Unit 3: Promoting Health and Wellbeing

Your world

'How are you?' What does that actually mean?

With a partner, discuss what you think is meant by the term 'health and wellbeing'. When you have reached a decision write down your definition. Do not look it up in this book or anywhere else!

Learning objectives

- Definitions of health and wellbeing
- Factors that affect health and wellbeing
- The effects of the factors affecting health and wellbeing
- Methods used to measure individual physical health
- Ways of promoting and supporting health improvements

Introduction

This unit is about how health, social care and early years practitioners promote the health and wellbeing of service users.

Definitions of health and wellbeing

It is very complicated to say what exactly each of us means by the expression health and wellbeing, but there are various **formal** definitions, which you will learn about in the first two topics of this unit. Many modern definitions regarding health and wellbeing are based on the hierarchy of needs set out by the psychologist Abraham Maslow, which you learned about in on page 67.

How we feel about our health and wellbeing depends on our life stage. As we get older, we generally become more contented and accepting of the person we are.

Factors affecting health and wellbeing

Numerous factors affect how we feel throughout our lives. These include:

- physical factors, such as illness, diet, exercise, alcohol and smoking
- social, cultural and emotional factors, such as family, friends and religion
- economic factors, such as income and wealth
- physical economic factors, such as housing conditions and pollution
- psychological factors, such as stress and relationships
- health monitoring and illness prevention services, such as vaccination.

The effects of these factors

All factors that affect health and wellbeing can do so in either a positive, good way or a negative, bad way. For example, following a healthy balanced diet helps us to have healthy bodies and maybe lose weight if we need to, but eating too little can lead to health disorders such as **malnutrition**.

Methods used to measure individual physical health

It is not always easy to measure health, but there are certain measures we can take and monitor by comparing what is normal for our age, such as blood pressure, peak flow and hip/waist ratio measures.

Ways of promoting and supporting health improvements

Health improvements for an individual can be promoted by designing a plan that sets targets, taking into account the individual's age and lifestyle. These targets can be monitored and supported by various **strategies** – with alternatives suggested for if those fail or do not appeal – and health promotion materials such as leaflets and videos.

123

Formal – official, not casual
Malnutrition – medical condition caused by improper or insufficient **nutrition**
Nutrition – parts of a balanced diet
Strategy – a long-term plan of action designed to achieve a particular goal
Pre-release – written materials to base your coursework on

How you will be assessed

You will be assessed by an internally assessed task based on **pre-release** material about an individual or group of individuals, which will include information and data about their health and wellbeing. You will need to show evidence of definitions of health and wellbeing, factors that affect health and wellbeing, the effects of the factors affecting health and wellbeing, methods used to measure individual physical health and ways of promoting and supporting health improvements. This task will be completed in controlled conditions.

The world view

This topic looks at how practitioners around the world define health and wellbeing.

Health and wellbeing

How do you define health and wellbeing? This is a complex issue! There are three main definitions – holistic, positive and negative – and this topic looks at the holistic definition.

Health means different things to different people, and any person's health can change from day to day. The word health comes from an old English word meaning 'the state of being **hale**, **sound** or whole, in body, mind or soul.'

Wellbeing means the state of being healthy, happy, or **prosperous**, so health and wellbeing can be described in terms of how people **function** and feel – physically, mentally and socially – and how they feel about themselves and their lives.

The World Health Organization (WHO) is an agency of the United Nations (UN) that co-ordinates international **public health**. It is based in Geneva, Switzerland, and was established in 1948. In the same year, it defined health and wellbeing as 'a state of complete physical, mental and social wellbeing, and not merely the absence of disease or infirmity' – a definition that was agreed by all during the first World Health Assembly and has not changed since. Health may be regarded as a balance of the physical, mental and social aspects of a person's life.

Mental health

This refers to an individual's emotional and **psychological** wellbeing, which enables him to use his intellectual and emotional abilities to function in society and meet the ordinary demands of everyday life (Merriam Webster dictionary). Mental health use to be viewed and treated as a totally separate part of a person's health, but is now seen as an integral part of health.

Your world

Healthy or unhealthy?

Think about people who live on The Green. Do you consider these people to be healthy?

- Mohammed, who is disabled and partially sighted
- Francesca, who has been deaf from birth
- Emma, who is a dancer and whose back always hurts when she dances
- Maud, who is lonely.

Explain each of your answers.

Think about it

When adults meet, they often ask 'How are you?' and just as often get the answer 'Fine, thanks', even if that isn't true. Most people, if they thought about it, would think about the fact that they were feeling physically well when they said this. How often, though, does someone who is feeling stressed or very unhappy or unable to cope intellectually, take it to mean that the person is asking about *that* aspect of their health as well as the physical aspect? Do you?

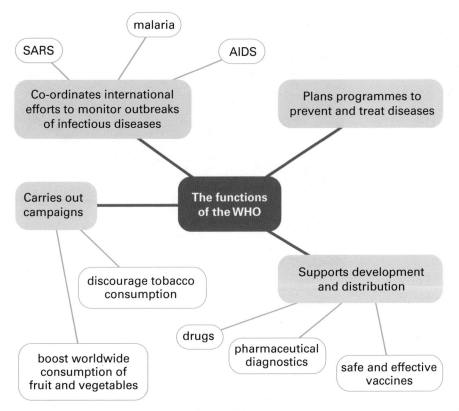

The World Health Organization (WHO)

Hale – free from infirmity or illness
Sound – free from defect, decay, damage, disease and injury; in good condition
Prosperous – successful, flourishing, well-off
Function – perform; operate
Public health – the field of medicine concerned with safeguarding and improving the health of the community as a whole
Psychological – relating to, or arising from, the mind or emotions

A holistic definition of health

A holistic definition of health assesses health based on a combination of physical, intellectual, emotional and social factors – so it looks at all parts of a person's health. This definition is based on Maslow's Hierarchy of Needs (see page 67).

Paula Radcliffe, the British marathon runner, offers a good example of someone with a holistic attitude to health. She keeps herself physically fit, eating a balanced diet and exercising. She learns about different training strategies and has written books (intellectual) and is happily married (emotional), with a family and lots of friends, meeting people all over the world as she trains and competes (social).

Just checking

1. What is the difference between health and wellbeing?
2. What is the WHO definition of health and wellbeing?
3. What is the holistic definition of health and wellbeing? Give an example of someone you think has a holistic attitude towards health and explain why you think this.

Activity

1. Write down how your own health is at the moment. On a scale of 1 to 5, with 5 being feeling as well as you've ever been, how well do you feel?
2. Write down how you feel about yourself at the moment. Try to think of all the different things in your life, such as your diet or your friends, that affect the way you feel. On a scale of 1 to 5, with 5 being feeling as good as you've ever felt about yourself, how do you think your wellbeing is at the moment?
3. Without sharing personal details (unless you want to), compare your scores with others in your group. How many of you have the same scores for health as you do, or for wellbeing? Try to explain the group's scores.

Positive or negative?

You have just learned the holistic definition of health. This topic looks at the other two definitions: **positive** and **negative**.

Positive definition of health

This is the assessment of health based on the achievement and maintenance of physical fitness and mental stability – similar to the WHO definition (see the previous topic). It is positive because you realise there is something you can do to improve your health and you do it.

An example of someone with a positive attitude towards health is Fern Britton. Although she is attractive, quick-witted and extremely well liked, has a loving family and an excellent career, she realised that she would be physically fitter if she lost weight, which she did successfully.

Your world

George is a war veteran. He is 90 years old, and has smoked in moderation all his life, but has always tried to keep himself physically fit by exercising and eating a healthy diet. He also sits out on The Green as much as possible to get fresh air. Discuss with a partner whether you think he has a positive or negative attitude towards his health. Then think about your family members. Do they have a positive or negative attitude? Explain your answers.

Negative definition of health

This is the assessment of health based on the absence of physical illness, disease and mental distress. It is negative because it is based on *not* having anything wrong with you.

A character like Eli Dingle in television's *Emmerdale* has a negative attitude towards his health. He assumes that, because he is currently healthy, he can keep on smoking and drinking to excess and presumes he will stay healthy in the future.

Health scares can make people change their ideas about their health. Jerry from the television soap *Coronation Street* is a popular person (social) who runs his own business (intellectual) and has a loving family (emotional). However, he is morbidly obese because he eats the wrong food (including food from his own kebab shop) and drinks beer. He had a negative attitude towards health, but after a heart attack he started to follow a healthy diet most of the time, cut

Positive – displaying certainty, acceptance or affirmation; moving forward or increasing

Negative – expressing, containing or consisting of a refusal or denial; indicating opposition or resistance

down dramatically on his drinking, and even took some very occasional exercise, so developed a more positive attitude.

Of course, television characters are not real, but you can no doubt think of real people who have had a similar change in attitude after a health scare.

Conclusion

It is best to look after all parts of your health if possible by adopting a holistic attitude (see the definition at the end of the previous topic), looking after the physical, intellectual, emotional and social aspects of your health. There are basic aspects, or factors, that we need, no matter what age we are.

- **Physical aspects** These are all the needs we have to keep our bodies working as well as they can. Even though people's bodies are different, there are certain needs we all have such as food, water, shelter, warmth, clothing, rest, exercise and good personal hygiene.
- **Intellectual aspects** These are all the needs we have to develop and keep our brains working as well as possible. They include mental stimulation to keep us motivated and interested, rather than bored, and we need to keep learning throughout our lives to keep our brains active.
- **Emotional aspects** These are the aspects that make us feel happy and relaxed, such as being loved, respected and secure. We need to be able to feel, express and recognise different emotions in order to cope with different situations that arise throughout our lives.
- **Social aspects** These are the aspects that enable us to develop and enjoy good relationships and friendships with others. These include opportunities to mix with others in an appropriate environment and access to leisure facilities and activities.

Just checking

1. What does having a positive attitude to health mean?
2. Name three consequences of having a negative attitude to health.
3. Give examples of three of each of the different aspects of a holistic attitude towards health. Which aspect does self-esteem fit into? Explain this.

Think about it

Do you think a homeless person, who chooses to live this way and is happy, makes some money by selling the Big Issue on the streets and goes to homeless shelters for food and a bed when he can, has a positive, negative or holistic health and wellbeing?

Activity

1. Write a list of all the things you could do to stimulate your brain. Compare your list with a partner's and add any you didn't think of. Pick one that you would like to try. What is stopping you having a go at it?
2. One such activity is to read. Have a group discussion to find out who reads books regularly out of choice, and who only reads when they are made to, such as in school. Decide who and what has influenced them to be like this.

What do you think?

This topic looks at how the same condition affecting different people will be viewed differently, depending on the life stage and culture of the individuals who have it.

Your world

Ninety-year-old George is gradually losing his sight. How do you think he will feel about this? Do you think he will still think of himself as being healthy? Will he still have good wellbeing? Before deciding, think about how he would be if the same thing happened to him at the age of nine. In pairs, draw a stick figure of George and in thought bubbles write his thoughts down for both situations.

Better late than early?

Social construction

Health and social care workers talk about health and wellbeing being **socially constructed** relative to an individual's life stage and culture. But what does this mean? It is about the way that factors such as your **social class**, religion, gender, sexuality, race, ethnicity and education determine your experience of reality and affect what your life is like on a day-to-day basis. For example, women live longer than men, but are more likely to seek medical attention and have higher levels of self-reported illness.

What counts as health and illness is relative to life stage, time, place and culture.

Life stage
Someone who is left blind after an illness or accident as a young adult will find this hard to accept and come to

Social construction – something invented by members of a culture or society, that exists because people agree to behave as if it exists. One example is **social status**

Social status – the honour or prestige attached to a person's position: for example, doctors and other professionals are considered to have a high social status; someone's position or rank within a group or society

Social class – where someone comes in a hierarchy of groups within a society: for example, working class, middle class and upper class, as determined by a person's occupation, education and income

terms with, and will at first feel they have poor health and wellbeing. Another person who is born blind will probably think of themselves as disabled, but is more likely to accept it and think of themselves as a healthy person with a disability, because that is how they have always been. Yet someone else, who gradually loses their sight as they approach the final stages of their life, will accept that it is part of the ageing process and will have many years of visual memories to reflect on.

Time

Certain conditions have existed for a long time but have only been recognised as illnesses later on. For example, ME (Myalgic Encephalopathy) or Chronic Fatigue Syndrome was only recognised as an illness in the late 1980s: before then, people suffering from it were thought to be lazy. Similarly, ADHD (Attention Deficit Hyperactivity Disorder) was only recognised in the 1990s. It is now treated with therapy and drugs, but before then those suffering from it were considered to have a behaviour problem rather than a medical condition. (If you have not heard of these conditions, ask your teacher to explain them to you.)

Place

In India, some people experience Dhat (anxiety and concern about semen loss); in North Africa, some people experience Zar (spirit possession).

Culture

Different social groups have different views about recognising symptoms and what action to take in response. For example, working-class women are less likely than middle-class women to see backache as a problem that needs medical attention. Working-class women encounter more life crises than other groups, and sometimes have less-developed coping strategies.

Case study **Steven**

Steven is 50 and a personal fitness instructor. When he was 40, he suffered a heart attack. Although he exercised regularly and looked fit, he smoked, ate a lot of red meat and drank to excess on a regular basis. He changed his lifestyle, cutting out the cigarettes and only drinking socially and in moderation, and ate a more balanced diet. His blood pressure went down and he lost some weight. He is now better able to do his job, despite the fact that he will need medication for his heart problem for the rest of his life.

1. Do you think Steven thought he was well before he had the heart attack? Explain your answer.
2. Do you think Steven considered himself well when he was in hospital recovering form the heart attack? Explain your answer.
3. Do you think he thinks of himself as well now, despite his medication? Explain why you think this.

Just checking

1. What is meant by social construction? Give an example to show that you understand this.
2. List five factors that affect a person's experience of life.
3. What are the four things that affect what a person's view of health and illness is? Which of the four things that affect what a person's view of health and illness is will affect you most in your lifetime? Explain your answer.

Activity

One example of social construction is how people with disabilities are viewed. Do some research into the medical model and the social model of disability. With a partner, prepare a presentation on why everyone should adopt the social model.

In your presentation, include:

- what the two models are
- why people with disabilities wanted and needed a change in the way society viewed them
- how the social model supports independence and choice for people with disabilities.

How do you feel?

This topic starts to investigate the physical factors that affect an individual's health and wellbeing, by looking at inheritance, **illness** and **disease**.

Factors that affect health and wellbeing

Factors that affect an individual's health and wellbeing fall into six main groups: physical; social, cultural and emotional; economic; physical environment; psychological; and health monitoring and illness prevention.

Physical factors

Inheritance

Some diseases are inherited – that is, passed from one generation to another. One example is haemophilia, which only affects males. It means that blood doesn't clot. A male with this disease would have to ensure that he didn't cut himself, because he could bleed to death. As a result, he may decide to avoid tackling do-it-yourself jobs in the home, taking part in contact sports or having a job that involves sharp objects, such as knives or spades.

Disability and illness

When we have a disease, we become ill. This affects our wellbeing, as does having a disability. People with disabilities have to adapt their lifestyles to cope with everyday situations that able-bodied people deal with automatically. A disability or illness may affect physical fitness, restrict access to varied learning activities, cause emotional distress and remove some social opportunities, thus affecting health and

Your world

Look up the meanings of any of the words in the introduction to this page that you do not understand, such as economic. Write down all the things in your life that affect you in a (a) positive way (b) negative way. Then try to fit them into the six main groups of factors mentioned by drawing a mind map, with you in the middle, a branch for each group of factors, and more branches off those that represent your life at the moment.

Illness – a state of poor health, sometimes referred to as ill health

Disease – an abnormal condition of an organism that impairs bodily functions; any condition that causes discomfort, dysfunction, distress, social problems and/or death to the person afflicted

Degenerative – gradually becoming worse

Acute – sharp or severe in effect; intense

Activity

Huntington's Disease is a **degenerative** disorder of the central nervous system that causes jerky and uncontrollable movements of the limbs. It eventually affects motor skills and speech and leads to loss of physical movement. Medical treatment can reduce the shaking.

1. What needs of a 45-year-old man with Huntington's disease will be met by continuing to work in an office after he is diagnosed with the disease?
2. What difficulties will he face that will affect his health and wellbeing, other than the disease itself?
3. How can his working conditions, such as the layout of his office, be adapted so that he can go on working for longer?

wellbeing. It may also affect the growth and physical development of the body: for example, a paralysed arm will lose muscle due to lack of use. Disability or illness can also affect the development of new abilities and skills, as well as emotional development.

Whatever condition a person has, their needs include all those of an able-bodied person, but they have important additional needs, especially in relation to access to both places and services. If these are met through the provision of an enabling environment, the impact of the disability or illness may be decreased.

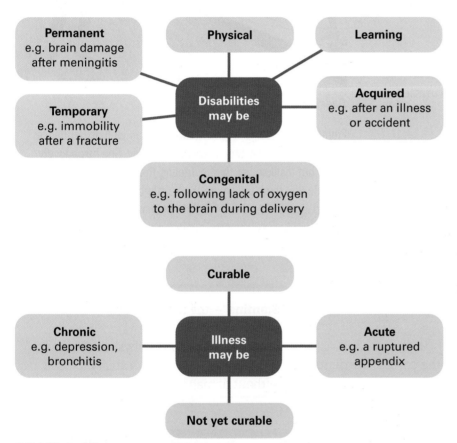

Disability and illness

Just checking

1. What is meant by 'some diseases are inherited'?
2. What is the difference between an illness and a disease?
3. Explain how three aspects of life might be affected by an illness or disability.

Fat or lean – fit or unfit?

This topic continues to look at physical factors that affect health and wellbeing, by looking at diet and exercise.

Lifestyle choices

If we make lifestyle choices that make us less healthy and feel less good about ourselves, we will not be able to take all the opportunities life has to offer.

For example, people who are overweight will be more prone to illnesses and conditions such as heart disease, will be less able to exercise, and will feel less confident about their appearance in social situations, feeling embarrassed and lacking in worth. This is more likely to shorten their life expectancy, will mean they are unable to take up many life opportunities such as hill walking, dancing or skiing, and will make them less likely to be successful at job interviews.

Diet

A balanced diet is one that contains the correct nutrients in the right proportions to keep our bodies and minds healthy. The essential parts of a healthy diet are fats (saturated and unsaturated), carbohydrates (sugars and starches), minerals, vitamins, water and proteins.

The food we eat affects the way we feel and look, and is very important to our health, wellbeing and life opportunities. Although our dietary needs vary throughout life, if we eat more than we need the body stores fat, which can lead to obesity, heart disease, high blood pressure, strokes, tooth decay and cancer. Eating less than we need can lead to anaemia, stunted bone growth, heart failure, depression, tiredness, cancer, mouth sores, scurvy and many other conditions. Both over- and under-eating can eventually result in death.

Your world

Dancing is excellent exercise

Emma is a dancer and goes to the gym, as well as her dance classes, to keep fit. She also eats healthily. She has a lovely figure but dislikes her thighs, feeling they are slightly too big. Why do you think they might be a little big? Does this mean she should change her lifestyle? Role-play a discussion between Emma and her housemate Felicity on the subject of her thighs.

Stamina – the heart's ability to work under strain
Strength – the body's physical power
Suppleness – the body's ability to bend without damage

Think about it

Many people drive to places of natural beauty such as the Lake District in Cumbria, but don't move more than a few feet from their cars. They even drive off the road to get closer to the edge of a lake to get a better view, often spoiling the view for others, and leaving wildlife damaged or dead and ruts in the mud where there should not be any. Why do people do this? What opportunities are they missing here to become healthier?

The eatwell plate

Use the eatwell plate to help you get the balance right. It shows how much of what you eat should come from each food group.

The plate model for a balanced diet

Exercise

Exercise improves our **strength**, **stamina** and **suppleness**, as well as our muscle and body tone. It also relieves stress, relaxes us, is enjoyable, makes us feel good, gives us a chance to meet others and gives us personal satisfaction.

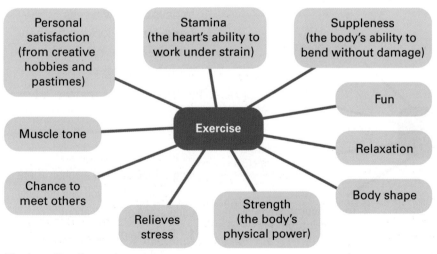

The benefits of exercise

Lack of exercise can lead to stiffening of the joints, poor stamina, strength and suppleness, obesity, stroke, coronary heart disease, a poorly developed heart and skeletal muscles, heart attack, sluggish blood flow, osteoporosis and other conditions. Any of these may mean that our health and wellbeing suffer, and we are less able to take life opportunities that come our way.

Under the influence

In this topic, you will continue to look at physical factors that affect health and wellbeing, by looking at alcohol.

Alcohol

Alcohol is a socially accepted part of many cultures. It is addictive, and excessive drinking causes many illnesses and problems, but in moderation it is both pleasurable and beneficial to health.

Recommended limits

If the recommended limits are exceeded regularly, there is an increased risk to health. However, they should only be used as a rough guide, as different brands of the same drink can have different strengths.

Your world

The Institute of Alcohol Studies says that young people in the UK are the third worst binge drinkers in the European Union

What do you think when you see young people looking like this and sounding loud and uncouth (rough, vulgar, common)? What do you think are the possible consequences of binge drinking?

Short-term – in the immediate future, measured in days or a few weeks
Long-term – looking further into the future, maybe six months or longer

---

Activity

Read the lists of short- and long-term effects of alcohol. There will be some that you will not fully understand or know about.

1. Do some research to find out what they all mean.
2. Produce an eye-catching and memorable poster, leaflet or fact sheet that warns young people of these risks. Include all the risks and make it clear what they all mean. Do not present them as boring lists!

As a habit | To relax | To be sociable

To accompany a meal

To relieve stress

Why drink alcohol?

To relieve boredom

To celebrate a special occasion

To quench thirst | To enjoy the taste | To overcome shyness and inhibitions

Why people drink alcohol

Other factors that affect the amount of alcohol in your bloodstream include your size (smaller people will be more affected), water level (dehydrated people will be more affected), your gender (women are generally more affected because of their size, and having more fat on their bodies), the amount of food in your stomach (alcohol reaches your brain more slowly if there is food in your stomach) and how often you drink (regular drinkers are more used to alcohol and so need more for the same effect).

In recent years, there has been growing concern about the way people drink in this country because many now 'binge drink'. There are many definitions of binge drinking; one is consuming more than half the recommended weekly maximum alcohol units in one sitting. Alcohol Concern adopts a stricter measure, and says that consuming too much alcohol – six units of alcohol for women or eight units for men – in too short a time is likely to count as a binge.

1.75 units   2.27 units   1 unit   1 unit
(50 ml)
(25 ml)

Recommended weekly limits: Female: no more than 14 units per week; Male: no more than 21 units per week

Effects of alcohol on health and wellbeing

Short-term effects

Alcohol is a depressant. It can make you feel more cheerful and talkative, but also reduces inhibitions, affects coordination so you become clumsy, causes blurred sight and speech, leads to loss of balance so you are more likely to fall over, makes your judgement less reliable, reduces your self-control so you become more aggressive or tearful and makes your reactions slower.

Long-term effects

The long-term effects of alcohol include weight gain and obesity, reddened and eventually permanently mottled skin, liver damage and eventually cirrhosis, stomach problems, brain damage, heart disease and ultimately heart failure, high blood pressure, increased risk of strokes, cancers of the mouth, throat, bowel and stomach, depression, ulcers, damage to unborn babies, insomnia and reduced sexual function.

Just checking

1. What does 'binge drinking' mean?
2. What are the recommended limits of units of alcohol for (a) females (b) males?
3. Why is the recommended limit less for women than for men?

Take it further

1. Think about the various adverts for alcohol you see in the media. How do they encourage people to drink more?
2. Do you think showing young people pictures of a healthy liver compared with the liver of a heavy drinker will deter them from drinking? Explain your answer.
3. You can work out the exact number of units in a drink by multiplying the volume in millilitres (ml) by the ABV (alcohol by volume), and dividing by 1000. Work out how many units there are in:

- a 25ml measure of gin, ABV 37.5%
- 130ml of wine, ABV 13%
- Half a pint (284ml) of strong cider, ABV 4.0%.

In a puff of smoke

In this topic we cover smoking, another physical factor that affects health and wellbeing.

Smoking tobacco

Smoking tobacco, usually in cigarettes, is legal and more socially acceptable than using other drugs, despite the recent ban on smoking in public places. However, it is addictive and a major cause of ill health, preventable disease and death. All smoking material packaging and adverts now carry a Government health warning.

Stopping smoking

Many smokers would like to give up, especially now that smoking is banned in public places. When you do give up smoking, your body begins to repair the damage done quite quickly. The benefits are:

- blood pressure returns to normal
- breathing is improved
- being better able to cope with sudden exertion
- loss of smoker's cough
- hair, skin and breath do not smell of smoke
- more money available for other uses
- improved senses of smell and taste
- a sense of achievement
- a reduction in the risk of smoking-related diseases
- less phlegm.

However, stopping smoking is not easy to do and you must really want to stop. There is a range of organisations dedicated to helping you give up, such as ASH, QUIT, GASP and the NHS Stop Smoking services.

Your world

Does everyone have the right to smoke?

What do you think are the rights of the woman in the picture? What are the rights of her unborn child? What about those of her partner, who does not smoke? What are the responsibilities of the woman and her partner for the unborn child?

Nicotine – a powerful, addictive drug found in tobacco

Carbon monoxide – a poisonous gas

Bronchitis – a chest infection

Emphysema – a condition that leads to severe shortage of breath, a dependency on oxygen, and death

Stroke – when part of the body is disabled due to a blood clot or a burst blood vessel in the brain

Did you know?

Smoking used to be considered good for you, so much so that doctors used to appear in adverts encouraging people to smoke.

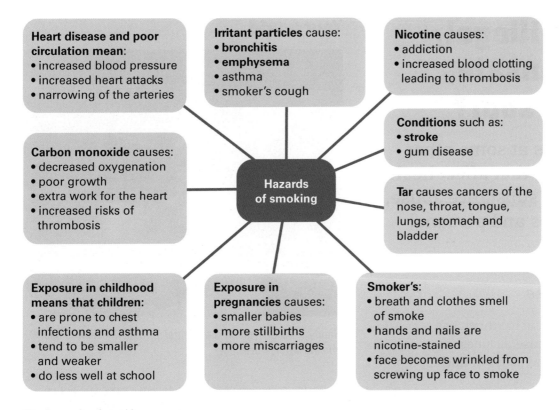

The hazards of smoking

Activity

1. Look at the risks of smoking. Draw up a table with two columns, one headed short-term risks and the other long-term risks. Put each risk in the correct column. Look at the internet to see if you can find any more.
2. Draw the outline of a person in the middle of a sheet of paper. Draw on its major organs. Label your drawing with the risks, putting each by the correct part of the body.
3. Look at the Tobacco Industry's Poster Child on www.tobaccofacts.org. What effect do you think such a poster will have on a young person?

Take it further

Use a website such as www.patient.co.uk. Divide up all the different organisations that help people stop smoking between everyone in your group, then each write to a different one asking for a set of leaflets to help with your GCSE Health and Social Care coursework.

Just checking

1. List five serious short-term effects and five serious long-term effects of smoking.
2. Describe three different ways to give up smoking. If you don't know any, look them up in a leaflet or on the internet.
3. What effect does smoking have on your blood pressure?

Legal or illegal, safe or unsafe, sweet or sour?

This topic looks at some other physical factors that affect health and wellbeing: substance abuse, sexual practices and personal hygiene.

Substance abuse

Along with smoking and too much use of alcohol, **substance abuse** includes the unsafe use of **solvents** and the taking of **illicit** or repeat-prescription drugs.

Solvent abuse	Drug abuse
Hallucinations	Anxiety
Headaches	Disorientation and depression
Liver damage	Blood infection
Lack of concentration	Heart and lung disorder
Kidney damage	Nausea, headache, giddiness
Heart failure	Raised body temperature
Suffocation	Raised blood pressure / stroke risk
Vomiting	Organ damage
	Suffocation
	Vomiting
	Mental illness

Some of the effects of solvent and drug abuse

Your world

Good personal hygiene is essential for both the service user and the service provider

Write down *everything* you have touched since you got up this morning. Now highlight all the things that other people might have touched as well as you. What will have happened to any bacteria on your hands? What are some of the possible consequences of not washing your hands regularly?

Substance abuse – the misuse or taking of substances such as drugs
Solvents – substances in which another substance is or can be dissolved, such as paint stripper
Illicit – unlawful, forbidden

Activity

1. Discuss with a partner the possible effects on health, wellbeing and future life opportunities of having an unwanted pregnancy. Think in terms of PIES. Present your conclusions on a large piece of paper.
2. Research the signs, symptoms and long-term effects of three sexually transmitted diseases.

Sexual practices

Unprotected sex can result in unwanted pregnancies and the possibility of contracting a sexually transmitted disease (STD). STDs include gonorrhoea, syphilis, HIV/AIDS, genital herpes, pubic lice and chlamydia. In the long term, diseases like these can cause mental illness, and even death.

Personal hygiene

Poor personal hygiene is not only unpleasant, but can affect your health.

Many bacteria are harmless, but some cause disease. They attack body tissue or release poisons that make you feel ill. Some examples of illnesses they cause are food poisoning, tetanus and sore throats.

Human beings are ideal for bacteria to grow in: our bodies offer the correct temperature and moistness, and provide food for them in the form of dead skin cells and in the chemicals in our sweat. Bacteria can be passed from one person to another and also in food, so it is important to reduce the number of bacteria that live on us.

When caring for others, it is often necessary to get physically close to them. If either of you have offensive body odour, it is uncomfortable and stops good communication taking place. It is also necessary to touch people, both to comfort and treat them, which is how infection can spread. Young babies or older people are less resistant to diseases and can suffer more damage from bacteria passed on in these ways.

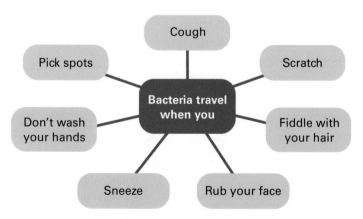

How we pass on bacteria

Think about it

If you have good personal hygiene and do not abuse solvents you will not offend others, so will not lose friends or your health. If you use safe sexual practices, you will not develop sexually transmitted diseases or have your life changed forever by an unwanted pregnancy.

Just checking

1. Name five effects of solvent abuse, and five effects of drug abuse.
2. Identify three consequences of unprotected sex.
3. Why is it important for service providers and users to have good personal hygiene?

How happy are you?

Here you will learn about some of the social, cultural and emotional factors that affect health and wellbeing.

Factors affecting your happiness

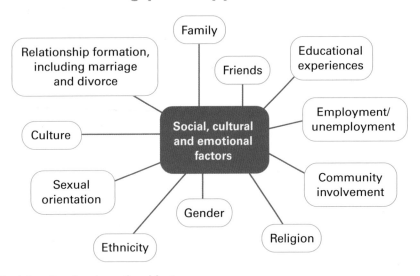

Social, cultural and emotional factors

Here we look briefly at just some of these areas. You will look at some of these factors in more detail in Unit 4.

Community involvement

Community involvement in a project – for example, raising funds to repair the church roof, planning a community use of a piece of land, or planning a street party to celebrate some local or national landmark – can improve the health and wellbeing of all those who take part. Even the local authority building, for example, new sports facilities can lead to more involvement of many of the local community in something that brings them together. Such projects might involve manual work, providing exercise (physical), and might stimulate the brain (intellectual). Being a useful part of a community can generate a feeling of happiness and wellbeing (emotional) and allow you to make new friends and relationships (social).

On the other hand, someone who is not involved in a community can become socially isolated, and their health and wellbeing will decline. One example is homeless people, who may have little choice about what they eat or what care they take of themselves because they do not have regular access to resources that meet their basic needs. Other people who can become socially isolated include older

Your world

Ben, Mike and Colin share a flat in The Green. Ben's girlfriend, Nicola, has also recently moved in. They enjoy each other's company and have a good social life. They drink in the Green Man, and know most people who live round the square to speak to. What do you think the benefits are to them of living in a community like The Green? How does this help their health and wellbeing?

Employment prospects – the chances of getting and keeping a job that pays well and has good opportunities for promotion

Activity

1. Think about a community project happening in your area. Describe the project and then identify how it will help community involvement.
2. How will such involvement improve a person's physical, intellectual, emotional and social needs?

people who are physically or mentally ill, or live alone after the death of their partner. Lack of company can lead to loneliness, depression and mental deterioration. Similarly, people can become socially isolated by illness, language or cultural difficulties, through loss of status and role in life, or through having to live alone in high-rise flats or bed-sits.

Educational experiences

Learning is something you do from birth. The amount and quality of education you receive will affect your health and wellbeing, as it will determine your choice of jobs and **employment prospects**, and so your income and standard of living. A good education will increase your status in society, make you feel good about yourself and give you a sense of security. For this reason, education is high up on Maslow's Hierarchy of Needs.

Culture and religion

The health and wellbeing of a person is influenced by the values, traditions, way of life and beliefs of the society or group into which that person is born. It is important for you to have opportunities to keep up your cultural and religious needs if you are to have positive wellbeing.

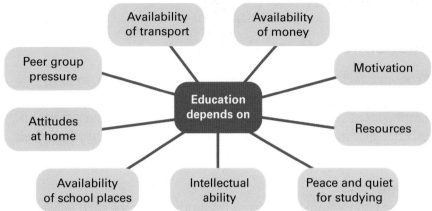

Factors that affect our education

The maintenance of cultural and religious needs

Just checking

1. List five social, cultural and emotional factors that affect health and wellbeing.

2. What is meant by community involvement, and how does it help health and wellbeing? Use three examples to support your answer.

3. Why is it important in any health and social care setting to allow people to follow and maintain their cultural and religious needs?

Can money buy happiness?

This topic looks at economic factors that affect health and wellbeing, such as income and occupation.

Economic factors

Economic factors include employment status, income, wealth, occupation, social class, poverty and material possessions. Employment is important to most adults because it gives them an income, and income has a major impact on the way they lead their life, as shown in the diagram on the next page.

Income

Income comes from earnings or from other sources such as welfare benefits, pensions and investments, and has a major impact on our **lifestyle**.

People who can afford to buy a range of healthy foods are more likely to be physically healthy and less likely to be ill, and so are able to exercise more (physical). They will also be able to afford to go to a variety of places and take part in a variety of activities, and so be less bored, and have more opportunities to learn (intellectual), to meet new people and to have a good time with their friends (social).

Another advantage is being able to afford good quality housing, with good schools to provide a quality education, and access to any other services the family needs to use. When a family has an adequate income, there will be less stress because they are not worrying about financial problems and so fewer arguments and less chance of relationships failing (emotional).

These factors therefore not only affect our health and wellbeing because they allow many of our needs to be met, but also affect our lifestyle.

Occupation

An occupation, or job, allows you to use expertise you already have and develop new skills and knowledge, which is intellectually stimulating. It not only provides your income but also gives you an opportunity to socialise and gives your days a routine, so giving you confidence and self-esteem.

The type of job we do also affects our health and wellbeing. If you are in a high-powered job, you will usually receive a salary that

Your world

Maud is recently divorced. Her ex-husband is a very successful businessman and, as part of her divorce settlement, she has kept their large Victorian house on The Green. She has plenty of money and a lovely home, but now finds herself on her own after 20 years of marriage. How will her financial position affect her health and wellbeing? How do you know this from your own experience of money so far?

Economic – to do with money
Lifestyle – a way of life or style of living that reflects the attitudes and values of a person or group

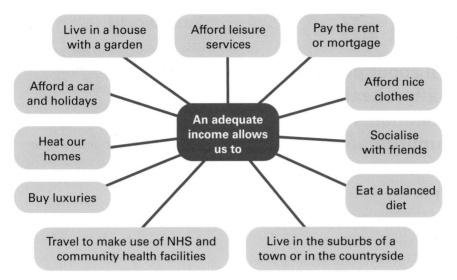

The importance of an adequate income

reflects the pressure you are under. You might become very wealthy. You might, however, find that you have a lovely home but never have enough time to spend in it, and the pressure might affect you badly and cause stress. If you have a very low-paid job, and even live in poverty, you would feel a different kind of pressure, because trying to make ends meet on a limited income is extremely stressful.

All types of work can put people under stress

Activities

1. Explain how social class (see page 128) affects health and wellbeing. To do this, you will need to research the lifestyles of people of different social classes.

2. Do you think money always makes people happy? To answer this question, research some famous people and some lottery winners.

Just checking

1. Explain how having an adequate income meets our needs.

2. What is meant by the expression 'material possessions'?

3. How can a well-paid job affect health and wellbeing, in both a good and a bad way? Explain your answer by giving an example.

Breathe that fresh air

In this topic, you will learn about physical environment factors that affect health and wellbeing. They include pollution, noise, housing conditions and rural/urban lifestyles.

Physical environment factors

The environment is everything that is around you, be it your bedroom, home, school or the area you live in, from the air you breathe to the noises you hear. Your environment has a major impact on your health and wellbeing.

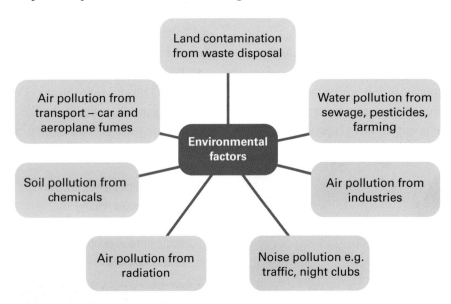

Environmental factors that affect health

Pollution

We all need clean air and water and proper waste disposal facilities, but in many cases these aren't available because of our modern way of living. Air pollution can cause and aggravate respiratory conditions and can irritate your eyes, nose and throat. Other sources of pollution are pesticides and herbicides on food, noise (such as aircraft taking off or drills) that can damage hearing, and even light. In the countryside at night you can see the stars; in the city, the lights can stop you seeing the stars.

A healthy environment can enhance your feeling of wellbeing, whereas a polluted atmosphere can make you ill (physical), stopping you going to school to learn (intellectual), making you feel low (emotional) and stopping you going out with your friends (social).

Your world

Look at the picture of The Green at the start of this book. How do you think living in an area like this will affect a person's health and wellbeing, positively and negatively? How does the area where you live affect you, positively and negatively?

Pollution – damage caused to living organisms by human activities disturbing the environment
Urban lifestyle – living in a town or city
Rural lifestyle – living in the countryside

Did you know?

The Campaign for Rural England says that, if current (2008) housing targets are to be met in the next 12 years, more than 2,250 hectares of greenfield land – including areas of land currently designated as green belt – are set to be developed for housing every year. By 2020, this would mean the loss of 27,182 hectares – an area equivalent to over 36,000 football pitches or the whole of the city of Birmingham.

Activity

Look at the two graphs.

1. Can you see any connection between the deaths from bronchitis and the distance from the city centre?
2. What is unusual about the number of deaths eight miles from the centre of the city? Can you think of a reason for this?

Hint: What comes up must come down!

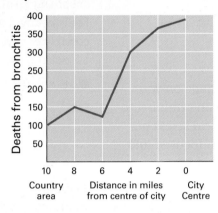

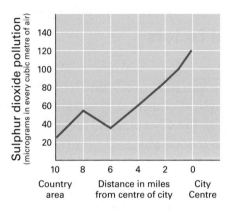

Housing

Our housing is where we spend much of our time. If a home is damp, overcrowded, cold and in the middle of a town (urban), you are more likely to become ill, with conditions such as arthritis. Overcrowding can cause infections and diseases to spread and can lead to accidents, sleeplessness and stress. Also, your health and wellbeing may suffer if, for example, you live in a high-rise apartment, with no garden space and a broken lift, so the children have nowhere to play.

On the other hand, if you live in a detached house with a garden in the suburbs or the countryside (rural), you will be able to get fresh air and exercise in the garden and sleep well (physical), so that your brain is more alert (intellectual), you feel happier (emotional) and you are less likely to fall ill, and so able to enjoy an active social life (social).

Urban/rural lifestyles

Although living in an urban environment can cause problems, some people prefer to live in a town. For example, if you are young, single and well paid, you might live in a high-quality apartment, with every modern convenience. With double or triple glazing to cut out the noise and no overcrowding, such a lifestyle might increase your feeling of wellbeing. You would be near to libraries, museums and theatres, which would enhance your intellectual life, and close to your friends, so you would always have someone to go out with. You would also be closer to work, so you would waste less time travelling, and near to all services you might need to access.

Just checking

1. Name three physical environment factors.

2. Explain how pollution can affect your health and wellbeing.

3. Describe the positive and negative effects on health and wellbeing of living in a big, comfortable farmhouse in the middle of the countryside.

No pressure then!

This topic covers psychological factors that affect health and wellbeing, such as stress, and relationships with family, friends and partners.

Psychological factors

Stress

Stress occurs when you have to respond to demands made on you, which could be physical or mental. For example, someone training to run the marathon in the Olympics will feel great physical stress on their body, but also mental stress, as they try to remain focused and determined for 26 miles. Stress causes the body to **secrete** the **hormone** adrenaline, which drives you on.

Most people suffer from stress at some time in their lives and a small amount can be good for us: for example, when you are nervous just before an exam or just before performing in public, stress makes your body respond more quickly to the demands made on it. It is stress for long periods of time, or very intense stress, that causes problems for health and wellbeing. This might be caused by a relationship breakdown, the death of someone close, being made redundant or illness.

> Dear Lindy,
>
> I have been going out with Clarissa for two years now and she wants us to get engaged. She keeps dropping hints but I don't feel ready to make such a commitment yet. The stress is making me feel ill.
>
> What should I do?
>
> Sam.

> **Secrete** – produce and discharge a substance
> **Hormone** – substance produced by one tissue and conveyed by the bloodstream to another to give activity, such as growth or metabolism

Lee Evans the comedian, sweats profusely during his act due to stress

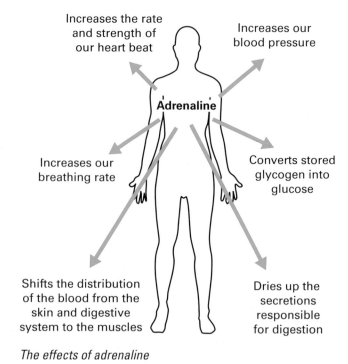

Increases the rate and strength of our heart beat

Increases our blood pressure

Adrenaline

Increases our breathing rate

Converts stored glycogen into glucose

Shifts the distribution of the blood from the skin and digestive system to the muscles

Dries up the secretions responsible for digestion

The effects of adrenaline

Short-term effects	Long-term effects
Feeling cold	Sleeplessness
Being less sensitive to pain	High blood pressure
Being more sensitive to touch	Irritability / becoming withdrawn
Tense muscles	Loss of appetite
Faster breathing	Heart disease
Dry mouth	Ulcers
Flared nostrils	Poor circulation
Wide eyes	Nerves / accidents / breakdowns
Pale face	Aching muscles
Hair on end	Body tension
Faster heartbeat	Headaches
Butterflies	Poor sex life / relationship problems
Urges to pass water	Anxiety / violent tendencies
Sweaty hands	Eczema
Diarrhoea	Asthma

The effects of stress

Relationships

Supportive relationships have a major influence on health and wellbeing.

As a child, you depend on your family very much. It is during childhood that you hopefully learn to form good relationships, building on the basics after being shown by example how to get on well with others.

As an adolescent you become much more reliant on your friends, who support you and give you confidence. With friends you can take part in activities that keep you physically fit, such as a sport, you can work together and help each other with homework, enjoy each other's company and have someone to go to different places and events with.

When you become an adult, you might become a partner, a parent, a neighbour and an employee – or even an employer. You will probably move out of your parents' home at some point into a home of your own. You will find it easier to form such relationships if you have already experienced supportive relationships.

Activity

1. Explain how supportive relationships earlier in life will help when you marry.
2. How does having supportive relationships help an adult's (a) physical (b) intellectual (c) emotional (d) social needs?
3. How will other supportive relationships help meet a person's PIES if their marriage is breaking down?

Just checking

1. List five short- and five long-term effects of stress.
2. How is stress sometimes helpful to us? Give three examples.
3. How will a lack of supportive relationships in early years affect a person's relationships later in life?

Prevention is better than cure

This topic looks at health monitoring and illness prevention services, such as screening and vaccination.

Health monitoring

Health monitoring

The aim of health monitoring is to make sure everything is as it should be and to continue to detect any problems that might arise as early as possible, to give the best chance of correcting the problem. If a problem does arise, it continues to be monitored during treatment and support is given to help the person cope with the physical, intellectual, emotional and social aspects of the problem. One example is if someone shows signs of having diabetes. Blood sugar levels will be monitored and, if diabetes develops, it is controlled either by diet and exercise, or with insulin, depending on the type.

Illness prevention services

These are services offered which aim to prevent people becoming ill. One example is the National Healthy Schools programme, which encourages schools to equip children and young people with the skills and knowledge to make informed health and life choices. It includes delivering a high standard of Personal, Social and Health Education, healthy eating, taking an active part in physical activities and enhancing emotional wellbeing through, for example, reducing the incidence of bullying. Another example is when someone with a history of breast cancer in the family decides to have her breasts removed to remove the risk of developing breast cancer herself.

Your world

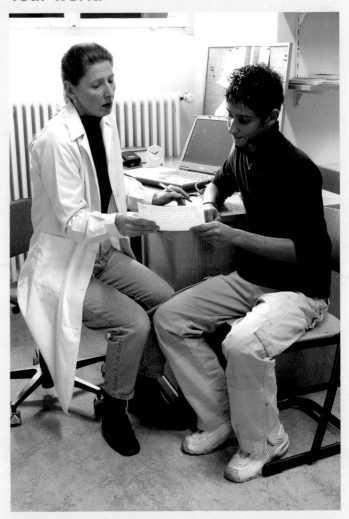

What do you do in your life to keep yourself free from illness and injury? Write down as many things as you can think of, in clouds around a stick figure of you, and then compare ideas with a partner.

Monitor – observe, record, watch closely or detect

Activity

Copy and complete the table below, by doing some research on the internet or by inviting the school nurses to come to talk to you about immunisation. The first line has been done for you.

Age group	Immunisation
Babies up to 15 months	Polio, diphtheria, tetanus, whooping cough, meningitis, measles, mumps and rubella (MMR), babies at high risk, also BCG against tuberculosis
Children aged 3 to 5 years	
Children aged 10 to 14 years	
Young people aged 13 to 18 years	
All under 25	Meningitis C for all those who were not vaccinated as babies

Screening

Health screening is a way of checking to make sure certain parts of our bodies are working well. One example of a health screening programme is the Ashton, Leigh and Wigan PCT'S Find and Treat, which aims to find people between 55 and 74 years old with high blood pressure, early diabetes and high blood cholesterol, and then to treat these conditions early. Those picked up by the scheme will also have the opportunity to discuss lifestyle issues and be referred to services that promote healthy lifestyles, including medication. Other examples include a dental check-up and screening for breast and testicular cancers.

Vaccination

Through immunisation – the administration of a weakened form of a disease, usually by injection, to help the body fight infectious disease – diseases such as tetanus, diphtheria and polio have practically disappeared in the UK. They could come back, however, so it is important that children are immunised. Practice nurses or school nurses usually do this.

Just checking

1. What do we mean by health monitoring?
2. Give three examples of health screening
3. What does immunisation involve?

Measures of health

This topic introduces the idea of **indicators** used by health practitioners to assess health and wellbeing.

Positive and negative aspects of lifestyle

You've looked at the ways in which you can tell whether someone is ill or not – but other aspects of a person's health and wellbeing are not so easily measured.

One way of assessing the positive and negative aspects of a person's lifestyle is to collect the information in a questionnaire or interview. This table shows some of the aspects you could ask about.

Positive	Negative
Balanced diet	Opposite of all positives: for example, unbalanced diet
Regular exercise	Inherited diseases and conditions
Supportive relationships	Substance abuse
Adequate financial resources	Smoking
Stimulating work	Alcohol
The use of health monitoring and illness prevention services: for example, screening and vaccination	Too much stress
Risk management to promote safety	Unprotected sex
Education	Social isolation
Leisure activities	Poverty
Enough sleep	Inadequate housing
	Unemployment
	Environmental pollution

Observation/interview

Healthcare service providers may ask a person for details of their **medical history**, at the same time taking measurements of the aspects that can actually be measured. The service provider will also gain information by observation. For example, a doctor will notice whether a patient is pale or has a heightened colour, is sweating, panting for breath, limping, behaving oddly, and so on.

Your world

Sketch as many ways as you can think of to tell whether someone is well or not. Put a tick by those you can actually measure with an instrument.

Activity

1. Draw a cartoon picture of yourself in the middle of a piece of paper as the centre of a mind map. Have branches coming off that say positive aspects, negative aspects and physical measures of health, then branches off each of those showing details about yourself. Include as much detail as possible. Your teacher may have equipment such as scales that you can use. If you don't want to write down your weight, decide whether you are underweight, average or overweight, and write that.
2. Write down what you need to change in your life and what you are willing to try to change.

Indicators – aspects of a person's health, some of which can be easily measured
Medical history – a complete description of a patient's physical and mental condition, past and present

Case study **Measures of health**

A man collapses after dancing very energetically at a wedding. He has pains in his chest, he is sweating, vomiting and groaning. He has also gone pale and his pulse is racing and erratic. An ambulance is called.

1. What aspects of his health can be measured by the paramedics when they arrive?
2. What aspects of his health can be measured once he arrives at the emergency room at the hospital?
3. What aspects cannot actually be measured but can be observed, recorded and monitored to judge his health?

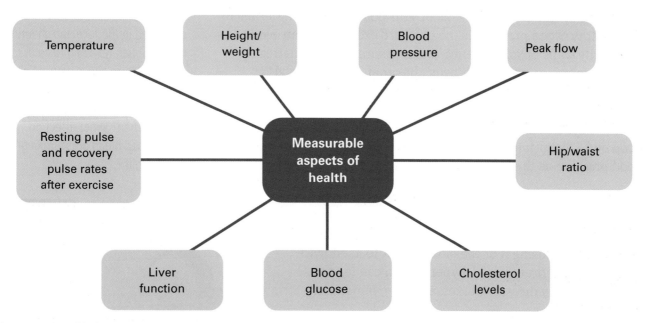

Aspects of health that can be measured

Notes/written report

The healthcare service provider will make notes of his or her observations and the answers to questions asked, then use this information to write a report if needs be, to be used by other service providers. For example, a doctor might write a report to send on to a hospital department if the person is being referred there, or might write a report on a person's mental capability to live in the community. Such a report will have recommendations as to further health assessment or treatment needed.

Just checking

1. Name five aspects of health that can actually be measured.

2. List three things a doctor might observe about a patient.

3. Why is it necessary for a service provider to collect as many details as possible of a person's medical history?

Heart and lungs

The first two health assessment measures you will learn about are to do with your heart and lungs, namely blood pressure and peak flow.

Blood pressure

Your blood provides all the organs of your body with the materials to stay healthy. Blood pressure is the pressure exerted by your blood against the walls of your arteries. It is measured in millimetres of mercury as two numbers, one 'over' the other. Healthy blood pressure varies from person to person, but normal blood pressure at rest is anything up to 140/90. The top number is the systolic pressure: the maximum pressure in the arteries as the heart pumps blood out. The bottom number is diastolic pressure: the minimum blood pressure as the heart relaxes between beats.

High blood pressure is called *hypertension*. It is a major problem that needs reducing quickly, either by removing the source of the stress causing it, or by treating either the condition causing it or the blood pressure itself with medication. If left untreated, hypertension can lead to heart and kidney disease, strokes, and even blindness.

Low blood pressure is called *hypotension* and is often normal for a particular person; in fact, it can even lead to a prolonged life. Sometimes, however, it can lead to dizziness, especially when standing up quickly, or, more seriously, can be a result of some underlying problem such as Parkinson's disease.

Peak flow

This is a measure of the maximum **rate** (the expiratory flow rate), in litres per minute, at which air is expelled from the lungs when you breathe out as hard as possible. It is measured using a peak flow meter. Blowing into it, with your lips sealed firmly round the mouthpiece, causes a pointer to move to a certain point, so you can read off your peak flow on a scale. You do this three times and take the highest reading.

The most common reason for taking and recording peak flow readings is to monitor a person's asthma to make sure it is being kept under control by the prescribed

Your world

Ahmad is a policeman. He lives with his wife Sabah and his two children, Aaron and Alina, on The Green. Aaron has just broken a window with his football playing inside the apartment and, instead of apologising, he has tried to pretend it wasn't him. Ahmad has had a stressful day at work and is cross, red in the face and shouting loudly. Sabah tells him to calm down because she is worried about his blood pressure. Why does she think about his blood pressure in this situation? What effect do you think raised blood pressure might have on him?

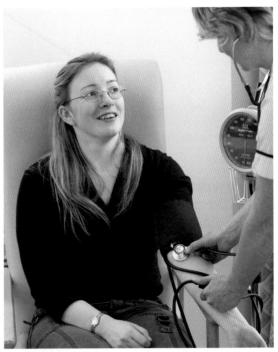

Blood pressure is measured manually or digitally using a sphygmomanometer.

Rate – measure of something compared with something else, such as litres per second
Diagnose – identify a medical condition

medication. It can also be used to **diagnose** lung problems, by comparing the reading on a chart of expected scores, based on age and gender. Someone with a lung problem has a lower score than is expected. Other conditions that cause shortness of breath are bronchitis, lung cancer, heart failure, cystic fibrosis and emphysema.

Activity

Maud has been asked by her doctor to record her peak flow reading three times a day. She is 54 and has had asthma since she was 16. She forgets, and only records it when she is feeling unwell.

1. Look at the chart shown. At what time of the day is her peak flow usually:
   • at its highest?
   • at its lowest?
2. Why is the pattern lower at the start of the period shown on the chart than at the end?

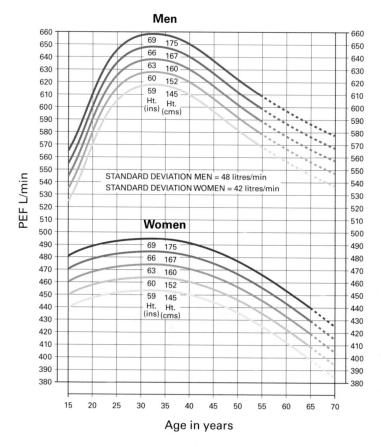

Chart showing peak flow reading against age for adults aged 15 to 70 years of age

In men values of PEF up to 100 Litres/min. less than predicted, and in women less than 85 Litres/min. less than predicted, are within normal limits.

Take it further

1. What might have made the reading so low on the evening of 7 January?
2. Why do you think her peak flows fall off a little on 15 and 16 January?
3. Do you think her peak flow will go up or down on the evening of 17 January? Explain your answer.
4. Why do you think the readings stopped on 16 January?

Just checking

1. What is systolic pressure? What is diastolic pressure?
2. What is the accepted upper limit of blood pressure? What are the names used if it is too high, and too low?
3. What are three different conditions that can be diagnosed using a peak flow meter?

Hips, bums and tums

The three measures of health you will learn about in this topic – body mass index, hip/waist ratio measurement and body fat composition – are to do with the amount of fat you have on your body.

Why measure body fat?

Someone who is severely obese is at risk of cardiovascular diseases, high blood pressure, diabetes, arthritis, stroke, and other conditions. Being very underweight is also very serious, and can be a sign of an undiagnosed illness or of eating disorders such as anorexia nervosa or bulimia nervosa.

Body mass index

This is a measure of the amount of fat in your body in relation to your height. BMI is worked out using the formula:

$$\text{BMI} = \frac{\text{Weight in kg}}{(\text{Height in m})^2}$$

People with BMIs between 19 and 22 appear to live the longest. BMIs are different for males and females, as shown in the table.

Female	Significance	Male	Significance
Less than 18	Underweight	Less than 18	Underweight
18 – 20	Lean	18 – 20	Lean
21 – 22	Average	21 – 23	Average
23 – 28	Plump	24 – 32	Plump
29 – 36	Moderately obese	32 – 40	Moderately obese
37+	Severely obese	40+	Severely obese

Hip/waist ratio measurement

Those who carry their fat around their waist and **abdomen** are more likely to suffer from the consequences of being overweight. To work out your hip/waist ratio, you divide your hip measurement by your waist measurement. This measure is a much better indicator of risk of cardiovascular disease in people over 75 than BMI, although BMI is a good indicator for younger adults.

Your world

There are now some babies who are too fat to crawl. Discuss with a partner the problems that will be facing them as they grow up to become adults. What problems do you think they will face as infants, as children and as adolescents?

Did you know?

Research suggests that people who feel constantly guilty about their fat don't lose weight – but people who focus on the positive steps they can take to exercise more do actually lose weight.

Also, having an extra 'spare tyre' around your stomach would make you hungrier. That's because stomach fat produces a potent hunger hormone, sending you signals that you are constantly hungry.

Abdomen – the part of the body that lies between the chest and the thigh

Body fat composition

The amount of fat you carry is called your body fat percentage (or composition) and affects your shape because muscle tissue is more compact than fat. If you exercise regularly, you will have a smaller body fat percentage and look slimmer than someone of the same height who doesn't exercise and so has a higher ratio of body fat.

The two most common ways of measuring it are by standing on a body fat monitor or by using a skin fold calliper to pinch at certain parts of the body – a gauge measures the thickness of the pinch. This latter method is better carried out by a professional. The average man has 15 per cent to 17 per cent body fat, while the average woman is between 18 per cent and 22 per cent. Typical values for elite athletes are 6 per cent to 12 per cent for men and 12 per cent to 20 per cent for women.

Activity

Copy and complete the table. Decide which category each person fits into.

Name	Age	Weight in kg	Height in m	BMI
Joanne	32	55	1.63	
Carmen	16	52	1.57	
Steven	15	76	1.89	
Lloyd	21	60	1.60	
James	38	94	1.70	

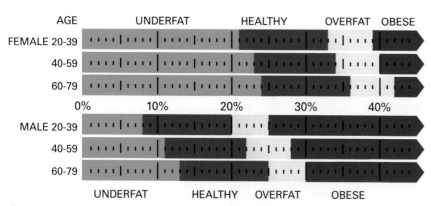

Chart showing body percentages and what they mean

Just checking

1. Why is it dangerous to be severely obese or very underweight? Explain your answer.

2. How do you work out BMI?

3. What is the significance of a male of 25 having 30 per cent body fat? What are the upper and lower limits of percentage body fat for a healthy 45-year-old female?

Testing, testing, 1, 2, 3

In this topic you look at some of the key tests that can be carried out on your blood.

Cholesterol level tests, blood glucose level tests and liver function tests are all blood tests that can be carried out at your GP's surgery. The doctor or practice nurse takes some samples of your blood, using a syringe, to be sent off for analysis and, within a couple of weeks, you will have the results.

Your world

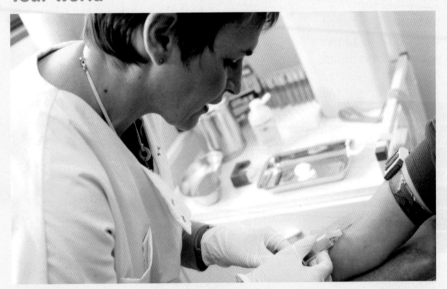

Three phials of blood are all that is needed to carry out a wide range of tests

Many adverts on television and in magazines now talk about cholesterol tests and reducing cholesterol levels. Do you know what that means? In a group, discuss whether any of you know of other tests for levels of substances in the body. You might have heard of these when you have seen medical dramas on the television, or someone in your family may have had one.

Blood tests

A variety of tests can be carried out on your blood to see that you have the correct levels of certain substances in your body, such as cholesterol, **glucose** and minerals such as sodium. Blood tests can also show whether organs such as your liver are functioning properly.

Cholesterol levels

Cholesterol is one of the body's fats (known as lipids) and is used to produce energy and hormones, and build body cells. It is made in your liver. A **fasting** blood sample is taken and cholesterol level is measured in millimoles per litre of blood, or mmol/l for short.

Activity

Beth has a cholesterol level of 7.0 and a high blood pressure. However, her proportion of good cholesterol is high. Miles has a cholesterol level of 6.8, but not as much good cholesterol and he also has high blood-sugar levels.

1. What advice would you give to each of them?
2. Why is it important to monitor the situation for both of them?

Case study **David**

David, the dentist on The Green, has just been told he has a cholesterol level of 6.7 and blood pressure of 110/76. His glucose level is normal, but his sodium is a little low. His wife, Wendy, has an even higher cholesterol level – 7.0 – blood pressure of 146/93, and a blood sugar level of 5.1. They both have healthy livers.

1. Do some research to see what causes low sodium and what foods to eat to improve cholesterol, glucose and sodium levels.
2. Plan a day's diet for both of them that will help improve all their problems.

There are two sorts of cholesterol: a good sort referred to as HDL, and a bad sort, called LDL. The more HDL you have in comparison with LDL, the lower the **cardiovascular risk**.

Cholesterol level	What does it mean? (www.netdoctor.co.uk)
Less than 5 mmol/l	Ideal level
Between 5 and 6.4 mmol/l	Mildly high
Between 6.5 and 7.8 mmol/l	Moderately high
Above 7.8 mmol/l	Very high

It is possible to have a high cholesterol level and a low cardiovascular risk if you don't smoke, have diabetes or high blood pressure, and have a high proportion of good cholesterol.

High cholesterol levels (hypercholesterolaemia) can occur because it runs in your family, your diet is high in saturated fats (such as full-fat diary produces, red meat, prawns) causing your liver to produce more bad cholesterol, lack of exercise, being overweight, age and drinking more than the recommended amount of alcohol.

Blood glucose levels

The amount of sugar in the blood is also measured in mmol/l and is normally between 4 and 8. It is higher straight after a meal and lowest in the morning. Having a high blood-sugar level can result in diabetes, eye, kidney and nerve disease and cardiovascular risk.

Liver function tests

Liver function tests measure amounts of various chemicals in the blood made by the liver. An abnormal result indicates a problem with the liver, so further tests may be needed to find the cause of the liver problem. This could include **hepatitis**, liver injury, or long-term alcohol abuse.

Glucose – a form of sugar
Fasting – not eating food and only drink water, as for the 12 hours leading up to the blood test
Cardiovascular risk – chance of developing heart disease or stroke
Hepatitis – liver **inflammation**, caused by a virus
Inflammation – redness, swelling, pain and sometimes a feeling of heat in the affected area

Did you know?

Seven out of ten people over 45 have high cholesterol.

In the UK the average total cholesterol level is 5.7 mmol/l.

Just checking

1. What is the range of cholesterol level that is moderately high?
2. Name three conditions that can be caused by a high blood-glucose level.
3. What aspect of a person's lifestyle might lead to an abnormal liver function result? What could be the cause of the problem?

A well-earned rest

Another way to measure health is to compare resting pulse rate and recovery pulse rate after exercise as this topic will explain.

Pulse rate

Every time your heart beats, it pumps blood into your **circulatory system**. These beats cause a pulse, or shock wave, that travels along the walls of the arteries. Your pulse rate is the rate (how fast) your heart is beating. It can be felt and so measured wherever an artery crosses a bone, most easily in the carotid arteries in the neck and the radial arteries in the wrist.

Pulse rate is measured by putting the tips (which are very sensitive) of two fingers on the radial pulse and counting how many beats there are in 10 seconds, and then multiplying by six to get the number of beats in one minute. This is then the pulse rate in beats per minute (bpm).

Resting pulse rate

The average resting heart rate for an adult is between 60 and 100 beats per minute, and for a well-conditioned athlete it can be between 40 and 60 beats per minute. Babies and children have faster pulse rates; a new baby's can be about 140 bpm.

It is best to measure your resting pulse rate when you are calm and have been sitting down quietly for at least five minutes. Take at least three readings and work out the average by adding them together and dividing by three.

Recovery pulse rate after exercise

Pulse rate increases during exercise and then returns to normal. If you watch an athlete running a race on television, you will notice that they can speak well enough to be interviewed straight after the race. A less fit person would find this very hard, because they would still be out of breath and panting and their pulse rate would still be high.

Measuring the pulse before and after exercise and seeing how many minutes it takes to return to normal is therefore another good way of measuring how fit you are.

Your world

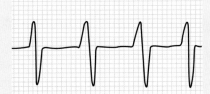

A heart beat

A typical training session for Steven, who is 50, may include 6 x 400 m sprints, with a slow jog between each one. Even after a session, his heart rate settles back to its normal pace in a couple of minutes. His sister, Liz, is 54 and is not an athlete. Any exercise leaves her out of breath and her heart rate higher than normal for at least six minutes. What do you think the dangers are for Liz?

Think about it

How do you feel after PE? What does this say about your fitness?

Activity

1. Work out your resting pulse rate. Then work out what your pulse rate after exercise should be.
2. Now run on the spot for five minutes and take your pulse rate immediately after. Take it and write it down every minute until it returns to your resting pulse rate. Write down how many minutes it takes.
3. Measure your own blood pressure, BMI, peak flow and hip/waist ratio. If your teacher hasn't got the equipment for some of this, finish the rest for next lesson, either by asking at PE or Science to see if they have what you need or by going to a chemist and asking for it to be measured.
4. What does all this tell you about your health?

A fit person will have a shorter recovery after exercise than a less fit person. The **predicted** maximum pulse rate is 220 minus your age, and the target for a healthy pulse rate during, or just after, exercise, is 60–80 per cent of this. For example, for a 22-year-old person, the predicted pulse rate is 220 – 22 = 198, 60% of 198 is 119 and 80% of 198 is 158, so his expected pulse rate after exercise is between 119 and 158 bpm. This tells you that, if you are 22, you will become fit when you reach a target pulse rate of between 119 and 158 bpm.

> **Circulatory system** – the system that moves nutrients, gases and wastes around our bodies; the main parts of the human circulatory system are the heart, blood and blood vessels
>
> **Predicted** – expected

Take it further

1. Draw a graph of time against pulse using your measurements from when you measured your recovery after exercise.
2. On the same piece of graph paper, plot your friends' measurements. What can you tell by looking at the lines on the graph?
3. Look at the table, which shows the effects of regular exercise on the circulatory and respiratory systems. What other conclusions can you draw besides the fact that regular exercise slows down your pulse rate?

	Before 6 months of regular exercise	After 6 months of regular exercise
Pulse rate (bpm)	82	67
Breathing rate (breaths per minute)	16	14
Heart volume (cm³)	126	139
Volume of blood pumped out of the heart by each beat (cm³)	63	74

Just checking

1. What causes a pulse?
2. What is the average resting pulse rate for an adult? And for an athlete?
3. Why is it good to have a short recovery after exercise?

What's the verdict?

This topic shows how to present conclusions from health and wellbeing assessments, and to make reasoned judgements from them.

Presenting assessments

Once measurements such as those covered on pages 152–9 have been made, they are collected together for assessment. In most cases these days they are collected on a computer.

It is important that all measurements and other assessments are presented clearly. For example, if a nurse handwrites something on a hospital chart in illegible handwriting, the doctor might make the wrong judgement based on the information he thinks is in front of him and might recommend the wrong course of action, such as surgery, or prescribe drugs.

It is also important that assessments made are taken and recorded accurately and precisely. If a measurement is taken carelessly and is just below the limit for a doctor to take any action, valuable time might be lost before action is taken – by which time a more serious, perhaps even life-threatening condition may have developed. For the same reason, it is important that evidence is **substantiated**: for example, someone having trouble breathing should not just have it recorded in that way, but must have a peak flow reading taken. The reading should be taken three times, and the best one should be used; the first reading taken in isolation might be inaccurate, perhaps because the person's lips were not sealed round the mouthpiece well enough.

Making reasoned judgements

The information is evidence and must be reviewed thoroughly, taking every piece of information into account. As you saw on pages 156–7, a high total cholesterol level on its own might suggest something is wrong, but once other factors, such as the percentage of good cholesterol and a history of high levels in the family, are brought into the picture, the doctor may feel there is less cardiovascular risk.

The health practitioner has to make considered judgements, based on all the facts. It is his or her responsibility to seek other opinions and to look at other sources of information if unsure, before making

Your world

Imagine you are a paramedic and you have been out for a few drinks the night before to celebrate your birthday. You drank more than you meant to and have a slight hangover. You are called to the home of a man who is complaining of chest pains. He insists he is alright now and does not want to go to hospital. You've got a headache, so you do just a couple of tests on him and because the readings are borderline, you let him persuade you that it was a false alarm. You leave him at home. He then suffers a major heart attack. How do you feel? How might his wife feel when she finds out that you didn't make him go to the hospital to be on the safe side?

Think about it

Information needs to be recorded in a way that is:

- clear
- accurate
- precise.

Can you think of any examples in your life when important information has NOT been one of these things, and this has created problems?

Activity

1. One man is average weight and another obese. Predict what BMI, peak flow, blood pressure and recovery after exercise each will have, by looking back over the information on pages 152–9. Explain why you think this.
2. Now imagine you are a doctor and you have to tell someone who is a really lovely person, always polite and cheerful, that she has developed heart disease, mainly due to her obesity. Role-play this situation with a friend.
3. Discuss with your friend how the role-play made you feel. Take it in turns telling each other what you did well and what you could have done better.

Who is fitter?

a judgement. All aspects of the patient's lifestyle have to be taken into account, such as age and lifestyle.

Presenting judgements

The health practitioner then has to make sure that the judgements reached are presented clearly and accurately, so there is no misunderstanding or misinterpretation.

This might be in the form of a written report, such as when a doctor has ordered a **biopsy** on a lump in a woman's breast, and the pathologist reports on his or her conclusions. The doctor then has to deliver the news by speaking to the patient, again clearly but, in the case of bad news, also sympathetically and with **empathy**. At the same time, he or she should not say anything that is inaccurate just to comfort the patient, as this will give false hope, making it even worse if the situation deteriorates.

> **Substantiate** – support with proof or evidence to make firm or real
> **Biopsy** – removal and examination of a sample of tissue from a human body for diagnostic purposes
> **Empathy** – identifying with and understanding another person's situation and feelings; 'putting yourself in someone else's shoes'

Just checking

1. What are three important facts about the way information should be recorded?
2. How might a health practitioner present findings and judgements? In what manner should this be done?
3. Explain what a doctor 'empathising' with a patient means – and what it should not involve.

162

Sounds like a plan

In this topic, you will learn about some of the features a health plan must have to be useful, with the focus on a group of individuals.

Health plans

Once assessments and judgements have been made, they are used to develop realistic health improvement plans for an individual or group of individuals. The best way to understand how the results of assessments are used is by looking at an example of a plan.

One such is *The NHS Improvement Plan: Putting People at the Heart of Public Services*, 2004 which sets out the NHS's priorities between 2004 and 2008. It builds on *The NHS Plan* of July 2000, in which the DoH committed to giving the NHS more money. This was for a steady increase in staff numbers, health facilities, equipment and better buildings, so people would have faster and more convenient access to care. The need for this was based on assessments of healthcare across the country.

Targets

The NHS Improvement Plan, 2004 makes some promises based on need, shown in the diagram, and then sets some **targets**, which include:

- by 2008, waiting time from GP referral to treatment will be no longer than 18 weeks
- by 2008, patients will have the right to choose any provider for treatment providing it meets clear NHS standards and does not exceed the maximum national price that the NHS is prepared to pay for such treatment
- by 2010, deaths of under 75s from heart diseases and strokes will reduce by at least 40%, and from cancers by at least 20%.

Your world

Think about your own measures of health that you collected at the end of page 159. Pick something you would like to improve. If a health practitioner were to write you a plan to help you do this, what features would you want the plan to have to help you stick to it? Collect ideas in a group to agree on the features of a perfect plan.

> **Target** – something to aim for or at
> **Review** – look at something again to improve it

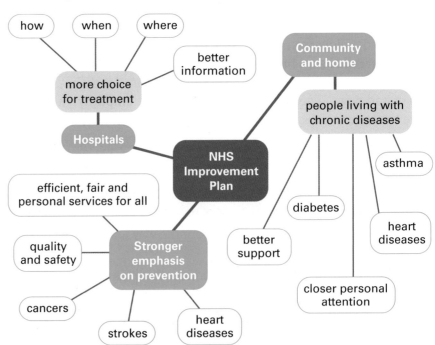

Promises made by The NHS Improvement Plan, 2004

Activities

1. Google 'Health Improvement Plans'. Read some of the plans identified to see how different Primary Care Trusts have responded to the NHS plan. Find the one for your own area and read it to find any targets they have set and the reasons for setting these targets.
2. Do some more research to find out what has actually been done in your area so far. Write a report of what your area is trying to do to meet the targets above and its progress so far.

Take it further

In a group, discuss whether or not you think it is correct that some NHS Trusts will not operate on a person unless their BMI is below a certain level or are more likely to target treatment for certain conditions to those under 75. Why do you think they have to make divisions such as this? Prepare a presentation, giving all the points for and against such an approach, and your group's conclusion.

Regional priorities

You will hopefully have seen from part 1 of the Activity that, although each area is striving to implement *The NHS Improvement Plan*, some regions have a slightly different emphasis. For example, some areas of the country have a higher proportion of incidences of illness caused by obesity, so might be directing a greater part of their efforts to reducing that problem, while other areas may have a higher proportion of patients with mental health problems, so will make that a priority.

Design of a health plan for a group of individuals

In order to draw up a plan for a group of individuals, such as the population of a region or whole country, it is necessary to:

- assess the present health status of that population
- set targets for health practitioners to meet, which will improve the situation
- provide support to help meet those targets, such as trained staff, better buildings, facilities and information
- identify any difficulties that might arise, and provide alternative strategies to meet targets to help overcome those difficulties
- monitor and **review** progress made towards meeting targets and, if necessary, set new targets as time passes.

Just checking

1. Why was *The NHS Improvement Plan* produced?
2. List three promises made by the plan.
3. List five steps in drawing up a health improvement plan for a group of individuals.

Assessment time

This topic looks at the most basic type of health plan, with the focus on assessing an individual's health and then receiving appropriate treatment for a health problem.

A basic health plan

A health and wellbeing improvement plan starts with the assessment of present health status through the use of physical measures of health and wellbeing, and the factors that affect them.

Baseline assessments

For most of the physical measures of health that you learned about in earlier topics, you were told what is normal: that is, what each should be for an average, healthy person, sometimes of a certain age. These normal measurements are called baseline measurements. By comparing a person's measures of health against these baselines, we can say whether there is a problem or not.

There might not be an illness yet, but a measurement can be a warning that, if you do not improve a certain aspect of your life, you are in danger of developing one. For example, high blood pressure, if allowed to continue, can lead to cardiovascular diseases and strokes, but decreasing weight or stress or alcohol intake, stopping smoking or something as simple as cutting out salt in your food can reduce the blood pressure, and so the risk.

However, there might be an illness. Normal body temperature is 37 degrees centigrade, and a raised temperature can indicate an infection.

A person's normal health

Some people live with chronic illnesses that are lifelong, such as asthma or diabetes. When such a condition is first diagnosed, they might feel shock and anger because at the time they feel ill and their normal activities are curtailed. They then come to understand that it can be, and needs to be, controlled. For example, ignoring diabetes can lead to consequences such as blindness, kidney diseases and strokes.

Once the condition has been diagnosed and controlled with drugs, they live a balanced, healthy life. Olympic gold medallist Sir Steven Redgrave thought his rowing career was over when he was diagnosed with diabetes but, by managing his condition, he went on to win

Your world

Look back at the mind map you constructed on page 150. Add anything that you missed then. It should include your weight, height, blood pressure, peak flow, pulse rate, recovery after exercise and BMI, as measured earlier in this Unit. Add words by each to say what it means: for example, normal weight. Also add positive and negative factors of your lifestyle. What does this information tell you about:

- your attitude to health?
- your short-term health?
- your long-term health?

Think about it

You have been learning about this since page 150. Before reading on, why not take a look back at these Topics, and see how much you can remember?

Did you know?

Other celebrities who live with lifelong conditions include musician Martin Kemp, who has had epilepsy since having two brain tumours in the 1990s. Comedian Rik Mayall has also had the condition since falling into a coma for five days after a quad bike accident in 1998. Another famous person with the condition is the musician Neil Young.

another gold medal four years later. It is only if there is a change in the condition that there is cause for concern and the need for medical intervention.

Sir Steven Redgrave, winner of five Olympic gold medals

Treatment

Once someone has been diagnosed with a condition, a course of action – or a plan – has to be agreed on. This might involve:

- no treatment: some conditions cannot be treated, such as 'flu, which is caused by a **virus**, so the symptoms such as headaches are treated with pain-relief tablets and the patient rests until the virus is gone
- pharmaceutical treatment: some conditions are treated with drugs, either bought over the counter from a **pharmacist** or prescribed by your doctor
- complementary medicine: these complement or run alongside rather than replace medical treatment, and include acupuncture, reflexology and hydrotherapy
- lifestyle changes, such as those mentioned earlier in this topic to reduce blood pressure
- therapy: examples include **therapeutic** exercise for a back condition with a **physiotherapist**, and occupational therapy, where a stroke victim is taught to do everyday things with a disability
- surgery: some conditions, such as appendicitis, require an operation.

Whichever of these is decided on, the condition is monitored until it is either controlled, needs further treatment or is cured.

Activity

Do some research into complementary medicine. In a group, produce an information pack for someone who has never used such treatments before.

Virus – a microscopic particle that infects the cells of living things
Pharmacist – a healthcare practitioner who specialises in drugs and medicines
Therapeutic – relating to the beneficial consequences of a medical treatment of any kind
Physiotherapist – a healthcare practitioner who treats physical problems caused by illness, ageing and accidents

Just checking

1. Explain two things it can mean if you have a measure of health that is different from the norm.
2. What can happen if you ignore a lifelong condition?
3. Name three different types of treatment and give examples to show that you understand what each means.

Read all about it

Another part of a health and wellbeing improvement plan is the use of appropriate health promotion materials to motivate and support people in following the plan. This topic looks at a range of such material.

Health promotion materials

Health **promotion** materials provide advice, information and support with the aim of helping people to take more responsibility for their own health. These materials come in many forms, including leaflets, articles on the internet, books, posters, DVDs, podcasts and **campaigns** on the television.

Getting the message across

Materials like this need to be carefully thought through and presented if they are to achieve what they are trying to do – but how do people do this? If you were going to produce health promotion materials, here are some factors you should consider.

- **Suitable for the target group**: if a leaflet is designed to encourage children under the age of 10 to clean their teeth regularly, it must have words that they can read and understand and have lots of colourful pictures, with children or animals in, to keep their interest.
- **Easy to understand**: people will lose interest in information delivered using lots of long words, jargon and medical terms.
- **Attractive**: someone is more likely to read something if it is presented in colour, with pictures and diagrams, and with key words or phone numbers standing out and on their own so they are easy to pick out.
- **Easy to read**: information written in a small point size (the size of the letters) or in a fancy font (the style of the letters) will not be accessible to those who do not have perfect eyesight, and will look like too much hard work to read even to those with 20:20 vision.
- **Attention grabbing**: for example, a television campaign to stop someone smoking has more impact and is more memorable if it has shock value, such as one that shows a child upset because her father is dying of lung cancer, and then shows the father breathing with great difficulty using an oxygen cylinder.
- **In your face**: every box of cigarettes has a Government health warning printed clearly and boldly on it.

Your world

With a partner, compile a mind map showing as many different ways you can think of that people receive information and advice on risks to health and how to remain healthy. Which method do you each personally find most effective? Would you expect others in your group to feel the same as you? Why do you think this? Check with your group!

Promotion – giving out information about something, with the aim of getting people to join in, take up an offer or change their views

Campaign – an organised effort to achieve something

Did you know?

Eyesight groups (such as the RNIB) and groups for older people (such as Age Concern) recommend a minimum point size of 12 pt for printed information, and preferably 14 pt. Find an example of 12 pt type so you can see what it looks like.

- **Informative by giving the required information**: a person suffering from a particular condition will want to be able to access information about that condition easily, in a leaflet on just that condition, rather than have to read through a general medical book. They will also want useful information, such as contact numbers.
- **Entertaining**: this is to grab the attention of someone who would not otherwise engage with the material, such as the 'Some of our bits ain't nice' leaflet, which is about personal hygiene and has amusing cartoons in it. These cartoon characters come to life in the video that is also available.
- **Available in a variety of languages**: this is necessary in our multicultural society, so that all can access the information they need.
- **Available in many forms**: on leaflets and on CDs with signing for those who have a hearing impairment, and in Braille or on audio tapes for those who are visually impaired.

Sources of information

In the 1950s, all health information came from health practitioners and books. Nowadays, there are health promotion materials everywhere, in places such as the doctors, dentists, opticians, hospitals, libraries – and even in supermarkets, about healthy, balanced diets. By having information so readily available, more people will be encouraged to help themselves, rather than relying on health practitioners.

One good example is the wealth of material available on how to give up smoking. Some people are more likely to pick up a leaflet or watch an advert, than make an appointment to go to the doctors: by having the material at hand, they may decide to have a go themselves, or join a support group.

Activity

1. Think about all the pieces of health promotion you remember on television or at the cinema. In a group, plan your own health promotion video for an aspect of health of your choosing.
2. Role-play your video to the other groups in your class. When each group has performed discuss which one was the best, which was less useful, and why.

A selection of health promotion materials

Just checking

1. Why do children need leaflets aimed specifically at their age group?
2. What sorts of health promotion information would someone who is short-sighted find useful?
3. What help has having so much health information available and readily accessible been to people?

Setting your sights

This topic looks at the setting of short- and long-term targets in a health and wellbeing improvement plan.

Your world

Think about a New Year's resolution you have made and kept, and another you have failed with. Then think about something hard you have tried to do. What made it easier to succeed? Explain your answer.

Targets

SMART

When drawing up a plan to improve health and wellbeing, it is important to include **targets**, not only to motivate the person following the plan but also so that progress made can be monitored.

Targets have to be **SMART**:

- **S**pecific: the target must be clearly stated, saying exactly what you mean, such as lose two kg in weight in one week. This is clear and cannot be misunderstood or used as excuse.
- **M**easurable: it is too vague to say lose weight: an amount must be stated, so that you can prove that you have met the target.
- **A**chievable: the person must feel it is possible to achieve the target set, otherwise they will give up. Asking someone to lose one stone in a week is not achievable, but losing two kg is reasonable.
- **R**ealistic: the target set must be realistic – you must be able to do it. It is unrealistic to expect someone who is older and not very fit to run for 30 minutes a day to aid weight loss, but it is realistic to ask the same of a fit, younger person.
- **T**ime-related: there should be a deadline set by which to reach a target, so that progress can be assessed: for example, by the end of the month.

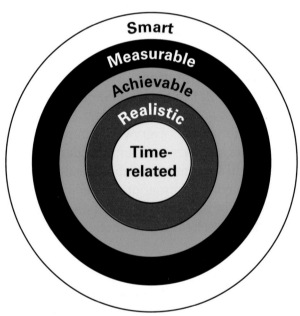

Targets must be SMART

Short- and long-term targets

As well as having a long-term target, it is important that a plan includes short-term targets too. The long-term target might be to lose five kilos in six months, but this can seem a long way off, with a lot of weight to lose – and it is easy to say that you will start the diet next week, and put it off. However, if you set a short-term target of losing one kg in a week, this is easy to think of doing, as it is only a short time and not a major thing to achieve. By breaking down the path to your final goal into these smaller steps, the task seems less daunting – and there is no excuse not to start that week!

Activity

Julie, the dental hygienist, smokes 20 cigarettes a day. She wants to give up. Design a plan to help her give up, applying what you have learned about target setting in this and previous topics.

Monitoring targets

Targets need to be monitored. You could do this yourself by, for example, writing down everything you eat and drink each day to look at any mistakes you are making with your diet. Alternatively, a health practitioner or a support group could be involved. Someone trying to lose weight might find it easier going to be weighed at the health centre, or at a slimming club, each week. Knowing someone else is going to know how you are doing can motivate you more, because you don't want to be seen to fail. At the same time, you'll know that other people are trying to do the same as you, so are also suffering.

Reviewing targets

By setting SMART targets, you can monitor progress regularly and amend your plan if necessary to meet your longer-term targets and **goals**.

Designing a plan for others is complicated, because you are asking them to change how they do something they have often enjoyed doing, perhaps something about their lifestyle. People might not manage to change straight away, so might fail to reach a particular target or their final goal, so it will be necessary to review the targets and even start all over again.

If a target is not being met, it is sometimes necessary to see if a different target will improve the chance of success. This may happen several times until someone succeeds in making the lifestyle change permanent: for example, someone who is overweight might start many diets before they manage to get to, and stay at, their goal weight.

Targets – short- and longer-term challenges to help you meet your goal
Goals – what you want to achieve in the long term; the final target

Think about it

If a teacher tells you that you have a year to design and make something in DT, what is likely to happen? You will probably do a bit each week, chatting away to your friends, and then end up rushing it all at the end and not doing a very good job. How would breaking it down into chunks, with a deadline to complete each part, help you?

Just checking

1. What does the phrase 'SMART targets' mean?
2. What is the difference between a target and a goal?
3. Why is it necessary to monitor and review targets?

That could be a problem

In this topic, you will look at possible difficulties in implementing a health and wellbeing improvement plan, and the features any good health and wellbeing improvement plan should have.

Your world

Enrico has decided to reduce his drinking as he drinks every night to relax when the restaurant closes. What difficulties does Enrico face in trying to do this? How can he overcome these difficulties? Do you or any of your friends ever binge drink? What problems are to be faced in stopping and how can they be overcome?

To drink or not to drink?

Difficulties

The final important factor in designing a health and wellbeing improvement plan is to assess the difficulties the person may face in trying to put the plan into action. What could stop them? What obstacles might they face? And how can you help them overcome these?

Getting started

Sometimes people make up excuses to put off starting on a health improvement plan. For example, they might not start a diet today because they say they haven't got the correct food in the house, don't really want to because they love food too much, are frightened of failing – or just feel it is too big a problem to tackle. For example, if a person is ten kilos overweight, that would seem a big mountain to climb, so they might just eat something else for comfort instead!

It can help to remind people of the positive benefits of the plan. If you tell them that their blood pressure will go down, so they will be less likely to suffer heart disease, their joints will ache less, and they will look much better too, they might feel more motivated. For this reason, it is important that you highlight the benefits of each part in a health and wellbeing improvement plan.

Knowing how to reach a target

Another difficulty is when someone does not know how to achieve a target, so you can suggest ways that they could do so. For example, as well as saying 'lose so many kilos in week 1', you could provide the person with a completely balanced, low-calorie and low-fat diet plan for a week. If someone is going to give up smoking, you could suggest they try nicotine patches.

Strategies not likely to work

Despite suggesting strategies, they might not work. For example, you may have included several items in the diet plan that the person doesn't like, or the person may have an allergic reaction to the sticky stuff on the nicotine patches. A good health plan will therefore include **alternative** strategies.

Lack of motivation

Sometimes the person might get bored and give up. This can be overcome not only by reminding them about the benefits or by providing more varied strategies, but also by building in rewards. For example, suggest to a person on a diet that they save any money they would have spent on takeaways and other fattening foods and use it to buy a new item of smaller-size clothing when they have lost their first five kilos.

Maintaining the change

Once a person has reached their goal, they may become **complacent** and fall back into old habits. Your plan should suggest ways to stop this happening, including targets to maintain the change.

Features of a plan

In order to be clear, compelling and likely to succeed, a good health and wellbeing improvement plan will have certain features.

- A statement of the problem to be tackled, based on the assessment of present health status through the use of physical measures of health and wellbeing and the factors that affect this
- SMART targets
- Short- and long-term targets
- Benefits of meeting targets
- Strategies to meet targets, including health promotion materials
- Alternative strategies to overcome any difficulties which may arise
- Regular monitoring and reviewing of targets
- Strategies to maintain improvement in health and wellbeing

Case study **Enrico**

Enrico has tried to reduce his drinking, but has not been successful. Draw up a health plan to help him. He drinks at least five units of alcohol in the restaurant every night, and even more on his night off. He is overweight, has high blood pressure and does not get enough exercise.

Draw up a plan to help him over the next year, maybe in the form of a table, with all the features in the list. Include some relevant health promotion materials to go with it.

Alternative – a different way of achieving the same thing
Complacent – satisfied with things as they are

Just checking

1. Name three difficulties that a person following a health and wellbeing improvement plan may face.

2. Explain how the three difficulties in question 1 can be overcome.

3. List five features of a good health and wellbeing improvement plan, and give an example for each.

Lean on me

This last topic of Unit 3 looks at the support available in implementing a health and wellbeing improvement plan, and the factors affecting its overall success.

Types of support

Informal support

Informal support is not paid for and is provided by family, friends and neighbours. If, for example, you were trying to lose weight you could ask them not to give you any gifts of chocolate at Christmas, to cook low-fat meals if you go to their house to eat, or to make sure they encourage you to stick to your diet when you are out shopping or for a meal.

Formal support

This is provided by health and social care practitioners who are professional carers. You might need this if you have no family nearby or you need more specialist help.

You might pay for this support. For example, you could pay to join a support group such as a slimming club, or to have hypnotherapy to help you give up smoking. You might receive help free: for example, your doctor might refer you to a dietician to help you stick to a weight-loss plan, or to a counsellor to help with a stress-reduction plan.

You have learned about some of the different health and social care practitioners you could call on for help in Unit 1 (see pages 50–51).

Voluntary and faith-based services

Voluntary services are organised by people who often give their services for nothing. There are voluntary support groups for most serious or chronic illnesses. For example, someone with diabetes could approach Diabetes UK, which is a charity, for help with sticking to a health plan to control his or her diabetes, when first diagnosed. Faith-based services support people of their own faith (as well as others) and might include a local church group that organises lots of different physically active activities, which a young person could benefit from if following a plan to become fitter.

Other support

You have learned about supporting yourself to meet targets by looking at information provided though health promotion materials, on pages 66–67. Support can also come in the form of prescribed

Case study **Rashid**

Rashid has had a fall and badly broken his ankle so now he cannot get out and about for at least two months, either to the gym or the shops. He really needs to lose some weight ready for an operation he is having in three months' time.

1. How can he use the various forms of support available to help him do this?
2. What is likely to happen if he doesn't use any support?

drugs, complementary medicines and practical aids, such as dummy cigarettes.

Factors affecting the success of a plan

There is one key factor in the success of any health and wellbeing improvement plan: the person for whom you have designed a health plan has to want to follow it.

This is far more likely if the person has been involved in its design from the start. If this is the case, they are more likely to use the support suggested to help them succeed too.

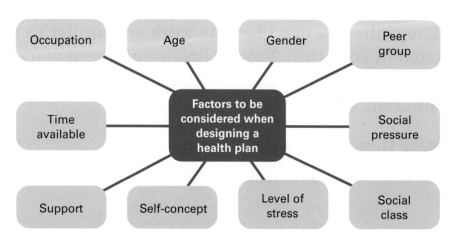

Factors that affect the success of a health and wellbeing improvement plan

To do this, you as a health practitioner would have to:

- discuss the health issue with the person to build a relationship with them
- discuss different options to tackle the issue
- **K**eep **I**t **S**imple and **S**traightforward (the KISS rule) – don't use lots of jargon or medical words that the person does not understand
- decide together which options are to be followed
- explain how they can access support
- draw up the plan so it is as clear and straightforward to follow as possible.

When designing a plan, you need to remember certain factors that will affect the person's ability to carry it out: for example, you would not give the same exercise plan to a 20-year-old, slightly overweight person and a 70-year-old, slim person. The various factors you should take into consideration are shown in the diagram.

Just checking

1. Name three different types of support. For each one, give three examples.

2. What is the KISS rule? Why is this important when discussing a health and wellbeing improvement plan?

3. Explain five factors that could affect the successful implementation of a plan.

Assessment for Unit 3

Welcome

Are you looking forward to completing your second piece of assignment assessment work in Health and Social Care? Having completed one piece of work you should be able to build on the techniques you already know.

The skills you need for this work are similar to those you have already used in your Unit 2 controlled assessment work. However, the tasks for Unit 3 are different, so the skills you use will be applied in a slightly different way.

How Unit 3 is assessed

Key things you need to know

- You will write a report for this piece of assessment.
- The task/s involved in the report will be set by Edexcel, your examination board.
- The report will be based on an investigation into the needs of one service user and how these needs are met.
- The report has to be written up over a 22.5 hour period of classroom-based work and is marked out of 50.
- The report will be written under controlled conditions. This may be completed in different ways. Your teacher will give you information about how this will be done in your school or college.
- You will be able to bring both the primary and secondary data you have collected to help you complete the tasks set.
- All written work, calculations and graphs must be completed in the lesson and supervised by your teacher.

What you will need to do

You will receive an Edexcel instruction sheet that sets the tasks to complete. These will require you to produce evidence, which will be assessed by your teacher against a mark grid.

You will need to show:

- knowledge and understanding
- the ability to plan and carry out investigations
- analyse and evaluate information
- draw conclusions and make reasoned judgements.

Top tips for preparing

- Read the pre-release material very carefully and select the individual/s you wish to focus your study on.
- Make sure you have a good understanding of the different definitions of health and wellbeing.
- Practice completing a range of health measure calculations so that you can do them under controlled conditions. You might even do the calculations on the data given as pre-release material, so you are familiar with them. In the write-up under controlled conditions you will have to do them yourself, without any teacher support.
- Look carefully at what the results of the calculations tell you about the individual's health and wellbeing as well as at any other background information that may be relevant. Many students just state the results but do not explain what these results show.
- Design a health plan based around the assessments you have made. If the information clearly points to the person having a weight problem and this is the main health issue, your health plan should focus on dealing with this. Often a student's plan will focus on something else, which isn't such a big issue.
- Collect a folder of information you will need to use in the writing up of your work in the classroom: for example, leaflets about health issues, types of support available, etc.
- Decide on how much time you are going to spend on the tasks set. Remember: you have twenty-two and a half hours. You do not want to spend fifteen of these hours on a task that only covers a small part of the evidence.

In addition the quality of your written work will also be assessed.

The sort of tasks that might be included as part of your report could be:

- defining health and wellbeing
- the factors which affect health and wellbeing
- the effect of the factors which affect health and wellbeing on a particular individual
- using the health methods and calculations to assess the health and wellbeing of an individual
- producing a health plan for an individual based on health assessment
- considering ways to promote and support the health improvement of an individual.

What is it?

One of the earliest tasks you are likely to be asked in the controlled assessment is to show that you understand the meaning of 'health and wellbeing'.

- Explain what you understand by the phrase 'health and wellbeing'.
- Use your textbook to help you understand the different issues involved in defining what health and wellbeing is.

Just checking

1. How many hours will you have to write up this report?
2. Explain why it is important to select carefully which person to focus your work on from the pre-release material.
3. Why is organisation and planning so important in completing this report?

How to approach pre-release material and use health measures accurately

Before you start your piece of work, Edexcel will give you a pre-release document. It is important that you get a good, thorough understanding of this background information, as all your work will be based on this.

You will probably have to select information based on one person from a number of people given in the material. Make sure you select the person you are most interested in. Your teacher may decide that the whole class is going to base the work round just one of the people, which is fine.

Example of pre-release material

Below is an example of a section of pre-release material, containing the general background and information about one person (in the real material, there were four people's information and data to select from).

We will spend some time here working from this pre-release material. We will look at the issues it raises and how it might help you be better prepared for the tasks in your controlled assessment work. Read the following sections carefully.

Activity

Produce a health plan for improving or maintaining the physical health and wellbeing for Andreas. This plan must include:

- an explanation of what is meant by health and wellbeing
- identification and explanation of the factors that affect the health and wellbeing of the selected person
- assessment of the current health and wellbeing status of the person selected
- the design of a health improvement plan, including short- and long-term targets
- an assessment of the difficulties the person may face in implementing the plan
- details of the support the person may be able to access to help implement the plan.

Background information

Beech Primary Care Centre

Beech Primary Care Centre provides healthcare for a large urban area in London. The centre provides general healthcare but also focuses on early intervention and prevention of ill health. The centre has a range of staff working together to meet the needs of a range of people. The staff at the centre include GPs, nurses, dentists, midwives, dieticians, physiotherapists, counsellors, reception staff and managers.

A range of services are offered alongside general healthcare. These include smoking cessation, sexual health clinics, dietary and weight advice, and regular clinics for a range of issues such as asthma and diabetes.

After an initial consultation with a service user, the health centre collects a range of data so that health plans can be developed to meet the needs of that service user. This includes:
- height and weight
- blood pressure
- pulse rates, both resting and after exercise
- information about lifestyle choices such as smoking, alcohol consumption and levels of stress the service user feels they are under.

The centre often refers service users to the local fitness centre, which has a full fitness suite, a swimming pool and a range of fitness classes on offer.

Background information

Andreas Costa

One service user is Andreas Costa. Andreas is a happily married man with three children. He has never enjoyed exercise and does not currently exercise. Andreas loves to spend time with his family and they eat fast food seven days a week. He has an office job and has a regular drink on the way home from work. On Friday and Saturday, Andreas spends time with his friends at the pub and drinks heavily. Andreas has recently been diagnosed as having diabetes and high cholesterol. His family has a history of heart disease.

Here is the health information the centre has gathered about Andreas.

- Age: 35 years
- Height: 1.78m
- Weight: 83.5kg
- Average peak flow: 350 1/min
- Resting pulse rate: 90 BPM
- Blood pressure: 160/95 mmHg

Using background information

- It is important to look at the information you have been given in the pre-release material. The clues as to what you have to do in the tasks set are often there – it is just a matter of drawing them out.
- Your teacher may choose to go through the pre-release material with you before you complete the controlled assessment task. If not, you need to do this yourself so that you will know what you have to do during the write-up period.
- You might also wish to practice your calculations before the controlled assessment, though you will have to do this yourself during the controlled assessment and you will not be able to take the completed calculations into the controlled assessment.
- You will need to practice understanding the significance of the health data you have been given, and of the calculations you complete yourself. If your BMI calculations show that the person is obese and they eat only fast food, there is a connection here. You can then think about how you might tackle this issue in the health plan you design.

> **Just checking**
>
> 1. Explain why is it important to read the background information with real care.
>
> 2. Explain why the health plan you design for a person may be inaccurate if you do not read the information and plan carefully.
>
> 3. Why it is important to make connections between the factors affecting a person's health and wellbeing and their current health status?

Note: You may need to refer back to earlier parts of this unit in the book.

1. Read the information about Beech Primary Care Centre carefully. What sort of services does it offer?
2. Read the information about Andreas again. What aspects of his life current lifestyle are a cause of concern?
3. Look at the data about Andreas's current health status. Calculate his current BMI.
4. What do Andreas's average peak flow, resting pulse rate and blood pressure tell us about his current health status?
5. What connections can you make between his current life style and health status?

Note: You may be asked to work on these tasks as a whole class, with a partner, or separately.

Student work and how to present evidence

Here we are going to consider some sections of the pre-release tasks that were presented to you earlier in this section. (You may wish to refresh yourself about the background information you were given).

We will consider how students presented their work and you will be given the opportunity to:

- assess the strengths and weaknesses of some student work
- complete some sections which have been started by other students
- attempt some sections of work yourself.

This will give you the opportunity to consider how you might structure your own work and practice writing at the appropriate level to achieve a high mark for this unit.

One section of the pre-release tasks

'Identify and explain the factors that affect the health and wellbeing of Andreas.'

Here are examples of how two students started their answers to this task, looking at one of the factors they identified.

Student A

There are a lot of things affecting Andreas's health and wellbeing. He is overweight and eats too much fast food. He has got diabetes and high cholesterol. He does not exercise. Exercise is really important to being healthy. It can keep your weight down and makes you fitter. There are many ways of exercising:

- swimming
- running
- going to the gym
- playing tennis
- playing golf

Andreas does not exercise and this is not good. Perhaps he should take up a sport and meet some new people rather than spending all his time in the pub.

Which is better?

With a partner, look at the two students' answers.

- Decide which you think is the better piece of work.
- Identify three ways in which this piece of work is better than the other.

What the examiners thought

This student has managed to identify some of the factors affecting the health and wellbeing of Andreas. Other factors have been missed. The factors identified are all related to physical health, and we assume that the student does not understand 'holistic' definitions of health and wellbeing. There is little development of the factors identified and they are presented almost as a list.

The student then goes on to consider exercise. There are some comments on the types of exercise people can take, but no real depth as to the value of exercise for Andreas. The student does, however, state that not exercising is not good for Andreas. The student also makes the positive point that exercising could provide the opportunity to meet new people.

If we assume that the student continues to write about the other factors identified in the same way, the final work will be at a fairly simple level.

Student B

We can see from the background information that Andreas is not as healthy as he might be. The lifestyle he has is having an effect on his health and wellbeing. By this I don't just mean his physical health, but also his intellectual, emotional and social health. Andreas needs to look carefully at the type of lifestyle he leads.

There are a number of factors affecting Andreas's health and wellbeing at present:

- The diet he has. Andreas eats a lot of fast foods, which are not usually healthy.
- He drinks every day, and heavily at weekends. This is not good for his health at all.
- Diabetes. This needs to be considered very carefully if he is to remain in good health.
- A history of heart disease in the family.
- Lack of exercise, which is not good. Andreas needs to keep fit if he is to control his weight and reduce the risk of heart disease.
- Having an office job, which means he burns very few calories during the day.
- A good social life. This is positive as we all need friends and it may make him handle the stress of work really well.
- A happy family life. This is important emotionally for Andreas as he probably gets a lot of pleasure from his wife and children.

There are many factors that affect Andreas's health and wellbeing. I am now going to explore some of these in more depth and look at how they will be affecting his health.

The sort of diet a person has is important to their health and wellbeing. Obesity is becoming one of the major problems in our society and to avoid this it is important to eat a balanced diet. A balanced diet consists of eating the correct proportions of different nutrients (protein, carbohydrates, fats, vitamins, minerals). These are found in different types of foods and drinks. It is important that people eat the correct proportions of different foods to give their bodies the right balance to work effectively.

Andreas does not appear to eat a balanced diet and eats a lot of fast foods, which are likely to contain a lot of fats and additives. As we can see, Andreas is overweight and needs to look at his diet in more depth.

The student continued to write about the various food groups, relating these to Andreas.

Just checking

1. Explain why is it important to structure your work clearly if you are to produce a good piece of work.

2. How does the background information help you decide which factors you need to write about in more depth?

3. Explain why it is important to apply the information on the factors you write about to the person your work is based on.

Carry on!

1. Read Student B's work again. Continue the work, and complete the section on diet.

2. Complete two more sections, explaining the effect of factors on Andreas's health and wellbeing. Select from the following list of factors:
   - exercise
   - a good social life
   - alcohol
   - office job
   - a happy family life.

What the examiners thought

This student has clearly read and understood the background material. They have identified a full range of factors affecting the health and wellbeing of Andreas. From the factors identified, the student shows a good understanding of the wider meaning of 'holistic' health. The student starts the work off clearly and the work is set out logically. The student looks at diet first. The evidence shows that this has been started really well and the information presented so far does not show any obvious errors. If the student continued to write in this way, the final work is likely to be of a high standard.

Unit 4: Health, Social Care and Early Years in Practice

Learning objectives

- The range of care needs of major client groups
- The care values commonly used in practitioner work
- The development of self-concept and personal relationships
- Promoting and supporting health improvement

Introduction

In this unit, you will further develop your knowledge and understanding of the core principles that underlie the work of health, social care and early years practitioners.

Very important point

This unit is **synoptic**. That means you will be developing some of the things that have been covered in the other three units in more detail. It is important, therefore, to go back and refresh your memory by reading topics earlier in the book when you are told to.

The range of care needs of major client groups

In Unit 2, you learned about the care needs of each of the major client groups. In this unit, you will look at the basic needs of all humans, as well as how life course events and lifestyle choices affect human growth and development and PIES. These events may be expected, such as starting school, or unexpected, such as a serious illness.

The care values commonly used in practitioner work

In Unit 2, you also learned about the care values commonly used in practitioner work. This unit revisits this, with more **emphasis** on

Your world

How would I expect to be treated?

Think about the units you have studied so far. What are the three most important things *you* have learnt about how people expect to be treated when being looked after? You are only allowed to pick three! Now compare your three with those of other members of your group. Is there much difference between them? Now you as a group must decide, by voting if needs be, which the group consider to be the most important overall.

how practitioners use them in their day-to-day work, interacting with service users. It also looks at the possible consequences if care values were not to be implemented by practitioners.

The development of self-concept and personal relationships

Unit 1 covered self-concept and personal relationships, although relationships have been included in Units 2 and 3 as well. In this unit, you will look at the factors affecting self-concept, such as age, appearance, gender and sexual orientation, and how self-concept is linked to personal relationships. You will also learn about how care practitioners can build and influence the self-esteem and self-concept of service users through their work.

Promoting and supporting health improvement

The final part of this unit looks at different ways health practitioners can support service users to change their lifestyles, and covers both the positive and negative effects of lifestyle choices. It also looks in more detail at the aims, approaches, and support for individuals, of health promotion, and how that relates to the implementation of the care values.

> **Synoptic** – presenting a summary of the main parts or a general view of the whole qualification
> **Emphasis** – special attention
> **Structured** – having a well-defined structure or organisation; highly organised
> **Case study** – a detailed analysis of a person or group
> **Scenario** – an outline of an event or situation
> **Compulsory** – no choice; required; must do

How you will be assessed

You will sit an externally marked examination paper, which will last 75 minutes. The paper will consist of a series of **structured** questions based on **case studies** and short **scenarios** requiring short and extended answers.

All the questions in the examination paper are **compulsory**, and will give you the opportunity to show examiners what you know.

Needs

This topic looks at the range of care needs of the major client groups.

Infancy

- **Physical**: Newborn babies are completely dependent on their parents or carers to protect them from harm, feed them, make sure they get enough rest and keep them warm and clean.
- **Intellectual**: Infants depend on their parents and carers to stimulate them with words, toys and books.
- **Emotional**: Bonding with parents or carers in the first year of life, through being loved and encouraged, creates a safe and stable relationship enabling the person to make effective relationships later in life.
- **Social**: Parents or carers who help an infant develop routines and meet other people, and encourage them to play with others, are building the foundations for the infant to know how to behave to get on well with others in later life stages.

Childhood

- **Physical**: Children need to be provided with opportunities to learn new physical skills and improve existing ones, through play: for example, by skipping, running and jumping.
- **Intellectual**: They need more advanced toys and books and more stimulating and new experiences, as well as being taught new skills such as letter and number recognition.
- **Emotional**: Although children will want to try new things, they still need their parents or carers to respect, encourage and love them, and depend on them to be there for them, to provide guidance and supervision.
- **Social**: Children continue to develop routines, but need opportunities to meet more people and play and learn with others, so they feel part of a group.

Your world

Look back at pages 68–71. How do the PIES needs of a person change as they move from infancy through to later adulthood? Produce a table to show this, showing something specific to each age group – for example, nappy changing for infants, and puberty for adolescents – in the physical column.

Activity

With a partner, look at each life stage and decide how the PIES would change if a person:

- was seriously ill
- had a physical disability
- had learning difficulties
- had mental problems.

Prepare a PowerPoint presentation to report your thoughts to the rest of your group.

Adolescence

- **Physical**: Adolescents need help to cope as they go though puberty and deal with all the changes to their bodies that this involves. They also need to keep fit, keep themselves clean and to be encouraged to follow a balanced diet.
- **Intellectual**: Young people need good educational opportunities, as well as varied experiences, such as the cinema, the theatre, museums, travel, and even work, to increase their knowledge and understanding of the world.
- **Emotional**: Adolescents need to experience more intimate relationships, learn about their sexuality, respect others and develop the confidence to become less dependent on their parents and carers.
- **Social**: It is important to develop **recreational** skills, to have different opportunities to meet people and to gain the respect and approval of their peers.

> **Recreational** – to do with the use of time in a manner designed for refreshment of one's body or mind; fun

Adults

- **Physical**: Adults continue to develop new practical skills, such as those needed for work or leisure, and most now have a regular sex life. Many women will give birth and all women go through the menopause.
- **Intellectual**: Adults need to continue to develop their knowledge and understanding: for example, through courses and work.
- **Emotional**: Adults need to learn to cope with their feelings as they develop relationships (some of which will fail) and face all the other events that happen during adulthood.
- **Social**: As adults pass through the different stages of adulthood, their social needs will change: for example, from going out often with friends, to stopping in more often because of having young children, so inviting friends round instead.

Later adulthood

- **Physical**: Many older adults are still fit and healthy, but eventually their bodies start to wear out, so they may need to be helped with everyday activities: for example, washing, feeding and going to bed.
- **Intellectual**: Older adults need to continue to stimulate their brains, reading books, watching the television, and so on, to keep their minds alert.
- **Emotional**: Older adults need to be allowed their dignity, to be respected and to cope with the loss of family and friends.
- **Social**: Older adults need opportunities to socialise with others or they may become socially isolated.

Just checking

1. How do physical needs change as we pass from infancy to adolescence?
2. Why is it important for adults and older people to keep their minds stimulated?
3. How do our social needs change as we pass from adolescence to later adulthood?

Who ate all the PIES?

In this topic, you will learn more about the basic needs of service users, divided into physical, intellectual, emotional and social needs.

Physical needs

Everyone has basic physical needs, whatever their age or life circumstances, although how they are met changes throughout our lives. Physical needs are those that we have to keep our bodies working as well as they can. They include food, water, shelter, clothing, warmth, rest, exercise and personal hygiene.

Intellectual needs

Intellectual needs are those that develop our brains and keep them working well, providing us with the ability to learn and develop new skills. Intellectual needs include **mental stimulation**, education and employment. If we do not have enough to keep our minds active, we become bored (and sometimes boring) and fed up with life.

One way to keep mentally healthy, as we grow older, is to keep doing and learning new things. Research shows that people who do this are more likely to keep their brains active and working well, as well as live longer and have more fulfilling lives.

As physical powers decline, intellectual needs become even more important. Carers must recognise the importance of maintaining intellectual health and keep service users interested in their world.

Emotional needs

Emotional needs are those that make us feel happy and relaxed, such as being able to express our feelings, love and security. We need to be able to feel, express and recognise different emotions in order to cope with relationships and different situations that arise in life.

Social needs

Social needs are those that enable us to develop, enjoy and maintain relationships, including friendships, intimate and sexual relationships and work relationships. These needs include the opportunities to mix with others in an appropriate environment.

Your world

Write 'Me' in the middle of a page. In each corner, write one of P, I, E and S. Think about your needs and write each one in the correct corner. Share your ideas with a partner, and add any more you think of between you. Remember that you will not have identical needs because you are each an individual, unique person.

Mental stimulation – something that produces an increase in activity in our brains and helps our brains to develop

Did you know?

There are many electronic games on the market now designed not only to entertain us but also to keep our minds stimulated. These range from word games to number games to games for the imagination. As you will realise when you watch the TV adverts carefully, these games are marketed for people of all ages, as it is just as important to keep the mind of an older person active as that of a younger one.

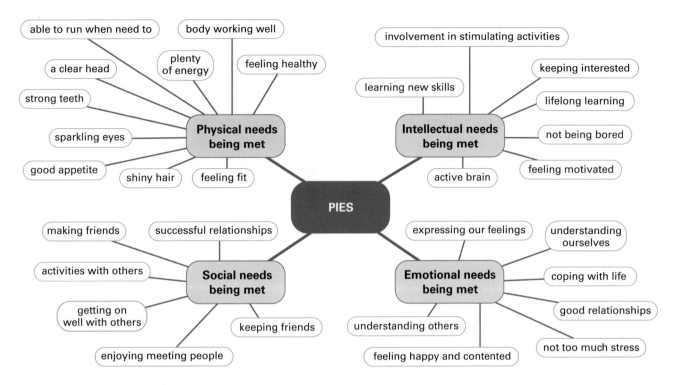

The results of your PIES needs being met

Activity

1. In a group, discuss and note down all the things you can think of to stimulate your brain. Include those that older and younger people than yourself might do.
2. Which are those that people older than you are more likely to do? Why do you feel this? Think of as many different ways that a person confined to bed due to age or illness can keep their minds active.
3. What do you think the expression lifelong learning, used on the diagram, means?

Take it further

Think of someone you know who does not get on well with others and does not have many friends. Do not give their name as this could cause offence and upset. Write down how that person behaves and what it is you think makes that person the way he or she is. Then write a list of things he or she could do differently to help him or her make more friends.

Just checking

1. What are the basic PIES needs that all people have?
2. Why is it important that a person's intellectual needs continue to be met?
3. If a person's social needs are not met, what might be the consequences?

Fate or choice?

This topic looks at life events and lifestyle choices that affect human growth and development.

Life course events

Life course events are important things that happen to people during their lifetime. These experiences, whether expected or unexpected, can have a major impact on growth, development, health and wellbeing. Those that are expected are those that, although not guaranteed to happen, most of us expect to happen to us at some stage of our lives. Unexpected ones are those that are not planned. Some examples are given in the table.

Life events involve change, which usually produces some level of stress, even when the life event is a positive one. Some of these events will be looked at in more detail in the next three topics.

Your world

What a difference a few months make

Look at the picture. With a partner, identify the lifestyle choices the girl and boy have made and the life events that have happened to both. Think of people you know, or know of, in a similar situation. How has it affected their lives?

Expected	Unexpected
Starting nursery and school	Birth of a sibling
Puberty	Moving house
Starting work/employment	Redundancy
Leaving home	Serious injury or illness
Getting married	Getting divorced or breakdown of a serious relationship
Parenthood	Bereavement
Retirement	Abuse
Menopause	Winning the lottery

Expected and unexpected life events

Activity

1. Find out:

   - why most Hindus believe the cow to be sacred
   - what is meant by 'halal'
   - why Jewish people consider some meats to be unclean.

2. Research and construct a table to show how the religions mentioned in part 1 of this Activity influence dress and hospital care. Add another religion, such as Jehovah's Witnesses.

Case study **Ben and Nicola**

Nicola met Ben at school. They are very similar in their tastes and abilities and have been together for four years so far. During that time, they have been on holiday to some lovely places, and they enjoy going to the cinema and socialising with their friends, Mike and Simone. They also go out with their own sets of friends. Nicola trained as a beautician, working in a pub as a waitress to make some money. She did so well that she is now at university studying for a degree – something she did not imagine herself doing. Ben has worked for several years as a chef, an area of work he got into through a Saturday job selling sandwiches arranged for him by a friend. He had always thought he would do something to do with sport. Despite doing very well and having managerial responsibilities and qualifications, he is considering a career change to gain better prospects, in either the police or IT.

1. Identify the expected and unexpected events in both Ben and Nicola's stories.
2. How has each led to the next event in their lives?
3. Are the changes in their lives for the better? Explain your answer.

Lifestyle choices

These are choices we make about how we live our lives. They have an important influence on how long we live and the quality of our lives. You have already learned about some of these, such as diet, exercise and substance abuse, in Unit 3. Another example of a lifestyle choice is a person's religion and other **beliefs**.

Religion and other beliefs

The religion someone follows can influence the way they live, such as their diet, dress and attitude to medical care. As well as religious beliefs, there are other beliefs such as cultural ones.

Travellers are one social group with a range of beliefs and customs. They mainly live in caravans, sometimes without running water and electricity, because that way of life is their tradition. Frequent moving about can result in apparent poor education, but in fact some groups of travellers have advanced vocabulary and social skills because of their strong verbal and musical traditions. Travellers can find it hard to access services such as healthcare because, for example, they might be in a remote area with the nearest healthcare service miles away, or they may not be registered to access care in the area they have just arrived in.

Health and medical beliefs also affect growth and development. For example, a Muslim woman would find being examined by a male doctor or nurse traumatic because strict Muslims forbid any physical contact between males and females unless they are married. This means Muslims need to be able to be seen by a doctor of their own gender. If this is not possible, a Muslim woman finds it less shameful to be seen by a non-Muslim male doctor. Fear of such a situation might put her off seeking help for a problem, such as a lump in her breast, before it is too late to treat it.

Belief – an opinion or conviction

Take it further

Explain how the quality of life of people who live by these religions is affected by their lifestyle choice.

Just checking

1. What is meant by a life course event?

2. Explain what is meant by lifestyle choice and give three examples to support your answer.

3. How do lifestyle choices and life course events affect growth and development? Explain your answer.

I didn't see that coming!

In this topic, you will learn more about the impact of expected and unexpected life course events on individuals, by looking at the example of marriage and divorce.

Expected and unexpected life events

Marriage and divorce are good examples to show how life events impact on growth, development, health and wellbeing.

Effects of marriage and divorce

Effects	Marriage (expected and positive)	Divorce (unexpected and negative)
Physical	Practical help, sex life; someone to do activities with, such as exercise; tend to live longer and are less ill	Short-term and long-term effects of stress
Intellectual	Conversation and activities; advice	Preoccupation; lack of concentration on other matters; travel and visits might be cancelled due to lack of money or a companion
Emotional	Good self-esteem; support in times of stress; happiness; humour; caring; self-confidence	Failure; disbelief; sadness; depression; anger; guilt; disappointment; low self-esteem
Social	Good relationship; sense of belonging; best friend	Friends often have to choose; loss of activities used to do together; harder to go out on own when others all in couples

Marriage is a big life change, and may bring some initial sense of loss on leaving the family and some stress due to taking on new responsibilities, but generally a happy marriage is positive. A supportive relationship contributes positively to our health and wellbeing by meeting many of our needs, helping us to achieve and maintain physical fitness and intellectual, emotional and social stability, and so to grow and develop as we should do.

Divorce may bring some positive effects, such as a feeling of relief from no longer living in an unhappy situation, but overall it is a negative event for almost everyone. When people get married, they believe it is for life, so divorce will bring a sense of failure, guilt or blame, low self-esteem and many other unpleasant emotions. This may mean many needs are not met. Stress may cause a lack of physical fitness and a poor intellectual, emotional and social state, affecting health and wellbeing – and this in turn will affect growth and development. For example, a loss of appetite due to stress may

Your world

Write down all the events that have happened to you so far in your life that you could have expected to happen, because they happen to most people. Then write down those events you didn't expect to happen. What effect did these unexpected events have on you?

mean that a person does not eat a balance of the nutrients needed to build and repair body cells.

Marriage and divorce show that, although life course events are generally considered to be either positive or negative, they cannot always be so neatly categorised, because there are negative and positive aspects to most events.

Was it 'til death do us part for Maud?

Just checking

1. Why is marriage an expected event, but divorce an unexpected event?
2. Why is a happy marriage considered generally to be a positive life event and divorce a negative life event?
3. How does marriage affect growth and development? How does divorce?

What a surprise!

This topic looks further at how life course events affect an individual physically, intellectually, emotionally and socially.

Lifestyle choices

Lifestyle choices can lead to both expected and unexpected events.

For example, a person who chooses to follow a balanced healthy diet and take regular exercise is more likely to have a fit, slim body than someone who doesn't. They are also more likely to have good self-confidence because they feel good about themselves, and to be more likely to take up recreational activities that keep them fit, active and mentally alert, as well as having more opportunities to meet others and build relationships. This in turn can help them get a job with prospects, make friends, meet a similar person to live their lives with, have children and enjoy a long, happy, healthy life.

On the other hand, a person who eats too much and smokes and drinks is more likely to suffer a serious illness, such as a stroke or heart disease, which will limit their employment chances and their recreational activities, and affect their chances of a long, happy, fulfilled life.

Expected events

These include starting school, marriage/partnership formation, employment, death and bereavement.

Your world

Look at the list you wrote at the start of page 188. Have you thought of any more events or effects you can add to your list? Now identify each of the effects as either physical, intellectual, emotional or social.

Activity

1. Pick an unexpected life event other than divorce, illness or disability that might happen in the family of a person of your age. Explain the ways in which it might affect that young person's growth, development, health and wellbeing.

2. Research the support available for a young person this event has happened to. Produce an information sheet suitable for such a young person.

Case study Carly

Carly is 14 years old. She lives with her two younger brothers and her parents. Her mother is wheelchair-bound after a car crash three years ago, and her father works long hours on a building site to support the family. There is no money to pay for any extra help, so Carly does a lot to help her brothers with things such as homework, and her parents with household jobs. She is happy to do this because she loves her family, but sometimes feels that life has been unfair on her.

1. How will her Mum's accident affect Carly physically, intellectually, emotionally and socially?
2. How will her lifestyle affect her:

- self-esteem
- education
- employment prospects?

Activity

Look at the diagram showing the importance of relationships. Use this, and the table on page 188, to explain how the expected event of moving in with a partner, either through marriage or **cohabitation**, affects the couple physically, intellectually, emotionally and socially.

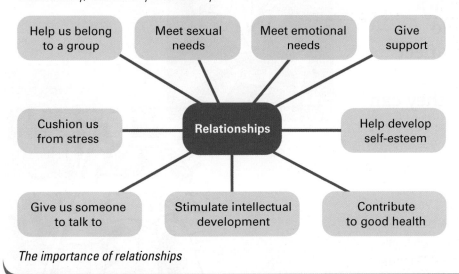

The importance of relationships

Unexpected life events

These include serious illness, unplanned pregnancy, relationship breakdown, financial difficulty, loss of a job and disability. They affect an individual physically, emotionally, intellectually and socially.

For example, an accident or illness can leave a person disabled. People with disabilities may have to adapt their lifestyle to cope with everyday situations that able-bodied people deal with automatically. A disability or illness may affect physical fitness, hinder access to varied learning activities, cause emotional distress and remove some social opportunities, thus affecting health and wellbeing. It may also affect growth and physical development of the body: for example, a paralysed arm will lose muscle due to lack of use. Disability or illness can also affect the development of new abilities and skills, as well as emotional development.

Whatever the condition, the needs of someone with a disability will include all those of an able-bodied person, but there may be important additional needs too, especially in relation to access to places and services. If these are met through the provision of an enabling environment, the impact of the disability or illness may be decreased.

Just checking

1. Why does a lifestyle choice affect an individual physically, intellectually, emotionally and socially? Give an example to explain your answer.

2. Explain how an expected life event affects an individual physically, intellectually, emotionally and socially by describing these effects.

3. Do the same for an unexpected life event.

Learn from experience

In this topic, you will learn more about how lifestyle choices and life events affect human growth and development, and how they can lead to new learning.

New learning

You have already considered how a variety of lifestyle choices and life course events can affect growth and development. To see how such factors and events lead to new learning, you are now going to look at one example of an unexpected life event: someone losing their job.

Having a job helps you:

- physically, by providing you with an income. The larger this is, the better the house, car, holidays, and all the other material possessions you could buy.
- intellectually, by giving you a busy life. This keeps your mind active. Also, having a job enables you to afford items such as books and theatre tickets, and means you can afford to travel to other places, so you learn more about the world you live in.
- emotionally, by helping you to have positive self-esteem. Knowing you can pay your way, not worry about money all the time and have social status will give you a good, positive feeling about yourself.
- socially, by giving you social status. People who have a job, particularly a job that is seen to be a good job, such as a doctor, teacher or lawyer, have social status and respect from others.

Your world

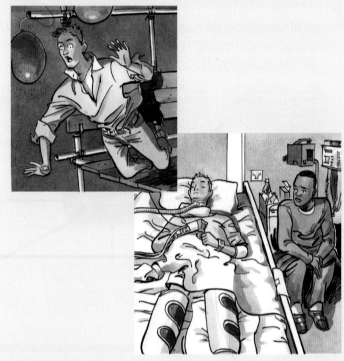

Alcohol changes lives

Look at the picture. How do you think Billy will learn from what has happened to Anthony when he was drunk? Can you think of a situation where you have learned from events that have happened to other people?

Think about it

If parents decide to send their child to a nursery as a baby, the child will learn so much from being with a range of people in a different environment. At nursery, children learn to play together and also learn from the different activities they do there. For example, they might have a play corner set up as a shop, where they learn about buying and selling things, so learning how to interact with others, practicing their numbers and learning that you have to pay for material possessions. This is an example of a lifestyle choice leading to new learning.

Think about your own early childhood. How did it prepare you for further learning?

If you suddenly lose your job you may be affected:

- physically, by stress, and by, for example, having a worse diet, less chance to pursue leisure activities that keep you fit and a worse quality of housing and environment.
- intellectually, by losing the chance to learn and use new skills and keeping your mind active, solving problems while tackling the job.
- emotionally, by losing your positive feelings about yourself. You may feel that society doesn't need you anymore and that you aren't bringing in money to support the family's finances. You might not know how to fill your time, so become very bored and depressed.
- socially, by missing the contact with other people that a job gives you, and by losing your status in society.

There are two options to choose from in such a situation. You could sit at home worrying and becoming more and more stressed, or you could get out and do something about it.

You can learn from the experience. You will now have the time to learn new skills and gain new knowledge, through taking a course. You could start your own business, doing something you really enjoy doing: for example, starting a gardening business. This might mean meeting a wider and different circle of people, and being out in the fresh air instead of maybe sitting behind a desk bent over papers or a computer. The new job could make you fitter and healthier and lead to you having a longer and more satisfying life. It could also give you more time to enjoy the outdoors and think about things you want to think about. As your own boss you might feel less stressed and more in control of your own life.

Just checking

1. How can having a job help meet a person's PIES needs?
2. How can losing a job affect your PIES needs?
3. Do you think that a life event like losing a job can ever be a good thing for a person? Could it lead to new learning? Explain your answer.

Activity

1. Think about someone taking retirement. This is an expected event, unlike losing a job, because everyone knows they will stop work at the end of their working life. How will retiring affect a person physically, intellectually, emotionally and socially, in a positive way and in a negative way?

2. Think about television health and safety adverts you have seen, such as the ones where people are dying from lung cancer or lying in the road dead after being knocked down by a drugged-up driver. How does seeing these situations lead to new learning, for you and others?

Take it further

Most people retire by the time they are 65 years old. Some retire earlier if their job and circumstances allow it and others chose to continue working if they are able or allowed to. Because people are living longer, young people now face the prospect of having to work well beyond the age of 65. What do you think of this? Discuss it in a group and ask teachers of different ages their opinions. Write a newspaper report on your findings.

Added values

This topic revisits the care values you learned about on pages 104–113 and looks at some of the possible effects and consequences if they are not implemented.

Care values revisited

You have already seen how health, social care and early years practitioners promote care values through their work with service users. The main care values used in interactions between service users and service providers are:

- promoting anti-discriminatory practice
- promoting and supporting individual rights to dignity, independence, health and safety
- promoting effective communication and relationships
- maintaining confidentiality of information
- acknowledging individual personal beliefs and identity.

By implementing these care values as a service provider, you can make sure that service users all receive the quality care each of them needs, and that they are treated with equality.

What is equality?

Equality means everyone having the same chance as everyone else to obtain or achieve something: for example, access to a service they need.

Different people see the world in different ways. Your way of thinking might seem as strange to someone else as theirs does to you. Think about you and your friends. Even in a small group of friends, you will have different opinions about certain things. If you respect each other's opinions, you will get on as a group; if you continually disagree, eventually the group will split up because you are all unhappy about the situation.

Your world

Look at the advert below, for a nursery nurse at The Green Nursery. Why would you want a nursery nurse to have these qualities?

Little People's Nursery

We are looking for a dedicated nursery nurse to join our team in delivering the highest possible quality childcare to our little people. The successful candidate will have a childcare qualification at level 2 or 3 and a thorough knowledge of 'Birth to 3' issues and the Foundation Stage.

We are looking for someone who:

- is a warm, committed individual with initiative
- has a desire to enhance the lives of children
- can be flexible, works well as part of a team and is highly motivated
- is positive and sensitive
- is literate and numerate
- has a current first-aid qualification

If you would like to apply please send a CV and a covering letter to Miss Little, Little People's Nursery, The Green, Littledon, London, SW111 6TJ

Rates of pay will depend on experience and qualifications. Closing date is 20th August 2008.

Depression – the condition of feeling sad or despondent
Anxiety – a state of uneasiness and apprehension
Aggression – hostile or destructive behaviour or actions

Case study **Mohammed**

Mohammed went on a holiday abroad with a group of male friends when he was much younger, able-bodied and single. He was taken seriously ill with a stomach condition and was admitted to hospital. His friends had to fly home without him because the end of the holiday had arrived, so he was alone. He found it hard to communicate with the nurses, and felt they didn't like or respect him because he was foreign and a Muslim. He was in a public ward with no privacy. When he was sick or couldn't get to the toilet on time, they dealt with it without drawing any curtains round his bed, and talked openly about him and his medical condition – he recognised some words such as his name, but couldn't understand most of what they said. He wanted to pray, but there was no room provided to do this.

1. Look at the list of values. With a partner, discuss whether Mohammed's carers implemented each one, write down what you decide and explain your answer.
2. Imagine how such treatment would make you feel. How do you think this treatment made Mohammed feel?
3. What effect would this treatment have on Mohammed's recovery?

It is the same when someone is being cared for. For example, think about someone living in a care home. If the carer does not respect their views and does not take them into account when helping the person, that person will feel unhappy and have low self-esteem, which will affect their health and wellbeing, and their growth and development.

As a practitioner, you should value and learn from these differences, rather than treat people differently because of them. If all the care values above are implemented, equality is assured.

What are the consequences of not implementing care values?

Some of the possible effects and consequences of practitioners not implementing the care values are:

- physical injury
- withdrawal from other people
- a feeling of not belonging
- loss of confidence
- stress and poor mental health
- a feeling of unworthiness
- **depression** and **anxiety**
- anger and **aggression**
- fear of others
- lack of security
- loss of identity.

Activity

Write a code of practice for the nurses in the hospital in the case study to follow to make sure they are implementing the care values above (see codes of practice on pages 114–5).

Just checking

1. What is meant by equality? Are there ever cases when it is fair to treat some people differently from others? Give three examples.
2. List the five main care values.
3. Under each care value, write two possible consequences of not implementing it.

Common values

This topic looks at some of the policies, procedures and guidelines used by various bodies in the health and social care sectors and compares them with the value base looked at in the last topic.

Policies, procedures and guidelines

Care practitioners follow a range of policies, procedures and guidelines to help them implement the care values in their work, as you will have learned on pages 114–5. Here we look at some of these, and see how they affect everyday practice in parts of the health and social care sectors.

Healthcare

The Nursing and Midwifery Council (NMC) has a code of professional conduct (2004) that starts by saying:

'As a registered nurse, midwife or specialist community public health nurse, you are personally accountable for your practice. In caring for patients and clients you must:

- respect the patient or client as an individual
- obtain consent before you give any treatment or care
- cooperate with others in the team
- protect confidential information
- maintain your professional knowledge and competence
- be trustworthy
- act to identify and minimise risk to patients and clients.

These are the shared values of all the UK health care regulatory bodies.'

(Source: www.nmc-uk.org)

Although there are seven points instead of the five given for this GCSE qualification, if you compare them, you will see that they combine to give the same values. Cooperating with others in the team and maintaining professional knowledge and competence are essential to providing the best possible care, to make sure service users maintain their independence, so keeping someone with good health and wellbeing – which is the main aim of health and social care practitioners.

There are many other such codes of conduct; using a search engine for 'NHS codes of professional conduct' yields a wide range for all of the many different parts of the NHS. Some of these only cover one

Implementing the care values means that service users' individual rights are met

particular care value: for example, many bodies have a separate policy on maintaining confidentiality of information.

Many health services such as GP surgeries, health centres and dentists have their own charters, which state the quality of service its service users can expect to receive.

Social care

The General Social Care Council (GSCC) worked with the other relevant bodies in Northern Ireland, Scotland and Wales to produce a code of professional conduct (2004) for social care employers and workers, which the Commission for Social Care Inspection (CSCI) takes into account in their enforcement of care standards. It states that:

'To meet their responsibilities in relation to regulating the social care workforce, social care employers must:

*   make sure people are suitable to enter the workforce and understand their roles and responsibilities
*   have written policies and procedures in place to enable social care workers to meet the General Social Care Council (GSCC) Code of Practice for Social Care Workers
*   provide training and development opportunities to enable social care workers to strengthen and develop their skills and knowledge
*   put in place and implement written policies and procedures to deal with dangerous, discriminatory or exploitative behaviour and practice
*   promote the GSCC's codes of practice to social care workers, service users and carers and co-operate with the GSCC's proceedings.'

Learning by doing

This topic continues to look at care values, considering how they are reflected through professional training and development of care practitioners.

Professional development

Service providers needs to be trained before they get a job, but training does not end there. Once they have a job, they should always try to improve the quality of their care they provide.

Continuing professional development (CPD) is how professionals ensure that they keep up to date with new theories, treatments, procedures, and so on. These are various types of CPD, and the main ones are looked at below.

Induction
When someone starts a new job or moves to a new department, they take part in an induction session or course. This introduces them formally to the workplace and teaches them all the policies, procedures and codes of practice they need to follow in that particular place of work.

Mentoring
A person new to a job may be assigned a mentor. This is a trusted person who is there to show them what to do and to help them if they have any problems. Mentors may receive training themselves – being a mentor is not always as easy as it sounds!

Work-based learning
Work-based learning is when someone learns knowledge and skills in the workplace, rather than in a school or other place of education. You may have done work experience while at school or have visited a workplace. There you will have learned aspects of the job that you wouldn't have learned in a classroom.

Work-based learning is important throughout your working life. Someone may be working full-time in a workplace as an apprentice and be being taught the job as they go along, by others in the workplace, and maybe by a trainer or teacher coming into the workplace. A surgeon will learn new operating techniques and procedures by watching another surgeon and helping them.

Your world

Carry out a simple survey in school to find out what training the staff in school have had in how to interact with the students and parents. Write a summary of what you find out. Remember to include a cross-section of staff, not just teachers.

Induction – a formal or informal introduction or entry into a position

Activity

1. In a group, plan what information you need to include in a display on training for various careers in health and social care.
2. Pick an area of work in health or social care that you think you might be interested in as a career. Do some research into the courses you need to follow to get a job in this area and the various sources of training available for CPD.
3. Produce an information sheet on the training for that job, following an agreed format, so that it fits in with those produced by the rest of the group.

Courses and qualifications

Practitioners can also develop their skills and knowledge by going on courses. Many one-day courses give the participants a certificate of attendance. Longer courses often lead to the participants being assessed in some way; if they have done well enough, they will gain a qualification.

Most job advertisements ask for specific qualifications. For example, an advert for someone to become an alcohol project worker might state that applicants need a relevant professional qualification, such as a degree or diploma in social work, nursing or addiction studies.

In order to continue to learn and improve their practice after they have started the job, practitioners may be sent on courses as and when appropriate. These may be run in house (i.e. within their own workplace) or by other professional bodies and organisations.

Sources of information

Sources of information on professional development include:

- **colleagues** in the same or a similar service provider.
- **professional bodies**. These organisations, which are usually non-profit bodies, maintain and enforce standards of training and ethics in their professions, to protect both the public interest and the interests of the professionals. For example, the General Teaching Council (GTC) is the professional body for teaching in England. Its purpose is to help improve standards of teaching and the quality of learning.
- **Sector Skills Councils (SSCs)**. These independent organisations work together to improve service provision. They are employer-led, but also involve trades unions and professional bodies.
- **professional journals**. These magazines will have articles on all aspects of that profession, as well as adverts for jobs and resources. Examples are *Nursery World* for nursery nurses and *GTC* magazine for teachers.

Some professional journals. Find some in your local library on the areas that interest you most

Just checking

1. What is meant by the term 'continuous professional development'?
2. What is work-based learning and why is it important?
3. List four possible sources of information on professional development.

No one to turn to?

This topic looks at some possible consequences if service practitioners have not effectively implemented care values, including the possibility of discrimination and of social exclusion.

Your world

It's lonely in this company

In a group, discuss situations when any of you have been made to feel lonely, even when you are in a group. How can this happen? Others in a group you have been in have maybe felt this way – how does this make you feel?

Discrimination

You learned about discrimination on pages 104–5. Take a look back at this topic now, and remind yourself of the main points before reading on.

Social isolation

Before accessing services

Social isolation is when people live without regular contact with other people, especially friends and family. Such people cannot rely on others around them to help them when they need health or social care, so it is important that practitioners recognise the possibility of social isolation – either already existing or developing – and act to prevent or help with this.

One group of people this can happen to is people in later adulthood.

- Physically, as people get older, their bodies slowly change, so they become less flexible and mobile and maybe suffer from ill health.

Think about it

Imagine what it is like to live on the 12th floor of a block of flats, with a lift that often breaks down, as an adult with small children. How would you meet other people? Would it be easy to go out? What are some of the problems you would encounter? Think about health and safety and the risk of letting the children outside on the landing or balcony to play. How would an older person living on their own manage in a similar flat? How would their needs be met?

This means they cannot continue some of the activities they have previously done, which can mean less contact with people.

- Intellectually, their memories may start to fail, or they might develop mental health problems.
- Emotionally, they may feel they no longer know their role in life, and ill health can also mean they view themselves less positively. Other people stereotype older people and this doesn't help either. The death of partners or friends can leave older people feeling emotionally isolated.
- Socially, they may not be able to take up opportunities because of ill health or lack of money.

All these factors can result in social isolation.

Another group of people who suffer from social isolation are homeless people, who may have little choice over what they eat or what care they take of themselves. They do not usually have regular access to the health and social care services they may need. Others include those with mental health problems, illness, language or cultural difficulties and those living in high-rise flats.

All these people may have difficulties accessing the health and social care services they need, and it is up to practitioners to recognise this and arrange appropriate transport or home visits.

After accessing services

Once people do access the services they need, the care values need to be implemented. If they are not, this can increase the service users' feeling of social isolation. For example, if someone is in a care home and the care assistants are too busy to get them up out of bed, washed and dressed, and help them move to a lounge where they would have company, they could remain in their room for long periods of time. The practitioners would have failed to promote the person's independence and have not promoted effective communication and relationships. The person will feel neglected and lonely, and will be more likely to give up and sink into depression. Leaving such as service user on their own with no-one to talk to can lead to **mental deterioration**, leading to social isolation, a poorer quality of life and even a shorter life.

All health and social care services aim to help people either develop or maintain independence. A young child who has suffered an accident might have paralysed legs. Practitioners need to do all they can to get the child walking again, or to help him cope with life in a wheelchair, so he can lead a long and fulfilled life. If the practitioners are too busy and don't spend time building a relationship with him, he will become upset and feel socially isolated when his family is not there. This will mean he will be less likely to respond to the treatment and therapy offered, feeling unvalued and useless, and so be less likely to walk again or accept his wheelchair and learn to make the most of the situation.

Activity

A male immigrant, who has not been in the country for long, goes to sign on with a GP. He wants to see the doctor about a personal problem but he does not speak good English. The receptionist does not understand what he is trying to say, and there is a long line of people waiting for appointments and becoming increasingly impatient.

1. What should the receptionist do in this situation? Discuss in a small group and role-play the situation, once so that the man gives up and goes away without help, and again so that the situation is resolved satisfactorily.
2. What might be the consequences of the man giving up, and not being able to access medical help?

Mental deterioration – intellectual power,s such as memory of words, gradually failing

Just checking

1. What is meant by social isolation?
2. List three groups of people who may become socially isolated and explain why for each one.
3. Give an example of how failing to implement certain care values can lead to social isolation.

Abuse

This topic continues to look at the possible consequences of practitioners failing to implement the care values effectively.

Forms of abuse

One very serious consequence of practitioners not implementing the care values can be **abuse**.

Abuse can happen for a variety of reasons, such as frustration with a person, loss of temper, a desire to exert power over someone else, prejudice or discrimination.

There are several different forms of abuse:

- physical abuse, when someone is physically assaulted in some way, such as being hit
- sexual abuse, when someone interferes with a person's body in a sexual and unwanted way
- verbal abuse, when someone assaults a person verbally, such as insulting them and calling them names
- neglect, when a person is ignored or not given the help they need
- exclusion, when someone is stopped from getting help or maybe the company that they need
- avoidance, when someone deliberately avoids contact with another person
- devaluing, when someone ignores a person's ideas and opinions or denies him something others are allowed, so making him feel less valued.

Just as it is inappropriate for the service user to abuse the provider, so it is also inappropriate for a service provider to fail to protect a service user from abuse. The exception to

Your world

Enrico could do more for himself with encouragement

Enrico from The Green has had a minor stroke, so he cannot use one side of his body very well. He is in hospital in a ward that is very understaffed. The nurses tend to do everything for Enrico rather than encouraging him to do them himself, because it is quicker for them. They have no time to talk to him or get to know him. What is the likely result for Enrico?

Activity

1. Using the list to the left, design and make a leaflet informing people about the different forms of abuse, the symptoms and who to go to for support, protection and advice. You will need to do some research to find more information to help you do this.
2. Think how it feels to be abused verbally and neglected by friends. Imagine this is happening to you, and write a letter to Dear Lindy at The Green Local asking for advice. Then answer your own letter, giving advice as to how to cope with and challenge this abuse.

this is when someone does not understand what they are doing, such as in the case of some mental illnesses.

Dealing with abuse

When abuse is suspected, of either a service provider or a service user, steps should be taken to protect the abusee, such as having two workers in a room instead of one. A service provider needs to look out for signs of abuse, such as bruises, mood swings, becoming withdrawn and feeling worthless.

There are many support organisations and telephone helplines to offer help, protection and advice about abuse, including the police and social services. A service provider should always report signs of abuse to the appropriate agency.

Analysis and evaluation of the consequences

Although most practitioners are very caring and implement the care values in all their work, you sometimes hear of cases where this is not the case. There are also cases where something bad happens even though the social worker has tried his best. For example, a family may have had a social worker assigned to them because someone has reported that the children in the family are not being looked after properly, but despite this one of the children has been hurt. Although this might not be the social worker's fault, the family will try to blame someone else for what has happened.

It is therefore important that the social worker makes regular visits, keeps careful notes and evaluates the risk to the children, taking action if there is any danger to them. If, for example, she calls round and the young children have been left on their own, the children should be taken to a place of safety while the case is assessed.

If the social worker is at fault, it is up to the local authority and the GSCC to **analyse** and **evaluate** the case and learn from it, introducing new guidelines and policies to try to prevent such a consequence happening again.

> **Take it further**
>
> Think about a recent case of child abuse that has made the headlines. Research the facts about it on the internet and, in a group, discuss how you think the services concerned could have done things differently and better.

> **Abuse** – treating someone wrongly, harmfully or inappropriately
> **Analyse** – examine something in detail
> **Evaluate** – examine and judge something carefully

Just checking

1. What are some of the reasons abuse happens? Give at least five.
2. Why is ignoring someone's ideas and opinions a form of abuse?
3. How does abuse happen because someone has not implemented the care values? Give three examples to explain your answer.

Feeling low

This topic looks further at the effect of poor care practice on the self-esteem and self-concept of service users: for example disempowerment and lack of self-worth.

Your world

What do you think Mohammed feels in situations like this?

Mohammed is sitting on The Green in his wheelchair, thinking about being unable to walk and his failing eyesight. He recently found himself stuck in the London Underground, because he couldn't use the escalator, and couldn't see where the lift was. How do you think he feels about himself? What would you say to him if you could meet him and try to make him feel better? Role-play the situation with a partner.

Social and medical models

The example we use here to show the differences between the social and medical models is that of people with a disability. However, these models could equally be applied to anyone receiving a poor quality of care.

Medical model

This is a model that was drawn up by able-bodied people who saw the person with the disability as the problem, and referred to their disability using words such as lack or abnormality, a restriction and a **handicap**. These are all words that can be offensive to someone with a disability, and can lead to poor self-esteem and negative self-concept. This in turn can lead to **disempowerment** and feelings of lack of **self-worth**.

In this model, the focus was on the disability rather than the person. The person tended to be pitied and seen as not able to do much for

Think about it

How do you feel when a teacher shouts at you and makes you feel small, particularly when you feel you do not deserve it? Does it make you feel good or bad about yourself? Are you more likely to try hard for that teacher in the future or are you more likely to resent him and so not learn much?

themselves and so dependent on others. It expects people with disabilities to fit in with society as it is. This might mean social isolation at home or in a medical institution.

Social model

This is a model developed by people with disabilities and their supporters based on how they saw themselves and how they wanted others to see and treat them. They want people to change society and the way they view people with disabilities: for example, expecting architects to design buildings to allow people with disabilities to access these structures. They say that it is not the fact that someone cannot walk that disables them, but the fact that they cannot climb steps to get into a building.

Medical model	Term	Social model
Any loss or abnormality of structure or function	Impairment	Some part, or parts, of your body, senses or mind are limited in their function, in the long term or permanently
Any restriction or lack of ability, resulting from impairment, to perform an activity in the manner or within the range considered normal for a human being	Disability	The loss or limitation of opportunities to take part in the normal life of the community on an equal level with others due to physical or social barriers

How the social model is less offensive to people with disabilities than the medical model

Imagine someone with a disability arriving at a service he needs to access but finding he cannot reach the door handle, or the door isn't wide enough for him to go through. He is either going to give up and go away, so not receiving the service he wants, or he will have to ask someone for help. This can be degrading and embarrassing and can lead to disempowerment and a lack of self-worth. This in turn can lead to depression and a feeling that it isn't worth going on.

There are many other problems less obvious than this, some of which were discussed in the topics in Unit 2 covering barriers to access (see pages 88–93).

These days it is much less likely that such a situation would arise as there has been a growing culture of acceptance of the social model, but unfortunately it does still happen. If service users receive poor care practice, they will have low self-esteem and a negative self-concept (see Unit 1). Think about that next time you meet someone with a disability.

Activity

1. As a group, discuss the image you have of people with disabilities. Did you watch the Paralympics? Produce a collage of images showing disabled people in a positive way.
2. Walk round your school with a friend wearing a blindfold and see what the problems are. Do the same with one hand tied behind your back. Write a report for your school governors stating how suitable or otherwise your school is for someone with a disability. Make recommendations to improve access.

Handicap – a disadvantage resulting from an impairment or disability, which limits or prevents the fulfilment of a role that is normal for that individual
Disempower – to deprive of (take away) power or influence
Self-worth – self-respect

Just checking

1. What is meant by lack of self-worth? What is meant by disempowerment?
2. How can these be caused by the medical model of disability?
3. How can poor care practice lead to low self-esteem and poor self-concept?

Self-concept revisited

In this topic, you will look at how self-concept is linked to personal relationships and professional relationships.

Your world

How do your friends make you feel?

With a partner, list how you spent the last 24 hours and the events that happened to you during this time. Split the events into positive ones which made you feel good, and negative ones which didn't make you feel good. For example, being at school might be a positive event for some people and negative event for others.

Select two from your positive list and two from your negative list and discuss with your partner how these events made you feel.

Self-concept

How is your self-esteem today? Did you look in the mirror this morning before you left the house?

In Unit 1, you learned that self-concept is a combination of self-image and self-esteem:

Self-image + Self-esteem = Self-concept

- Self-image is how we see ourselves and is influenced by other people and what we see in the media. A person's self-image is constantly being reshaped by the events that happen to them and their experiences.
- Self-esteem is how we value ourselves and this also changes over time. A person's self-esteem can be either positive or negative, and people are said to have either good or poor self-esteem.

As we pass through different life stages, a person's view of who they are changes frequently. For example, if someone chooses to marry, they are no longer a single person and are now somebody else's

Think about it

We are all affected by the relationships we have in our life. How important do you feel that the quality of relationship a child has with its carer is to establishing good self-esteem as an adult?

husband or wife. This may affect their self-image and their self-esteem – the two parts of self-concept.

Core values that affect self-concept

As you develop from infancy, you create a set of **core values and beliefs** about yourself. Many people think that these stay with you throughout your life and shape your future.

It is this set of core values and beliefs that establishes the pattern of whether someone generally has a positive self-concept or a negative self-concept. The same sorts of everyday events can happen to different people and they may be affected totally differently. If someone has a positive self-concept, they might not be affected as badly by the difficult events as somebody with a negative self-concept. If that person believes they are good-looking and they are turned down by someone they ask out on a date, this may not affect them too badly. They already believe they are good-looking. They may even think that it's the other person's bad luck – they've missed out on a great opportunity! However, if someone has a negative self-concept and believes they are not attractive, the rejection may just reinforce the core value of unattractiveness that they already hold.

Core values are thought to be established in infancy and childhood, and to become more difficult to shape and change as we pass through the life course. What happens and is said to a person at home and at school is really important in them developing a positive set of core values.

We all have important core values and beliefs about our:

- appearance
- intelligence
- importance to our families
- importance to our friends
- value and contribution to society.

Care professionals sometimes work with service users who have low self-esteem and a negative self-concept. Time is often spent exploring the person's core values and beliefs and looking at the events that shaped them in their early years.

Activity

Maud has been divorced for a short time and has not yet established another long-term relationship. She lives alone and works part-time as a volunteer care assistant. She often feels lonely.

1. Explain why Maud may have a negative self-concept. Remember to use the self-concept equation to help you do this.
2. Identify and explain two changes Maud may make in her life to improve her self-esteem.

Core values and beliefs – strong views and ideas about who we are which influence our actions

Just checking

1. Why is family so important in helping create a person with a positive set of core values?
2. Describe two events that may happen during the course of a day that may help build a person's self-esteem.
3. Explain how receiving negative feedback about a completed piece of work may affect a person's self-esteem.

How positive am I?

In this topic, you will learn how self-image and self-esteem are developed and influenced during the life course, particularly in infancy and childhood.

Your world

Mike is a professional football player. David is a dentist. Both live on The Green and have good self-esteem.

Draw up a list of the possible benefits of the two men's work for their self-esteem. What other positives in people's lives contribute to having good self-esteem?

Self-concept

If you looked at a glass of water on a table that has been partly drunk, would you say it was half full, or half empty? The answer you choose says a lot about your outlook on life. Some people take a positive approach to life, while others tend to approach life more negatively.

An individual's self-concept – the combination of their self-image and their self-esteem – is closely linked to their emotional and social development in infancy and childhood.

Self-image

A person's self-image can often be traced back to early childhood and, in some cases, infancy. How we see ourselves is developed in response to what people say to us and how people behave towards us.

In infancy and early childhood, the response of parents, carers, brothers and sisters is very important. Children quickly learn from

Think about it

Parents can have a big effect on the self-image of their children. This is through what they say and do and how they respond to what other people say to their children.

How would you a handle a situation where your son came home upset because other children had been calling him names because he had long hair?

You may wish to discuss this case with a partner.

others and begin to paint a picture in their own minds about themselves and who they are. It is important that positive messages are given to children and negative comments are challenged.

When children start nursery and primary school, they are greatly influenced by the other children they meet. Before starting nursery or school, children can lead quite a sheltered life, so this change can play a key role in their emotional development. At this stage, children begin to compare themselves with others, and their self-image changes in response to what they see, what others say and how others respond towards them. Children begin to look at themselves in comparison to others with particular regard to:

- appearance
- **gender**
- height and weight
- income and wealth
- home background and environment.

People generally like to fit in with what is the average, so if children see themselves to be very different from other children, this can affect their self-image.

Self-esteem

How people respond to being similar or different to others depends very much on their self-esteem. A person with good self-esteem will be confident in who they are and in being different; a person with low self-esteem may not find being different from other people easy.

It is important that parents and carers work hard at building a child's self-esteem. This can be done in a range of ways:

- telling children that they are loved
- telling children that you are proud of them
- telling children that they are special
- challenging unfair negative comments said by others to a child.

Establishing good self-esteem in infancy and childhood is important, as a good self-esteem base can last throughout adult life. As we pass through the life course, a number of different life events can affect self-esteem. These might include things like:

- marriage
- divorce
- redundancy
- illness and injury.

People with good self-esteem generally find it easier to handle these life events and the challenges these can present.

Dear Lindy,

I retired from work six months ago from a busy and satisfying job. I felt as if I helped the business and had a contribution to make to the world. When I retired, I was really looking forward to having a more leisurely life. I have found retirement to be very different. At present, I am very down and feel as if I have nothing to contribute to the world, people consider me to be old and I feel I have no real place any more.

What can I do to feel good about myself again? Should I just come to terms with these feelings?

John

Gender – the roles, behaviour and activities that society considers appropriate for men and women

Just checking

1. Why do parents/carers have such an important part to play in the development of a child's self-esteem and self-image?

2. Describe two ways in which parents/carers could help children feel more positive about themselves.

3. Why is it better to take a positive approach to life and its challenges rather than see things negatively?

How do I look?

In this topic, you will learn how important age, appearance, gender and sexual orientation are in determining someone's self-concept.

Many factors combine to determine a person's self-image, self-esteem and self-concept.

Age

One of the most important factors that can influence a person's self-concept is their age.

Different people handle the ageing process in different ways. Some are comfortable with the changes it brings and are happy becoming older; others find the loss of youth a challenge. However, being older does have many benefits, both emotionally and socially. People often become more contented with themselves and who they are.

During infancy and childhood, young people are still dependent on their family but, during adolescence, many people look forward to the day when they will become independent – this is a natural feeling for most young people. Becoming independent certainly changes a person's self-concept. For example, moving away from home, securing a job, and becoming an employed, productive member of society usually affect self-esteem positively.

How people handle retirement often affects self-concept in later adulthood. As many people now remain healthier for longer in later adulthood, this can be a time of development and change. People can take on new challenges and contribute to society in different ways. Some people become involved in voluntary work, which raises their self-esteem as they continue to feel like active members of society who have a role to play. However, a number of people find the

Your world

George lives on The Green and is 90 years of age. He is a war veteran and has a number of friends. He exercises regularly and lives alone in his own flat. George has a positive self-concept.

With a partner, list the reasons why George has a positive self-concept and be prepared to feed these back to the class in a discussion session.

Activity

Select two magazines that you or your family buy. Look carefully at the images in these magazines and write a short report on how the media could influence young people's self-image and self-concept.

move into later adulthood a challenge. They feel they no longer have a role in society, and this can affect self-esteem and self-image negatively.

Appearance

Society places a high value on appearance and this does affect self-concept across all life stages. People's physical characteristics and their non-verbal behaviour tell others a lot about their self-concept. In adolescence and early adulthood, a high emphasis is placed on how a person looks, and people are often measured by others on this basis. People often consider themselves attractive or unattractive – and this is reinforced by the images portrayed in the media.

As we pass through the life course, we begin to realise that appearance is just one small part of a person's identity. The saying that 'beauty is only skin deep' becomes easier to understand and, for most of us, the importance of appearance declines as we age.

Gender

Ideas about masculinity and femininity exist in all societies and these also affect a person's self-concept. As children grow and develop, they learn about the roles and behaviour expected of men and women. Most people conform to their gender role, and this is an important part of self-concept. Over the last 20 years, gender roles have become a lot less traditional. For example, many men now are happy to be fully involved in family life and raising children, while many women are the 'breadwinners' for their families.

Sexual orientation

In general, society has become much more accepting of different types of sexuality. There are many role models in the media who are gay and lesbian, and this makes it easier for other people to be comfortable with their sexuality. This has not always been the case, and there are still groups within society who find difference hard to accept.

It is important that people can express their sexuality as it can affect self-esteem and self-image. People need to feel that they are accepted by others. A person's sexuality is an important part of everyone's self-concept, but possibly more so if a person is part of one of society's minority groups.

Think about it

In most families there are arguments about who should do which jobs in the house and for the family. These include things like:

- who cleans the house
- who does the cooking
- who washes the car
- who puts the children to bed and reads goodnight stories
- who comforts the children when they are really upset.

In the past, there were often strict divisions as to who did which jobs. Today, many people feel that the jobs are shared much more equally.

How are the jobs divided up in your household? Are some jobs still seen as work for men and some jobs seen as work for women?

Just checking

1. Explain why appearance is such an important influence on a person's self-concept.

2. Why is it important for young gay and lesbian people to be able to be accepted by other members of society?

3. Explain how gender roles have changed in the family and how you think this affects the self-concept of men.

Did society make me feel this way?

In this topic, you will learn how ethnicity, culture and social class can influence a person's self-concept.

Your world

How many different ethnic groups do you encounter each day?

The UK is a multicultural society with people from a range of different ethnic groups, each with their own cultures.

In small groups, identify two ways that a person's ethnicity may influence how a person is expected to behave. Next, identify three different opportunities available in your local community to experience the culture of a different ethnic group.

Society's influence

Have you ever felt that you needed to change your behaviour to be what other people expect of you? Do you sometimes feel that you cannot be yourself in the company of other people? If this is the case, you are experiencing how society can affect your behaviour and who you are.

A person's self-concept is influenced by the society in which they live. UK society consists of many different ethnic groups and social classes. These different groups and classes often have their own social values and expected behaviour patterns. These can affect an individual's self-concept, as people often feel that they need to measure themselves against the expectations of their local community.

Ethnicity and culture

People often classify themselves according to the community in which they live. This may be based on having a common history and

Think about it

Have you ever been in a position where you felt that you did not fit in and came from a different social class from other people? What made you feel different?

culture, similar values, speaking the same language, practising the same religion or having the same-coloured skin.

The UK has many different ethnic groups, including:

- Asian
- Asian British
- Black
- Black British
- Chinese
- Eastern European
- Mixed race.

Many of these groups have their own culture and this does influence a person's self-concept. If this culture is distinctive and has strong expectations of individuals, people may feel they have to measure how they live their lives against these expectations.

Many cultural groups still maintain **traditional values**. This can be a challenge for younger members of the community, who may choose to lead their lives according to values common to modern British society.

Although British society is multicultural, some people are still discriminated against, and this can affect a person's self-worth.

Social class

In the UK, it is possible to identify different groups of people based on income, wealth and occupation. People often see themselves as working class, middle class or upper class. Although this is just one simple way of looking at class, it does help us understand how class is still an important influence on a person's self-concept. Social class can influence many aspects of a person's behaviour and life experiences: for example, many people choose friends who are of a similar class to themselves, and marry and settle down with people of the same social class.

Occupations such as medicine and law are strongly class-based, and it may be difficult for working class people to get into these occupations. If a person from a working class background does access one of these **professions**, this may lead to radical changes in their self-concept.

Some people are discriminated against as a result of their social class. For example, in adolescence, young people may find that they are excluded from friendship groups if they are from a different social class. This can affect a person's self-esteem, self-image and self-concept.

Activity

Imagine you have fallen in love with and decided to marry a person from a different ethnic group than your own.

1. Explain how you think your own family would be affected by this decision.
2. Identify ways in which your own self-image, self-esteem and self-concept might change as a result of the marriage.

Traditional values – beliefs or moral codes passed from one generation to another in a particular culture

Profession – an occupation or career with a specialist field of knowledge

Just checking

1. Identify four different ethnic groups that exist in the UK.
2. What are traditional values?
3. Explain how a person's self-concept might be affected by marrying a person from a different ethnic group.

Under the influence

In this topic, you will learn how education, relationships with others and emotional development can influence a person's self-concept.

Your world

Do you feel comfortable with who you are?

When Joy told her family and friends that she was gay, she was lucky as they were accepting and supportive. This made Joy feel safe and secure in who she was.

List the sorts of things Joy's family and friends could have said to show they were accepting of her sexuality. Why do you think a lot of people do not react in such a positive way? How could this sort of reaction affect a person's self-concept?

The influence of others

Have members of your family or friends ever helped you to handle a difficult situation? The support of friends and family is important in the development of self-concept. What those close to us do and say affects how we feel.

Education

The experience people have in school has a significant influence on their self-concept. It is during this time of life in particular that a person's identity and self-concept are being formed. There are two main types of influence at school: other students and teachers.

Interaction between children at school is important. These experiences will contribute to how people see themselves and how they value themselves. Young children can often be cruel in what they say and what they do to others who appear different. It is important that adults challenge this sort of behaviour and handle any bullying that happens at school quickly. Bullying often leads to a

> **Diversity** – difference or variety
> **Emotionally mature** – able to handle your own emotions and accept the person you are

person feeling worthless and negatively affects a person's self-concept. It has been shown that the effects of bullying can affect self-esteem levels well into adulthood.

School is also important as it educates children about **diversity** and difference. This is done through the curriculum, directly in subjects such Citizenship and Personal and Social Education and indirectly through the other subjects such as English and History. This allows us to see 'difference' as positive, and to reassess our own opinions about issues such as age, ethnicity, gender and sexuality.

Relationships with others

The relationships we have in our lives have a great impact on our self-concept. Most people are influenced by family relationships, work relationships and friendships.

Family relationships are central to a person's self-concept. The family builds a person's self-concept in infancy and childhood. A family that lets its members know they are loved will help maintain good levels of self-esteem. Although we would like to think that the family is always supportive in building a positive self-concept, this is not always the case. Relationship breakdown can affect the self-image and self-esteem of the two people directly concerned, but can also be damaging to the self-esteem and self-image of the children within the family.

Work and working relationships are important to many people and their self-concept. People often define themselves by their occupation, such as a nurse, teacher or a social worker. As you saw in Unit 1, redundancy, retirement and unemployment all have a great affect on a person's self-concept. As people spend a lot of time at work, the relationships formed there can have an important influence on self-concept.

Most people develop friendships throughout their lives, and friends can be important in helping us handle life course events.

Emotional development

As we grow and develop across the life course, we become better able to handle difficult life events – we learn from experience and become more **emotionally mature**. As people pass through adolescence and have a number of intimate relationships with others, they learn how to handle problems better without it negatively affecting their self-concept. This helps us to come to terms with who we are and be comfortable with ourselves. For most people, this happens in adulthood, but a person's self-concept is never totally fixed. We all change as we experience new things.

Activity

1. Design a questionnaire to give to men about the experience of becoming a dad. Ensure the questionnaire asks about how becoming a dad affected:

   - the man's self-image
   - the man's self-esteem
   - the man's self-concept.

2. Present the results of your findings in the form of a local newspaper article of not more than 200 words. Ensure that you have a good heading for the article to grab people's attention when they open the newspaper.

Just checking

1. How might having supportive friends help a person handle becoming single again after a marriage breakdown?

2. Why is it important that bullying is handled quickly and effectively at school?

3. Why is work such an important influence on a person's self-concept?

Can I help you?

In this topic, you will learn how care professionals build positive care relationships and **empower** service users to improve their self-esteem and change their self-concept.

Your world

How can Steven help Tom feel better about himself?

Steven is a personal fitness trainer. He works with people looking to make a change in their lives, often not just in terms of their physical health but in all aspects of their health and wellbeing. He is presently working with Tom, who is overweight, has poor self-esteem and has a negative self-concept.

With a partner, list five actions Steven may take to help Tom reach his goal of losing weight, gaining self-confidence and developing a more positive self-concept.

Empowering people to change

Have you ever sat down with a friend who has a problem and helped them come up with a plan for how to handle the situation? Care professionals frequently work with service users in a similar way, to help them deal with poor self-esteem and a negative self-concept.

People often find the support of care professionals crucial in building their own self-esteem and change their self-concept. Friends and family may be good at listening, but it can be good to talk to people who are not directly in your life, to whom you can say exactly what you feel.

Many different sorts of care professional employed in the health and social care sector are trained and skilled in this sort of work. **Counsellors** and **psychiatric nurses** spend a lot of their time working with service users looking at

Counsellor – a person who sees service users privately to explore difficulties being experienced in life

Psychiatric nurse – professional mental health nurse

Think about it

Friends and care professionals can both offer people different types of support. How might the support of a friend be different from that of a care professional?

self-esteem and self-concept issues. Some service users may have had a negative self-concept throughout childhood and adolescence; others may have experienced a significant life course event that has affected them at some point; all can benefit from what care professionals offer.

Positive care relationships

The work care professionals do with service users is broadly based around using the core care values. The aim is to try to build service users' self-esteem and enable them to look at their lives from a new perspective.

It is important that the care practitioner builds a relationship based on trust. A person needs to know that everything they tell a care professional is treated confidentially, and that the care practitioner has the interests of the service user at heart.

As you have seen, the UK is a multicultural society, with a wide range of cultures and religions. A care practitioner needs to be able to understand the service user's beliefs and values in order to work with them and be able to give appropriate support.

Communication skills are important too. The care practitioner needs to be sensitive to people's thoughts and feelings, and to treat each person as an individual, with respect and dignity.

Empowerment

Supporting people to improve their self-esteem and develop a more positive self-concept is not easy. The service user has to want to change, and the care practitioner, rather than deciding for people, needs to empower the service user, so that they are better informed and can make sensible choices once they know all the facts.

To empower a service user in this way, a care practitioner could discuss:

- the service user looking at what has influenced the view they have of themselves at present
- the service user looking at how they would like to be and be seen to be by others in an ideal world
- the service user looking at the changes they could make in areas of their lives to improve their self-esteem
- the service user designing an action plan to promote change, and the care practitioner supporting the service user through the changes they want to make.

Activity

Jenny is recovering from a serious car accident that has left her wheelchair-bound. Although she is recovering from the physical injury well, Jenny is finding it difficult to be positive about her life and future. She was an active sportswoman, and enjoyed socialising with her friends.

At present, Jenny has lost her self-confidence; once a positive person, she now sees the future as a challenge.

1. List the different options available to Jenny that could help her become more positive about the future.

2. Select two of the options you have suggested and explain how these could improve Jenny's self-concept. (Remember to look at the effect of the actions on Jenny's self-image and self-esteem).

Just checking

1. Describe two actions care professionals might take to empower service users.

2. Why is it important that service users trust the care professionals they are working with when discussing self-concept issues?

3. Why might it be necessary to ask service users to consider what happened in their childhood if they have low self-esteem?

The feel-good factor

In this topic, you will learn how relationships with family members, partners, work colleagues and friends can affect self-concept.

Relationships and self-concept

Which people in your life make you feel good about yourself? How do they do this? Care professionals often work with service users exploring the relationships they have with the other people in their lives. How people relate to other people often has a big impact on self-concept.

Family relationships

As you saw in Unit 1 (see pages 32–33), family relationships are important in the formation of a person's self-concept. There are two types of relationship within family groupings: those between parents/carers/adults and children, and those between brothers and sisters.

In these relationships, a number of factors influence self-concept:

- the quality of the relationships between family members. Carers who are both supportive and positive are likely to help their children have a positive self-concept.
- the level of security children feel. A child who feels loved is more likely to have good self-esteem and a positive self-concept.
- the 'roles' people adopt within the family. If a child sees that the household cleaning tasks are always done by the women in the family, they might come to believe that this is a female task.
- the degree of conflict between family members.

Love and support is a great benefit in the formation of good self-esteem. Feeling secure is important to all

Your world

With a partner, list the different types of events that could happen in a typical day at school, and how these could affect a student's self-esteem. (This might include such things as bullying, or receiving results from a recent examination.) Ask your teacher to 'hot seat' and discuss how they would handle these situations if they faced them. How might the teacher's response to these situations affect a person's self-esteem and self-concept?

Activity

Identify two events that have affected how you feel about yourself while you have been at school, and share with a friend how they affected you.

Did you know?

In 2004, in a typical day, the average person spent:

- 7.6 hours at work
- 7.6 hours sleeping
- 5.1 hours on household activities
- 3.7 hours on activity outside the household.

You can now see why the relationships we have with people at work and the time we spend there is such an important influence on self-concept.

children, and the level of conflict between family members contributes to how secure a child feels. The roles taken by adults in a family can also influence how children look at themselves. If a family has traditional family roles, it is likely that children will see this as normal, which might affect their own future expectations.

Care practitioners often ask service users to reflect on their childhood experiences, and to think about their current family relationships. This can lead to a deeper understanding of why they feel the way they do and can help people can make important changes to their relationships, which can lead to a more positive self-concept.

Relationships with partners

The intimate and sexual relationships people have in adulthood can have a big effect on self-concept. Having a supportive partner can help in handling difficult life course events, such as serious illness. A long-term partner can help give you a feeling of security and self-worth, and help you to have a positive self-concept.

Not all intimate and sexual relationships have a positive effect on self-esteem and self-concept. Relationships can be **destructive**, and people can damage each other's self-esteem and self-concept by what they say and how they behave. In some relationships, one person is expected to look after the children while the other person is able to continue with their social life. This may affect the person who has to stay at home as they may feel less important and that their needs are not being met.

Relationships with work colleagues and friends

People spend a lot of their time with friends and work colleagues. It is important that you choose your friends carefully, as they can contribute to how you see and value yourself. If friends are supportive, this helps create a positive self-concept; if they let you down, this can be damaging.

The time you spend at work can also contribute to having a positive self-concept: for example, when an employee receives positive feedback from colleagues and feels valued. However, if the person receives negative feedback and does not feel valued, this could lower self-esteem and change the person's self-concept.

Care practitioners often ask service users to look at their friendships and working life, so that they can get a greater understanding about why they feel the way they do about their lives.

Activity

Most people have a review at work on a regular basis. This is to find out how well they are doing their job, and whether they need any training to help them do their job even better.

1. How would a positive review affect a person's self-concept?
2. Why should people giving feedback to employees always start with the positive comments, and then move on to the areas for improvement?

Destructive – damaging

Just checking

1. How might a person's self-concept be affected if they are taken from their parents and placed into local authority care?
2. How might exclusion from being part of a friendship group affect a person's self-esteem?
3. Why is it important for a person to be told by their manager that they are doing a good job?

One of many

This topic looks at one of the factors that can affect health and wellbeing, and the impact it can have on an individual throughout life, in detail.

Factors affecting health and wellbeing

In Unit 3 you learned about a range of factors that affect health and wellbeing throughout the life course, and the effects of those factors on an individual. This topic looks at just one of those factors – so, before you read on, look back at the other factors you read about on pages 134–147.

Diet

Diet is a good illustration of how a factor can affect an individual throughout life. In the UK, childhood obesity is increasing. Every year, children aged between 5 and 11 are weighed and measured in UK schools (provided their parents give permission). Of those who are weighed and measured:

- 10 per cent of those aged 4 and 5 are obese, and a further 13 per cent are overweight.
- 17.5 per cent of 10- and 11-year-old children are obese, and a further 14.2 per cent are overweight.

Research suggests that children's diets are now worse than ever in terms of healthy growth and development. A child under the age of five needs more carbohydrates for energy – a young body is growing rapidly – and, until the age of 13, up to 15% extra fat. However, too many calories can cause weight and health problems and unhealthy eating patterns for life.

Many children have a weight problem

Your world

Ninety-year-old George is sitting on a bench on The Green watching the world go by and reflecting on how his lifestyle choices have affected his life. He fought in the Second World War, when he started to smoke, but he has tried to keep fit by eating healthily and exercising. How do you think his lifestyle choices have affected him throughout his life? Discuss this with a partner.

Activity

Consider someone who is **malnourished** as a child. Explain how that will affect her PIES (a) as an adolescent (b) as she grows older in later life stages

Take it further

Do some research into the effects of anorexia on a young person's PIES at various stages of life. Produce an information sheet showing ways in which someone who is worried they are becoming anorexic can get help.

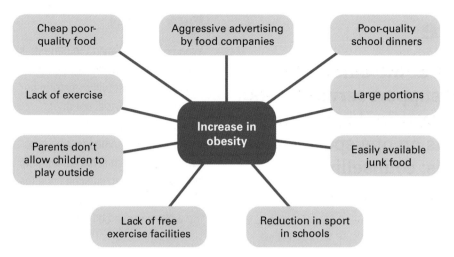

Reasons for increase in childhood obesity

Look at the picture opposite. Obesity will affect him:

- physically, as he is less able to run around and take an active part in sports and other games, and might be more **prone** to illness if he does not get much fresh air
- intellectually, because his brain will be less alert due to his more **sedentary** lifestyle, and he will be more likely to have time off school due to illness, embarrassment and other social problems
- emotionally, as he will be unhappy because he may be teased by other children and called names, and won't be able to join in all their activities because he is hampered by his weight
- socially, as he will be more likely to be ignored or taunted by other children due to his weight, or feared if he uses his size to threaten others, and less likely to be asked in join in with others.

If the obesity continues throughout his life, he is more likely to suffer:

- physically, because he will be more likely to develop conditions such as high blood pressure, Type 1 diabetes, heart disease, strokes, tooth decay and cancer. His lifestyle will be more sedentary and, ultimately, he is likely to die at a younger age
- intellectually, because he will become less mobile and be less able to travel to new places, or go to places such as the theatre and museums, as well as becoming less alert mentally, unless he reads a lot and watches documentaries on the television
- emotionally, as he may be embarrassed by his weight, worrying if, for example, he will fit into a cinema seat of if the seatbelt will fasten round him in a plane, and being concerned about what others think about his weight
- socially, because others can be dismissive of obese people, and he will not be able to join in fully with the activities his friends undertake as he will struggle to, for example, walk far.

Malnourished – physically weak due to lack of healthy food
Prone – likely, inclined
Sedentary – sitting or taking very little exercise

Just checking

1. What percentage of 4 to 5-year-olds, and 10- and 11-year-old children, is at the weight that is considered normal for those ages?

2. Why is an obese child likely to find life harder at school than a child of normal weight?

3. How might obesity affect an adult's social and emotional life if his friends like to go walking or travel to different places for the weekend together?

Help me, please

In this topic, you will look at the different ways health professionals can support service users to change their lifestyles in order to improve their health. You will focus on one specific area of support to illustrate this: counselling.

Health professionals

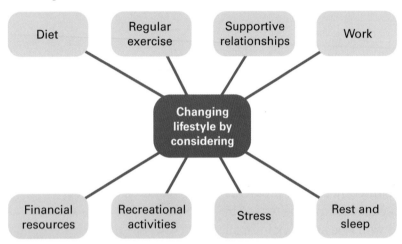

Health professionals can support lifestyle changes by helping with a range of factors, including those shown here

In Units 2 and 3, you learned more about the health and social care services and how they support service users. Some factors that service users need help with are shown on the diagram.

Health and social care professionals can support service users:

- physically, by providing drugs and support aids: for example, sleeping pills and access to a special reclining mattress to help someone sleep
- intellectually, by providing advice and information: for example, leaflets giving strategies on how to reduce stress
- emotionally, by providing a sympathetic ear and advice when a service user is tired, worried or upset: for example, when someone has lost their job
- socially, by helping someone to become less socially isolated: for example, when an individual has lost their spouse or partner, by helping them get a place at a local day-care centre.

Counsellors

All factors that affect our health and wellbeing affect us in some way psychologically. Many people with long-term medical conditions

Your world

Wendy, wife of David the dentist, is obese, with a BMI of 44. She needs an operation that will transform her life, but the NHS will not do it because of the danger of the anaesthetic for someone who is so overweight. What services can help her lose weight so she can have the operation? Draw a spider diagram of the ways she can be helped.

Activity

1. Draw up a table showing the skills, qualities and characteristics you would need if you wanted to become a counsellor.

2. Think of an issue a person might need counselling for, and do some research to find out which organisations exist to provide support and counselling for that issue. For example, Relate helps people with relationship problems. Produce a poster advertising the organisation, giving details of the issues they offer help with, the name, address and contact number, their logo and a brief description of their aims.

Case study Zac

Zac used to be a roofer but two years ago he fell and broke his back. He is now in a wheelchair and is paralysed from the neck downwards. The last two years have been spent in various units in hospitals and convalescent homes, but Zac is now well enough to return home, and needs a lot of help to cope with day-to-day life. His wife Sarah has given up her job to look after him. She gets daily help from various service providers. However, the enormity of what has happened and the reality of what lies ahead has now sunk in. Both Zac and Sarah are depressed but trying to make the most of the situation. Sarah loves her husband and tries to stay cheerful for his sake, despite how she is feeling deep down.

1. What are the issues that Zac and Sarah each face physically, intellectually, emotionally and socially?
2. How can a counsellor help them?
3. Role-play a session with a counsellor for (a) Zac on his own (b) Sarah on her own (c) both of them together.

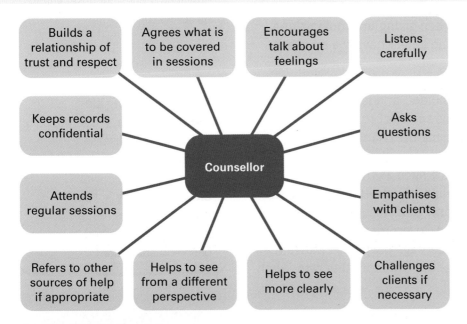

A counsellor's job description

or problems such as obesity, relationship breakdown, stress or lack of financial resources, require counselling and support.

Counsellors provide service users with time, attention and a safe environment to help them explore their feelings. They also encourage the service user to consider their options and find their own way to make a lifestyle change, to help them come to terms with, and if possible solve, their problems. These problems might be due to relationship difficulties, bereavement, coping with a disability or terminal condition, or simply coping with everyday life.

Some counsellors work with people with a wide range of issues, while others specialise in an area such as eating disorders or addiction to food, drugs, alcohol, smoking, gambling, sex or relationships. They work with people on a one-to-one basis, or with couples, families or group, either face to face or via the phone or internet.

Just checking

1. List five factors that a service user may need help with to change their lifestyle.

2. Describe the job of a counsellor, giving at least five aspects of her or his job.

3. Write a list of qualities and skills required for a job as a counsellor in Relate, a service that helps people with relationship problems.

A healthy influence?

In this topic, we will look at how factors that affect health and wellbeing can do so in both a positive and a negative way.

224

Positive influences

Changing your lifestyle can influence health in a number of positive ways.

- Health improvement: this may be a short-term improvement, such as reduced blood pressure when giving up smoking, or a long-term improvement, such as no longer having a smoker's cough or breathlessness.
- **Longevity**: giving up smoking means that a person is no longer taking in nicotine and carbon monoxide, and is less likely to develop life-threatening conditions such as bronchitis, emphysema or a stroke, so increasing the chance of leading a longer life.
- Reducing **morbidity rates**: statistics, such as those for arthritis and rheumatism shown on the graph, show details such as the morbidity rate for different ages and genders, and for different areas of the country. This helps the Government and health professionals target support to encourage people to change their lifestyle in certain ways, and so reduce the morbidity rate, when and with whom it is most needed.

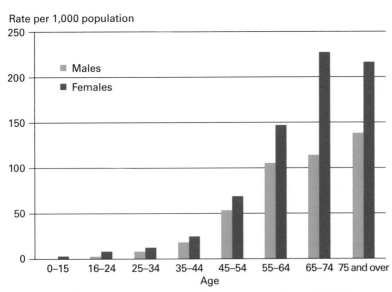

Rate per 1,000 population

Arthiritis/rheumatism prevalence: by age and sex, GB, 2003

Taken from the national statistics website, www.statistics.gov.uk

Morbidity rates for arthritis

Your world

On page 222, Wendy needs a hip replacement operation, as she has very bad arthritis. What might be the short- and long-term effects on her if she has the operation? And what might they be if she does not? Do you know anyone who has had a serious operation? How did it help them, or not help them? Discuss this with a friend, providing it does not upset you to do so.

Longevity – long life
Morbidity rates – the rate of incidence of a disease
Premature – unexpectedly early
Life expectancy – the number of years that an individual is expected to live based on statistics

Activity

Look at the graph.

- What does it tell you about the morbidity rate for arthritis and rheumatism among men compared to women?
- How does the morbidity rate change with age?
- Why do you think this is?

Negative influences

Failure to improve an unhealthy lifestyle can lead to:

- an increase in sickness rates: people who lead an unhealthy lifestyle are more likely to become ill. For example, an obese person being more likely to develop heart disease, so increasing the percentage of people with heart disease.
- **premature** death: statistics suggest how long an average healthy person can expect to live to, according to factors such as the area of the country they live in, their age and their weight. An unhealthy lifestyle can reduce a person's **life expectancy**, and lead them to die before they reach the expected age.
- poor mental health: this is a disorder that affects the functioning of the mind and the brain. An unhealthy lifestyle can lead to poor mental health in a number of ways: for example, taking illegal drugs, such as LSD, can lead to depression and feeling that everyone is against you; cannabis can lead to hallucinations; and many others, such as cocaine and crack, lead to anxiety.

Also, research suggests that people eating diets that lack one or more of a combination of polyunsaturated fats, minerals and vitamins, and/or that contain too much saturated fat, seem to be at higher risk of developing conditions such as Attention-Deficit/Hyperactivity Disorder (ADHD), schizophrenia and dementia, including Alzheimer's disease.

Activity

1. In a group, put together the facts about the short- and long-term effects of taking each of the common illegal drugs. Divide the drug names up between the group, with a deadline for research to be finished by.
2. Produce a drama piece that shows the dangers to mental health of taking illegal drugs. Write the script and rehearse it, ready to show to the rest of your class. Include a rap, or song, or some other memorable device, which really gets the message across.

Just checking

1. Explain what is meant by the terms 'morbidity rate' and 'mental health'.
2. Explain how giving up smoking can improve longevity.
3. How does diet affect mental health? Answer in terms of (a) overeating (b) undereating (c) eating an unhealthy diet.

Helping health happen

This topic looks at the aims and approaches of health promotion, and how health professionals support individuals to change health-related behaviour.

Health promotion

Aims

Take a look back at what you learned about health promotion on pages 166–7. Health promotion aims to:

- raise awareness: for example, the leaflet pictured advises service users that antibiotics have been overused in the past and this has led to super bugs such as MRSA developing. It advises people to only take antibiotics when it is strictly necessary and points out that they don't actually work on viruses such as the common cold.
- prevent ill health: for example, by giving information about the risks of smoking, in the hope that it will stop some people from starting and so prevent them developing smoking-related conditions
- Improve fitness levels: for example, showing diagrams of exercises that someone can do if they want to improve their **cardiovascular** fitness
- improve life expectancy: for example, highlighting the dangers of alcohol, giving the recommended weekly limits, so that people are discouraged from drinking excessively and so improve their life expectancy.

Approaches

The approaches used in health promotion to improve health and wellbeing include:

- disease prevention: one example is through promoting the need for a certain vaccination, to stop a particular disease, such as the National Department of Health HPV vaccination programme, started in September 2008, which is given to 12 and 13-year-old girls to protect against the commonest cause of cervical cancer

Your world

Health promotion leaflet

Look at a selection of health promotion leaflets. What do these leaflets aim to do? Which leaflet does its job best and why? Which is the least effective leaflet and why?

Think about it

How have you and others in your group been helped by health promotion? What sort of health promotion do you tend to take most notice of? Hard-hitting television promotions such as drink driving, binge drinking or smoking? Leaflets? Health warnings on packets? Any others? With a partner, discuss one promotion on the television or at the cinema that has made an impact on you recently and say why.

Cardiovascular – relating to the heart and the blood vessels

- adoption of healthier lifestyles: for example, hard-hitting television campaigns about how children copy their parents and so learn habits such as smoking in the home at an early age
- actions taken at a national level to improve the nation's health: examples of this are the social policy goals set to reduce obesity, to encourage young children to eat fruit and to ensure schools promote a healthy lifestyle through the Healthy Schools programme, and by teaching more about food for health, food safety and food and employment on the curriculum.

Support from health professionals

Health professionals play an important part in supporting individuals to change health-related behaviour – that is, any behaviour that affects health, such as unprotected sex, an unhealthy diet, lack of exercise or substance abuse.

Health professionals support individuals to change this through:

- diagnosis
- monitoring progress
- health planning
- advice and counselling
- evaluating progress against targets.

You have looked at all these areas on pages 160–173. Make sure that you re-read these Topics before your exam. You should also look back at pages 222–3, which deal with counselling – another key area where health professionals can offer support.

Just checking

1. State four aims of health promotion.
2. Name and give examples of the approaches used by health professionals to improve health and wellbeing.
3. How can health professionals support individuals to change health-related behaviour?

Activity

1. The Department of Health's campaign 'Small Change, Big Difference' aims to persuade people to make a small change to their lifestyles in order to make a big change to their future health and wellbeing. Read about it on www.dh.gov.uk.
2. As a class, identify the issues that affect people in your school, such as teenage pregnancy or smoking. Decide which one you feel most strongly about. Plan a campaign to encourage students to make a change to their lifestyle. It must include the production of health promotion materials, such as posters, leaflets or videos.

Take it further

If your teacher will let you, arrange to spread the campaign into the wider school community.

You've got the power!

228

This topic looks at how effective health promotion and support is built on through careful implementation of the care values.

Implementation of the care values

In Unit 2, you looked at the care values implemented by health and social care professionals. Here, you look at how these are implemented, through promoting choice, respecting identity and culture, and empowerment.

Promoting choice

When a service user, or the service user's family, is faced with a decision to make, they need to know what choice is available to them, so information has to be readily accessible to them. For example, if a person has dementia and it is not safe for him to live on his own anymore, his family will want to know what residential homes are available in the area and which will be best for him.

It is therefore important that there is information available on the internet and in leaflets, as well as from health care professionals, so that the family can research their options. They can then arrange to visit any homes they like the look of, to see if they will meet the needs of their loved one, and then can make an informed choice.

Your world

A life-changing experience

As Aaron has grown, it has become clear that he has special needs. He has struggled to communicate until recently, when his mother read a magazine about a new method being used in a nearby special school. He is now a pupil there and is making amazing progress. How will he have felt before and after the move to the new school?

Have you had an experience, no matter how small, that enabled you to move forward in your life? Have any of your group? Discuss this.

Activity

1. By talking to someone and finding out their preferences and dislikes, and giving them choices, a care assistant can start to help a person newly arrived at a residential care home to settle down and feel happy to be there. Think about someone who is of a different culture from most other people in the care home. What should a good care assistant do to help them settle in quickly? Explain your answer.
2. Answer the same question for someone who does not believe in taking medicinal drugs unless it is unavoidable. Explain your answer.

Respecting identity and culture

If a person's identity and culture are not acknowledged and taken into account in their care, it will affect how their needs are met, and affect their state of mind and willingness to use the service concerned. For example, a health promotion leaflet in a selection of languages will mean that someone from a particular culture will be able to access the information they need, and so will have a better understanding of the situation and will be less frightened.

Another example might be that of a service user with a disability that means he has to use a wheelchair, on a visit to the doctor with his mother. If the receptionist addresses her questions to his mother rather than to him, assuming that the disability means that he is in some way mentally impaired too, he could feel insulted and unvalued. In fact, all that makes him different from her is that he has a mobility problem.

Empowerment

It can be difficult for some service users to express their preferences and needs. This may be because they have become used to their carers speaking for them. If a service user is given health promotion information, encouragement and support to enable her to understand what is happening and to say what she wants and what is important to her, she is empowered, and is making progress towards being more independent and making a better recovery.

It may be that someone has been fighting a long battle against cancer and has now decided that he would rather spend what time he has left at home with his family, rather than suffering more treatment that makes him really sick and reduces his quality of life, just for the sake of a few more months of life. If he is given a choice, and his wishes are respected, he will feel empowered and back in control of what is left of his life. This will make him happier, and so help him through the rest of the illness.

Free to choose

This topic continues to look at how effective health promotion and support is built on the careful implementation of the care values, including promoting independence and respecting an individual's right to choice.

Implementation of the care values

Promoting independence

Promoting independence has been mentioned several times in this book because it is so important. The main aim of any health and social care service is to enable a person to develop or maintain their independence, so that they have as much control over their own life as possible.

The development of independence in childhood and adolescence helps to support a positive self-image and self-esteem. People of all ages may need support to maintain their independence, but it is important for this to happen to preserve a positive self-concept.

Respecting individual right to choice

If someone has developed a condition or illness such as a stroke that has affected one side of his body, and is not consulted about any aspects of his treatment, he will feel that things are happening to him over which he has no choice. As a result, he will not feel valued or part of the process and may become depressed and less able to cope with the situation mentally.

If, however, he is offered choices, such as whether to stay in the hospital he was first brought to, or be moved to a specialist unit where he will get more one-to-one help with his condition, he will feel as though he still has some control over his recovery, and will be in a more positive frame of mind, so helping his recovery.

Promoting health improvement

Before a person can be persuaded to follow a health improvement plan, he has to be motivated. He needs to want to make the necessary changes to his lifestyle enough to overcome the difficulties faced in following the plan. This is often hard: someone who is overweight or smokes or drinks too much may well recognise the need to make change, but has to really want to change in order to have a chance of succeeding.

Your world

Carmen is 21 and has Down's Syndrome, and her mother is very protective of her. She lives above the mini market with her family, but now wants to live on her own. A social worker intervenes and persuades her mother to see it Carmen's way. What will be the effect on Carmen and her mother in the short and long term?

Have you ever been in conflict with your family? How did you resolve the issue?

Think about it

Some parents don't allow their children to be vaccinated against diseases such as measles, because they are concerned about the small risk from the vaccination itself. If more parents do this, there is a danger that illnesses that are now very rare become more common again. It is their right to make this choice. What do you think about this issue? Have you had all your vaccinations? If you don't know, ask at home.

Halal – food fit to eat according to Islamic rules, such as pure and good foods, including fruit, vegetables, milk, lamb, beef, poultry and nuts; to be halal, meat must be killed according to the Islamic way

Case study **Mohammed**

The Qur'an is treated with utmost respect by Muslims

Mohammed is a Muslim and reads the Qur'an, which is the Muslim holy book and contains the words of Allah. He treats it with the utmost respect, washing his hands and feet as best he can in his wheelchair before touching it. He does not eat, drink or speak while reading it. He never allows it to touch the ground and places it on a stool when he puts it down for any reason. When he puts it away, he wraps it in a special cloth and puts it on a shelf, with nothing stacked on top of it. Mohammed prays five times a day in Arabic. He can only eat **halal** food, must avoid certain foods, including pork, and does not eat or drink during daylight hours during the month of Ramadan.

1. Explain how Mohammed's religious beliefs have to be considered in order to (a) allow him choice, (b) respect his identity and culture, (c) empower him, (d) promote his independence and (e) respect his right to choice, if he has to go into hospital.
2. Remember that Mohammed is a wheelchair user and is partially sighted. How will this affect his care and need for independence?

Factors that can help motivation are:

- incentives: for example, the promise of having a reward for each week that a person loses weight, or the thought of being applauded by fellow slimmers at a slimming club, can encourage people to lose weight. They may also stick to it if they are convinced that the benefits of the plan are worth the struggle to follow it, such as looking better, being fitter and having more money
- belief: a person is more likely to stick to a plan if it is not too complicated and he believes he can do it
- being realistic: a person is more likely to stick to a plan if they feel it is possible: for example, a person trying to lose weight is more likely to believe he can lose one kilo in a week than four kilos.

Activity

Think of something about your own health that you could do with improving. What would make you stick to a health improvement plan? Explain your answer.

Just checking

1. What is the main aim of any health and social care service?
2. Why should health professionals respect an individual's right to choice?
3. What are the three factors that can help persuade someone to follow a health improvement plan?

Assessment for Unit 4

Welcome

Are you looking forward to the examination you will sit for Unit 4? If not, why not? It is important to be confident. In this unit, you draw from all the knowledge and understanding you have already gained from Units 1, 2 and 3. You already have a head start! By practising what you have learned in the tasks set, you will be able to enter the examination well prepared and confident.

Remember what we have said before – examinations are a lot less stressful if you:

- know what sort of questions you will be asked
- have prepared and revised properly
- know what sort of evidence examiners are looking for in your answers to the questions they set
- understand what the command words are expecting you to do.

You may wish to look back at the assessment section at the end of Unit 1, to remind yourself of the basic principles.

Try to be confident. The more you practice, the better you will get. Remember: there is no point in worrying on the day as you will already have done all the hard work!

How Unit 4 is examined

Key things you need to know

- The examination is 75 minutes long and you can get a maximum mark of 70. If you manage this, you will be awarded an A star. Some people will, so let's try to make sure it is you!
- Examiners work on a principle of 'a mark a minute', with 15 minutes extra to let you **read** the questions, **think** about them, **plan** your answers, **write** your answers and **review** what you have written, to check that it does actually answer the question set.
- The Unit 4 examination is about the 'core principles' used in health, social care and early years by practitioners. This unit will develop the key principles from Units 1 to 3 in more depth.
- The examination paper for Unit 4 will consist of a range of questions based around short case studies or scenarios, and can range in marks from two to ten. Split your time carefully in the examination. *There are no multiple-choice questions on this paper*.
- Some questions ask you to draw information 'from the background information'. If you are asked to do this, make sure your answer comes from the background information.

Remember:

R = read
T = think
P = plan
W = write
R = review

Top tips for preparing for examinations

Make sure:

- **you have covered all the content you need to**, as set out in the examination board's *Specification for GCSE Health and Social Care*. Your teacher will have this in booklet form, or you can look it up for yourself on the internet.
- **you remember that in Units 2 and 3 you produced pieces of portfolio work**. You may need to make sure that you have a good set of notes about the parts of these units that make up Unit 4: for example, human needs, care values. Your teacher will help you do this.
- **you have revised**. Don't leave the revision all for the days really close to the examination. Write out a revision plan for the weeks before the examination.
- **you know how to answer the different types of questions** that will appear on the examination. We will practice this later, looking particularly at the longer type of questions.
- **you know what the different 'command words' used by examiners mean** and how these guide you to write accurate and detailed answers.
- **you have practiced** doing all the different types of questions regularly well before the examination.

If you do all of these things, you are likely to be able to show what you know, what you can do and what you have learned.

- The shorter questions require short and to-the-point answers. If you write too much, you are wasting valuable time. The longer questions require you to think about what you have to do and construct an answer that does exactly what you are asked.
- There are more longer questions on this examination paper than on the Unit 1 examination.
- A range of 'command words' will be used in the examination – see pages 58–59.
- Some marks are awarded for the quality of your written English. You need to show that you can write in a sensible and structured way.

Getting it together

Pull together all the work you have which is relevant for this unit into one folder for revision purposes. This must include:

- the work you have done in preparation for this examination
- your work from Unit 1 on self-concept
- your work from Unit 2 on the care needs of the major client groups
- your work from Unit 3 on promoting and supporting health improvement.

Having this in one place will help you to prepare really well for this examination.

Just checking

1. How long is allowed for the Unit 4 examination and how many marks is the maximum you can get?
2. Why are the questions on the examination more applied to the work of health, social care and early years practitioners?
3. Is there a different range of command words used in the Unit 4 examination?

Writing extended answers

One of the skills you will have to show in the examination for Unit 4 is that you can write at some length in a clear and concise way. Some questions will have eight or ten marks given to them. There will a large space available for you to write a detailed, well thought-out and constructed answer, which does what the question asks.

It is important that you develop the skills you need early in the course, and you will certainly need to develop them more if you intend to continue to study on courses at post-16 level. In the world of work, you will also need to be able to write in an extended way to produce reports or summaries of events that have happened. It's a valuable skill to have.

In the longer questions, the assessors will also be looking at your 'QWC':

QWC = Quality of Written Communication

You will need to show and use a number of general written skills that you will have been developing throughout your time at school or college. In the box on the right are some basic rules that are really simple, but are often forgotten.

In the longer questions, you will have to make sure you answer the question set, show your knowledge and understanding and show QWC.

Example

'Discuss the importance of education and training for an individual's development'. (10 marks)

Before you attempt a question in the examination, you need to do some thinking and planning. You need to work out:

- what information you need to use to answer this question
- if there are any clues that might help you in the background information given – there usually are!
- how many paragraphs you might use and what might be in each
- if the question is insisting you write about the people in the case study, or whether you can write more generally. In this question, you have the opportunity to write generally, but a lot of students will use the people in the background information as examples in their answers. So, although it might not seem that the information given about Amy and her life is central to answering the question, it gives the student some ideas to use.

Basic rules

- Use capital letters and full stops.
- Write in sentences.
- Use paragraphs to structure what you want to say.
- Include examples to show what you mean.
- Check what you have written and be sure it makes sense.

Background information

Amy works in the Willows Nursing Home and is Norman's named nurse. She is 24 years of age and lives with her partner, Sean. Amy is currently completing her NVQ Level 3 in Care qualification, and would eventually like to train as a nurse. Sean is at university studying accountancy. They plan to marry when Sean leaves university and gets a job.

The examiner who marks your work will have been given a mark scheme to assess your work. This gives them a structure to use when marking your answer. They will read your answer and then:

- decide which band best describes your answer
- decide where in that band your answer fits.

Level	Mark	How marks are gained
Level 1	0-3	The student presents a few points about the importance of education and/or training for an individual's development. eg helps to get a job, earn more money. **One to two** factors are identified and explained. Discussion will largely be missing and extended writing will be repetitive and poorly structured. In addition the student may have misinterpreted part or all of the question.
Level 2	4-6	The student can identify and explain accurately. **Three** factors are identified and at least **one** is explained. Generally accurate knowledge and understanding shown in the work. The answer will tend to read like a story and there will be a lack of discussion in the work. Structure of the work will be adequate. There will be limited skills in writing although a good interpretation of the question. There will be some omissions of content.
Level 3	7-10	The student identifies a range of factors and explains them fully. Links will be made between factors and the work will be logical. An excellent level of knowledge and understanding will be shown. The student's work will present a good level of discussion. There will be accurate interpretation of the question. Students will have the ability to see or argue both sides of a question.

Mark scheme

Above is a mark scheme used for a ten-mark question like this. You can see what the examiners actually have to do when they look at your answer. If you understand this, you will know better how to get to the top band of the mark scheme when you write your answer.

Interesting, isn't it, when you see what the examiners are looking for? Students think that writing an answer is just about how much knowledge you have but it is also about how you write the information down and use it.

What's your answer?

Working with a partner write a plan to answer the example question. Share your plan with the class in a discussion with your teacher then write up your answer.

Just checking

1. Why does it help to use examples in your written answers?
2. Why is checking an important task for you when you have finished writing in the examination
3. If an answer you have written to a question falls into mark band two, what written skills have you been able to show? What would you have to do to get to mark band three?

Marking work

In the previous part of this assessment section, we looked at one particular question and how mark schemes work. The question we looked at was:

'Discuss the importance of education and training for an individual's development.' (10 marks)

Here are two attempts at answering this question. Read them carefully.

Student A

Education is important for a person's development. The better you do at school, the more money you earn. If Amy had worked harder at school, she might be at university like her boyfriend.

If Amy completes her NVQ Level 3, she might be able to train as a nurse as she is better qualified. She could meet new people as well which could be good as she might get out more. Overall, education and training are good.

Student B

Education and training are usually seen as a good thing for most people. Having a good education and passing examinations helps people get into better jobs. This means a person is likely to earn higher pay. Most people want this. Well-paid jobs often have better pension schemes, which are good for later adulthood. Working hard to achieve a good education helps a person's intellectual development as they learn new things and can see things differently. Training is important as it helps people to learn new skills, which might get them promoted later. Training also helps people to keep up to date with the latest technology. A doctor may be well educated, but will always need new training to use new techniques.

Education can also give people confidence and boost their self-esteem and change their self-concept. It might also improve someone's social life as they meet new people and make new friends.

Education may not always be good as it can stress people out if they are pushed too much.

Activity

Now you have read the work, look at the answers again and look at the mark scheme given earlier in this assessment section.

- Which mark band would you place each piece of work in?
- How many marks would you give each answer?
- Which piece of work is the better piece of work?
- Why is this piece of work better than the other?

Key words and phrases

Here are a few words and phrases you can use in your answers to show the examiner that you are assessing or discussing an issue:

- 'however'
- 'on the other hand'
- 'some people may see this in another way'
- 'there is more than one way of looking at this issue'

These will help you assess and discuss in your answers. You will then need to follow on the word or phrase with some more information.

What the examiners thought

Answer A: 3/10 – Mark band one

This is a fairly weak response to the question. The student makes a few relevant points and one or two points are made. This would place the student in mark band one. The question asks for some discussion and this is not really evident in this answer.

There are not three things identified so the student cannot be placed in mark band two.

Answer B: 8/10 – Mark band three

The student identifies a range of factors about how education and training can affect an individual's development. The points made are discussed, though on some occasions the discussion is limited. Examples are used to good effect. There is a good link made to self-esteem and self-concept. At the end of the answer, the student does raise the fact that on some occasions education may not always be a positive as it can cause stress.

A good attempt that would place the student at the top of mark band two or the bottom of mark band three. The examiner gave the student the benefit of the doubt and gave the student 8/10.

Writing and marking answers

In this section you will further practice and improve:

- **understanding questions**
- **writing answers to a mark scheme**
- **assessing student work.**

Remember that practice will help you in the long run. The more prepared you are, the better you will perform in the examination.

On the right is some background information for two different questions, the first for 4 marks and the second for 10 marks. Try to do the tasks in order and not to look at the section which follows.

Sample questions

'Explain two possible benefits for Thomas of the nursery effectively implementing care values.' (4 marks)

Sample answer 1

If the workers use care values this might help Thomas. If he is treated is respected he will develop good self-esteem. Being respected makes people feel good and build self-esteem. It is good to keep confidentiality and treat people equally. The workers should not discriminate against Thomas and put him at risk.

What mark did you give the work after applying the mark scheme? Where did the student go wrong?

'Assess how life course events may have affected Jane's self-concept.' (10 marks)

Sample answer 2

Jane has gone through a lot of changes over the last few years. She has got married, had a child, and moved from Ireland to England. These things will all have affected Jane's self-concept. Self-concept is a combination of self-image and self-esteem – how you see yourself and how you value yourself.

Getting married will certainly have affected Jane's self-concept. She is no longer a single woman but is somebody's wife. She will have responsibilities and

Background information

Jane is 30 years of age and married to Stephen. They have recently moved to Liverpool form Northern Ireland. Jane married Stephen two years ago and they have recently had their first child, Thomas. Jane decided to give birth in a hospital. She has now returned to work part time and Thomas attends a day nursery.

Mark scheme

0 marks – no rewardable material

1-2 marks – one or two benefits identified but not explained (1 or 2), or 1 benefit identified and explained (2)

3-4 marks – two benefits identified and one explained (3) or two benefits identified and both explained (4)

What the examiners thought (Answer 1)

This answer was given 2/4 marks.

The student wrote quite a lot but there was only one part which gained any marks – 'If he is treated with respect he will develop good self-esteem'. This is explained more to get the second mark. The rest of the student's work was about care values generally and not benefits of applying them.

will not be as free as she was before to do what ever she wants. This might have made her self-esteem go up as she feels someone wants her and is attracted to her. Her self-image will be good I would imagine. She might have good self-esteem anyway though.

When she had her baby her self-concept will have changed again. She is now a mum as well as a wife. She will have to look after the baby show her son how to behave properly. This might make her feel good too. It might stress her out though. She might also find it difficult to manage a job as well as being a wife and a mum.

Moving to England from Ireland could have been upsetting and have knocked her self-confidence.

Level	Mark	How marks are gained
Level 1	1-3	The student presents a few points about how life course events might have affected Jane's self-concept **One to two** factors are identified and considered. Eg. education, having a baby. The student will have a limited or no understanding of the meaning of self-concept. Assessment will largely be missing and extended writing will be repetitive and poorly structured. In addition the student may have misinterpreted part or the entire question.
Level 2	4-7	The student can identify and explain life course events which might affect Jane's self-concept. **Three** life course events are identified and at least **one** is explained. Generally accurate knowledge and understanding shown in the work. The answer will tend to read like a story and there will be a lack of discussion in the work. Structure of the work will be adequate. There will be limited skills in writing although a good interpretation of the question. There will be some omissions of content.
Level 3	8-10	The student identifies a range of life course events which might affect Jane's self-concept and explains them fully. Links will be made between factors and the work will be logical. An excellent level of knowledge and understanding will be shown. The students work will present a good level of discussion. There will be accurate interpretation of the question. Students will have the ability to argue see or argue both sides of a question

Mark scheme

What's your answer?

Answer the questions, and ask a friend to mark your work according to the mark scheme.

What the examiners thought (Answer 2)

This answer was given 9/10 marks.

This is a good piece of work. Three points are identified and two of them are discussed in some depth. The student applies the factors identified to Jane's self-concept and certainly knows what self-concept means. The work is logical, well presented and accurate so it falls in mark band 3. The third factor identified, the move from Ireland, was not fully developed because the student ran out of time. The writing is good and this student can use paragraphs accurately to structure their answer.

Just checking

1. What words could you use to show you are discussing or assessing something?
2. How can you show the examiner that you can use good written English?
3. Why is it important to look at the background information in planning your answer for a long question?

Last-minute preparation

As the examination approaches, it is useful to go through practice questions, to test that you know the basics and can shape answers for each type of question. Check you know these and with a partner test each other to see how well you do!

You might want your notes or textbook with you at the first try at the questions. As you get closer to the examination date, see if you can do them from memory.

Basics

1. Identify two basic needs of service users.
2. Identify two life course events and two lifestyle choices.
3. Describe two ways in which a serious illness may affect a person's development.
4. Identify and describe how care workers might integrate two care values into their work.
5. How might the breaking of confidentiality affect a service user's self-esteem?
6. Define 'self-concept'.
7. Identify two ways care practitioners can build the self-esteem of service users.
8. Identify four factors that may affect a person's self-concept.
9. Identify two consequences of care values not being used by care practitioners.
10. Identify two aims of health promotion.

Short written questions

Here are some short written questions for you to do to check that you can put what you know into words. The answers to each of these questions would be worth between 1 and 3 marks. You may not need to write in full sentences and some answers may just need one or two words.

1. John is 27 years of age. Identify one physical and one social need John will have.
2. John is overweight and suffers from asthma. Describe how these health problems affect his social wellbeing.
3. Describe one way in which health professionals may help John become healthier.
4. Why must health professionals treat John with dignity?
5. Describe two measures health professionals may use to assess John's health.
6. Identify two aims health professionals may set John.

7. If John loses weight, how might this affect his self-image?
8. Identify two factors that may be a cause of John's obesity.
9. Why is it important that health professionals find time to talk to John about his health plan?
10. Identify two targets that could be set in John's health plan.

Longer written questions

Four- to six-mark questions

Here are some longer written questions for you to try close to the examination date. These questions would all have a mark ranging between four and six.

1. Explain two care values used by care staff in a residential home.
2. Explain two benefits of 'empowering' service users.
3. Explain two ways in which early years practitioners could promote the language development of children.
4. Explain, using examples, why it is important for people in later adulthood to continue to exercise.
5. Describe two ways in which health professionals could support service users to lead healthier lifestyles.

Eight- to ten-mark questions

You will need to write in full sentences and paragraphs in your answers. The examiner is looking for you to show your extended writing skills.

The questions tend to focus on the command words 'assess' and 'discuss'. Remember the general rule of 'a mark a minute', as you will not have much more time than this!

1. Assess the importance of care workers implementing care values in their work with service users. (10 marks)
2. Discuss the effects of gender and age on an individual's self-concept in middle adulthood. (10 marks)
3. Assess the importance of health plans being carefully monitored. (8 marks)
4. Discuss the importance of care workers having positive care relationships with service users. (8 marks)
5. Assess the importance of recreational activities to health and wellbeing. (10 marks)

Just checking

1. Is it always important to write in full sentences for 'identify' questions?
2. How are your extended writing skills examined in this unit?
3. Why is it important that you practice longer questions and use them to revise from close to the examination?

Index